THE VALLEY OF KASHMIR

THE VALLEY OF KASHMIR

A Geographical Interpretation

Vol. I : The Land

MOONIS RAZA

AIJAZUDDIN AHMAD

ALI MOHAMMAD

CAROLINA ACADEMIC PRESS
Durham, North Carolina

Published in the United States by

CAROLINA ACADEMIC PRESS

2206 Chapel Hill Road, Box 8791 Forest Hills Station,
Durham, N. C. 27707

ISBN 0-89089-058-7

Library of Congress Catalog Card No. 77-93391

PRINTED IN INDIA

To

the Vitasta

united with the Valley

in every fibre of its being

Preface

The present volume marks the partial fulfilment of the senior author's desire, cherished since his long stay in Kashmir in the sixties, to grasp, in the medium of geographical expression, the indescribable and bewildering mysteries of the Valley's personality. The authors are, however, fully aware that this volume is but a poor substitute for what was originally conceived.

The work has been planned to produce a systematic geography of Kashmir in three volumes dealing with the land, the people and the economy. This, being the first in the series, presents a systematic account of the physical setting of the Valley, dealing with its remote origin in the geological past, its surface features as evolved through the alternations of glacial and fluvial cycles during the Pleistocene, the network of streams and their hydrological peculiarities, the complexities of weather, the magnificence of its flora and the riches of the soil. The two forthcoming volumes will bring out the essential features of the social and economic geography of the Valley.

Kashmir is an area of perennial interest both to the scholar and the layman. The scenic beauty and the grandeur of its physical form have invited interest since the very early stages of the peopling of the Valley. Numerous references found in the early texts such as the Puranas and the literary works from Kalhana to Iqbal provide ample evidence of this eternal interest. Literature and aesthetic arts apart, scholarly writings on Kashmir belonging to the genre of formal science, perhaps with the singular exception of geology, are absent. Geology seems to have benefited most from the storehouse of material embedded in the mountain ramparts surrounding the Valley and offering clues to the processes of Himalayan orogeny, sedimentology, glaciation and prehistoric cultures. In sharp contrast to this is the largely untapped source material scattered throughout the Valley and throwing light on the facets of its physical geography, its settlement history, social and economic parameters and its cultural ethos. It has awaited a meaningful analysis for too long. The present work on the geography of Kashmir is an humble step in that direction.

Despite the pioneering works of C.D. Deshpande and Enayet Ahmad on western India and Bihar respectively, regional geography continues to be a thoroughly neglected field in India. No regional monographs worth the name on any of the macro or meso regions of India exist, so much so that Oscar H.K. Spate's masterly work on India is the only standard reference source. Its deficiency in regional aspects is too well known and many of India's regions have merited an account of a hundred words only. The edited works by a large number of authors are bound to be unequal and fragmented and cannot be a substitute for a regional geography of India. In the context of this general dearth of regional material on India, the present work seems to have some justification.

A word on the coverage of this volume may not be out of place. It confines itself to the Valley alone for reasons of its uniqueness. Nestled within the frame of the northwestern Himalayan complex and marked out clearly by the enveloping crest, the Valley of Kashmir has a distinct and clear geographical identity. The parameters of this identity are undisputed. Its uniqueness within the cultural mosaics of the northwestern Himalayas, its partially and largely self-sufficient enclosed system and the limited nature of its interactions with the surrounding lands more than justify such a singular treatment. It may be hoped that parallel studies on its other regions, such as Ladakh and Jammu, will compensate for the gap left by this volume in the geographical understanding of the northernmost state of the Indian Union.

The present volume owes its origin to a grant from the University Grants Commission under its university level textbooks programme which the authors wish to gratefully acknowledge.

For the materials borrowed from different primary sources, such as the *Records* and the *Memoirs* of the Geological Survey of India, India Meteorological Department, departmental records of the Central Water and Power Commission and the like, due acknowledgement has been made at the relevant places. So also some of the notable secondary works, such as those of the late D.N. Wadia on geology; of S.N. Bhan and V.M. Meher-Homji on climate; and of R.C. Hoon and M.L.

Kaul on soils, have been acknowledged in the text.

The authors owe a debt of gratitude to a number of students and staff members of the Centre for the Study of Regional Development of the Jawaharlal Nehru University, who helped them in different capacities. Particular thanks are due to Dr Rais Akhtar for collecting material on soils; to Mr A.N. Sharma, a doctoral student, for cartographic assistance; and to Mr Chinmoy Nath for processing the photographs for the plates. Special thanks are due to Mr A.N. Talwar for preparing the typescript for the press.

Centre for the Study of Regional Development
Jawaharlal Nehru University
New Delhi, 110057

MOONIS RAZA
AIJAZUDDIN AHMAD
ALI MOHAMMAD

The Valley of Kashmir—
Its Space Relations

Kashmir Valley has been a half-closed ecosystem, opening up slowly in space and across time.

The *Vitasta* has been and continues to be the key element of the system. Kashmir is, indeed, the gift of the Jhelum. It is born of it, made up of the detritus brought down by its numerous tributaries; and is united with it through every fibre of its being. The sons of the soil have come to terms with the natural elements of the system, through millennia of settled life, by sticking to the Valley floor and developing the technology of the *khul* based paddy monoculture symbiotically linked with handicrafts activity, concentrated in the winter months when the seeds slumber under the snows. Natural fertility of the alluvium, the abundance of precipitation, the nature of the enveloping slopes, permitting terrace culture linked with indigenous irrigation, and the favourable temperature regimes of the growing season have not only given to the Valley a unifying homogeneity and a socio-economic viability at a low level of technology but have also infused into the system an internal strength and vitality which is the basis of the historical continuity of the Kashmiri tradition, which has contributed no less to the inward looking characteristics of its ethos.

The natural configuration of the enveloping crest has tended to strengthen the closed character of the system and has acted as a serious constraint on the processes of its opening up. Kalhana, using mythological symbolism, refers to this as follows: "To protect, foresooth, the *Nagas* (who came to seek shelter) afraid of *Garuda*, it stretches out its arms high above in the guise of mountain walls." Hieun Tsiang and Au-Kang made special note of the impregnability of the surrounding mountains and of the difficulties of its passes. Alberuni referred to the fact that the Kashmiris "are particularly anxious about the natural strength of their country." The mountain ramparts have not only been important from the strategic point of view but have considerably buttressed the sense of identity of the people and their deep involvement in the Valley environment. It has, on the one hand, given to the endogenous system of man-nature interactions a specific regional stamp and, on the other, has led to the weak induction of exogenous influences. It has strengthened homogeneity within and sharpened the gradients of both natural and socio-economic diversities from without.

Though the mountains have stood as sentinels guarding the Valley, historically they have the character of no man's land. The Kashmiri peasant never came to terms with the mountains. They remained alien to him—the abode of gods and demons, to be dreaded and revered but not to be assimilated into the tamed environment. Where the realm of the alluvium ends in the side valleys, where the maple, the poplar and the willow do not grow, that is the land of the transhumant Gujjar and Bakarwal. Such a negative attitude towards the surrounding mountains has led to the squeezing in of the peasantry within the restricted confines of the Valley floor and has further accentuated the sense of identity of the people.

The closed character of the ecosystem should, however, not be overstated. The Monsoons during the summer and the Mediterranean cyclones of the winter months bring the Valley within the orbit of climatic phenomena of far wider dimensions. The rhythm of the seasons which, more than anything else, characterizes the subcontinental ethos, underlies social activity within the confines of the Valley as well; only, there it acquires a wider range. When nature is kind, it is too kind; when it is cruel, it is alarmingly so. In the sphere of social life as well, ideas and institutions have moved across the mountains, having neither been accepted in their totality nor rejected entirely but assimilated in an ambience which is, consequently, composite in character. Shaivism, Buddhism or Islam; nationalism, communalism or communism; land reforms, adult franchise or women's lib, sericulture, trout-farming or textile designing, all these have been interwoven into a peculiarly Kashmiri fabric.

The interactions of the Valley with the surrounding territories were motivated, in the historical perspective, by six factors.

First, it may be noted that though the Valley did not lie along the highways of ancient and medieval times, it never acquired the character of a *cul-de-sac* or a blind alley and continued to be an important source of and destination for commodity flows. It is not without reason that the Pir Panjal route was till recently known as the salt route. The trade linkages between the Valley and the rest of India have been strengthened at a considerable rate since independence. What was previously a minor appendage to the subcontinental trade system is now becoming an integral part of the national home market. This may perhaps be considered as the most potent mechanism for the opening up of the semi-closed system. With every consignment of saffron, apples or handicrafts that goes out of the Valley, and of foodgrains and manufactured goods that flow into it from the rest of India, symbiotic links of interdependence are being forged and strengthened.

Secondly, the fertile Valley with a healthy climate, a flourishing agriculture-cum-handicrafts economy but a small population have attracted, during the past, military expeditions from the great empires surrounding it and based in the Indo-Gangetic valley, Central Asia and the Pathan lands. In the wake of military campaigns, economic and cultural interactions of far-reaching significance came in. However, the difficulties of access and the relative isolation of the Valley did not permit these interactions to seriously weaken the semi-closed character of the system. The exogenous elements were either fully or partly assimilated in the Kashmir polity itself, or were ejected out after an ephemeral existence as a superimposed superficial layer. The historical experience of aggrandizement by great empires has generated a deep suspicion against "aliens" which is now being strongly eroded by the new ethos of India's pluralistic democracy.

Thirdly, while itself under tremendous pressure from the great empires, Kashmiri power has had its own expansionist ambitions at the cost of small little worlds in the mountain basins surrounding it. This not only led to the establishment of Kashmiri-speaking enclaves beyond the crest but also to increasing interactions with these territories—the "barbarians" of the mountains being brought within the orbit of socio-cultural processes generated within the Valley. The situation became further complicated when the roles were reversed—for example, when the Dogras of the southern foothills brought the Valley under their control. The tension and strains of this interregional system at the meso level still continue within the framework of the Jammu and Kashmir state, particularly in the light of the unequal levels of development and of the rates of growth.

Fourthly, the system of shrines of local and regional importance in the Valley, though complete and self-sufficient, has, within itself, at least three subcontinental nodes—Amarnath, Martand and Sharda. These have attracted pilgrims from all parts of the country since ancient times, and have led to economic and cultural interactions of various degrees between the Valley and the outside world. It may however be noted that the differences between the religious persuasion of the majority of the Valley dwellers on the one hand and that of the pilgrims on the other, renders the cultural interaction between the two weak and anaemic. It is surprising that, with an overwhelming Muslim population, the Valley does not have any Muslim shrine of subcontinental status. While Kashmiri Muslims visit Ajmer or Sirhind in substantial numbers, a corresponding inflow of Muslim pilgrims to Aish Muqam, Khanyar or Chrar-i-Sharif is conspicuous by its absence. In the recent past the influx of tourists, who visit the Valley for non-religious motives, has increased considerably. This not only provides a significant input into Kashmir's economy but also leads to cultural interactions which are by and large restricted to tourist resorts and urban centres. The Kashmiri peasant accepts the tourist but generally does not interact with him.

Fifthly, the transhumant communities move across the mountains with the rhythm of the seasons, from the summer to their winter pastures. They enter into economic and trade relations with the people of the Valley. These relations are generally symbiotic and very rarely competitive. But, over the centuries, they have continued to be a distinct stream, with their own economic and social structure and their own religious shrines and institutional frame. The semi-closed system of the Valley is perhaps most strongly reflected in the fact that in spite of centuries of interaction, the Gujjar *kafila* continues to be a seasonal phenomenon in the Valley. It is generally accepted as friendly, fertilizing agricultural plots, bartering commodities, but is still considered as an ephemeral intrusion repeated year after year, leaving the placid life of the villages unaffected. The *kotha* of the Gujjar pastures, their settlements—now that some of them are settling down—and centres of their seasonal congregations are all located on the higher lands in the side valley outside the realm of the *shali* fields on the Valley floor.

Sixthly, the Kashmiri peasant, traditionally dependent on a one-crop economy under climatic constraints, has been from ancient times forced to migrate to the surrounding regions in search of livelihood during the difficult winter months, to return to his fields as soon as the thaw sets in and the *shali* shoots start sprouting. Such annual to and fro flows across the mountains have contributed to the opening up of the semi-closed system. But the rate of this process should not be over-estimated. These seasonal in-migrants in various cities of northwest India live generally huddled together in colonies of their own, with a high degree of intra-group interactions.

The space relations of the Valley have historically evolved through the interactive mechanism discussed above. An understanding of these relations is of crucial significance in any meaningful geographical interpretation of the land, the people and the economy of the Valley. These can be studied at two levels:

i) At the macro level of relationships, in terms of the political geography of ancient, medieval and modern Asia; and

ii) At the meso level of relationships, with the regions in the immediate vicinity.

From the first point of view, the Valley is located in a region where East, Central, West and South Asia meet and has been consequently in contacts of varying degrees with four major geopolitical elements:

i) The Indo-Gangetic plain with the geostrategic node at Delhi;

ii) The land of the Pathans and the Afghans and through it with the extensive realm of West Asia;

iii) Central Asia, all along the arc stretching from Balkh and Badakhshan in the west through Dushanbe, Samarkand and Bokhara to Kashghar, Yarkand and Khotan in the east; and

iv) Tibet, and through it with China.

Before the centrifugal pulls of colonial economies, linking export oriented ports with metropoles, started the processes of disrupting the natural linkage systems of Asia, the Kashmir Valley was an important link in the communication system at the hub of Asia, centripetally uniting all its important realms. Even after the destruction of the traditional linkages, Knight could still refer to this region as the meeting point of the three empires. But the statement is true in a far deeper sense than that intended by him. Is it not also, for example, the zone of interaction of the three empires of the spirit, of Hinduism, Islam and Bhuddhism, and of three linguistic realms, of the Indo-European, Dardic and Tibeto-Mongol? The unifying role of this Central Asian diamond withered away when the continent lay at the feet of imperialist conquerors and intra-Asian links fell into disuse and decay. While

colonialism is dead and a number of independent nation states have emerged on the Asian scene, the dragon's seeds sown by centuries of imperialist domination continue to bear fruit in the form of boundary disputes and interstate tensions. But these are bound to be shortlived. The advice given both by geography and history cannot be disregarded for long. One can confidently look forward to a future when the renaissance of Asia will be reflected in the rejuvenation of the arteries of its circulatory system, its heart, when the decaying *carvansarais* will be replaced by petrol pumps and motels, and in the bazaars of Srinagar and Anantnag traders from Tibet and Sinkiang, Tajikistan and Uzbekistan, Balkh and Badakhshan, from Kabul and Lahore will rub shoulders with their hosts, their Indian counterparts.

Having had a cursory look at the space relations of the Kashmir Valley at the macro level with the geopolitical realms of Asia, it may be worthwhile to focus attention on the links with the micro units lying on and along the mountain ramparts across the bounding crest. They may be analyzed in four sections:

1. ACROSS THE PIR PANJAL RANGE

To the south of the valley, across the Pir Panjal range, lies that complex web of small worlds of valleys and side valleys which, over the centuries, have sustained *thakuriats* and principalities, living, by and large, as closed systems, interacting with each other rarely—through wars, feuds and matrimonial alliances—some expanding at the cost of others, some contracting and becoming assimilated and all living under the shadows of the power based in the Kashmir Valley and within the wide orbit of Delhi-centred geopolitical entities based in the Indo-Gangetic plain. This multi-tiered system of suzerainties within suzerainties underwent kaleidoscopic changes over time and crystallized into the twenty-two principalities led by the clans noted against each on the following page.

With the dawn of independence, these self-sufficient micro worlds which were being sustained in their feudal decadence by British bayonets and trickery, have been assimilated into the Jammu and Kashmir state of India.

The role of some of the main passes through which the Valley of Kashmir was linked with the regions across the Pir Panjal range is discussed below:

a) The Banihal pass, situated at the eastern extremity of the Pir Panjal range, has been a convenient route towards the upper Chenab and the eastern portion of the Punjab hills. Owing to its low elevation, it

Principality	Clan
Jammu	Jamwal
Mankot	Mankotia
Jasrota	Jasrotia
Lakhanpur	Lakhanpuria
Samba	Sambial
Tirikot	Tirikotia
Akhnur	Akhnuria
Riasi	Riasial
Dalpatpur	Dalpatia
Bhau	Bhauwal
Bhoti	Bhatial
Chanehni	Hantal
Bandralta	Bandral
Basohli	Balauria
Bhadrawah	Bhadrawahia
Bhadu	Bhadwal
Kashtwar	Kashtwaria
Punch	Mangral
Kotli	Mangral
Rajauri	Jaral
Bhimbar	Chibh
Khari-Khariyali	Chibh

provided the only route across this range over which communication is never completely stopped by snowfall. It may be noted that the old route through the Banihal took a slightly different terrain than the one used by the national highway now. Even as recently as the later years of the 19th century, Drew mentioned the stages as Jammu, Dansal, Kiramchi, Meer, Landar, Bilaut and Ramban, the route crossing the crest between Lander and Bilaut through the Loro Lari (2,500 metres; 8,200 feet) pass. The construction of the Jawahar tunnel has for the first time in history provided a safe all-weather link between the Valley and the rest of the world. It is in this direction that the inter-regional bonds are being strengthened and the process of the opening up of the semi-closed system of the Valley is taking place most effectively.

b) The Siddau or Budil pass lies on a route which is along an almost straight line connecting Srinagar with Akhnur. It is suitable for pedestrian traffic only but has been quite popular, owing to the short duration of the trip in spite of the difficulties of terrain. According to Drew, the distance from Jammu to Srinagar by the Siddau route was 120 miles (192 kilometres), whereas along the Banihal route it came to 177 miles (225 kilometres). The name Siddau is given to the pass from the first village reached by it on the Kashmir side, while the name Budil is associated with the name of the first village across the crest.

c) Beyond the snow peak, from where the main range turns northwest, lie the passes of Rupri and Darhal, both above 3,900 metres (13,000 feet) and provide the most direct access to Rajouri—ancient Rajapuri —and are comparatively easy to traverse. Near the Darhal pass lies the Nandansar, probably the Nandana Naga of the *Nilimata*—a place of some religious significance. The route leading to it through the Darhal pass has been used by pilgrims on a considerable scale since ancient times.

d) The lowest dip in the central part of the whole range is situated about eight kilometres to the north of Nandansar. It is marked as the Pir Panjal pass, 3,491 metres (11,400 feet), and in the historical context has been the most important link with the Valley across the mountain ramparts. It has been mentioned repeatedly in ancient as well as medieval chronicles. Traditionally there have been three variants to this route:

i) The Hasti Bhanj or the Hasti water route which, according to Abul Fazal, was the route for the march of troops before the time of Akbar;

ii) The Pir Panjal route which, according to Abul Fazal, was commissioned by Akbar himself; and

iii) The Tang-Tala route.

The route which crosses the Pir Panjal pass proper is the most important of these variants and is also known as the Imperial Road or the Mughal Road, connecting Poshiana in the south to Aliabad Serai in the north. Akbar passed through this road thrice. During his first visit to Kashmir, during his stay at Poshiana, he asked Prince Saleem to go via the Hasti Water route and return by the Pir Panjal route; it was only on the basis of the report of the Prince that Akbar chose to go through the Pir Panjal pass, thus commissioning what was later to be known as the Mughal Road. Since the ceasefire line demarcating Pakistan-occupied territories of Jammu and Kashmir state of the Indian Union lies close to this route, and it has previously been involved in the military designs of Pakistan, it has fallen into disuse and an important line of communication has been thereby blocked.

e) Beyond the Pir Panjal pass to the northwest, the summit ridge is crossed by a number of high passes; for example, Sang-e-Safed, Noorpur, Chorgali. These are all difficult but may have been used for pedestrain traffic between Kashmir and ancient Lohara, and are used now by transhumant Gujjars for their seasonal migrations. It is only at the Tosh Maidan pass that we meet again with an important and ancient line of communication. It was the shortest, the safest, the easiest and the most frequented route through Poonch to the Sindh-Sagar Doab, the land of the

Ghakkars and other Pathan tribesmen. This explains the close political relations between Lohara and Kashmir in the past, as well as the presence of a substantial Kashmiri population in the present Loharin. Unfortunately, Pakistani occupation of a part of the Jammu and Kashmir has blocked this important outlet.

2. ALONG THE GORGE OF THE JHELUM

The gorge of the Jhelum from Baramulla to Muzaffarabad was the transition zone between the Khasa homelands lying to the west and the projection of Kashmir influence in the east. The dividing line was the town of Bolyasaka. This fact is corroborated by Kalhan, Abul Fazal, Jahangir and other chroniclers of ancient and medieval times. All are unanimous in explicitly stating that the territory of Kashmir started from Bolyasaka. To the west of Bolyasaka, the Valley was divided among several chiefs of the Khakha and Bomba clans who seem to have acknowledged as their nominal head the Khakha Raja of Muzaffarabad. The portion of the Valley between Muzaffarabad and Bolyasaka bore the old name of Dvaravati, from which the modern designation of this tract—Dvarbidi—is derived.

To the west of the gorge lay the territory of Urasa which occupied the Sindh-Sagar Doab in the present district of Hazara. Urasa was in constant touch with the Valley and is referred to frequently in ancient chronicles. During the medieval times, this tract was included in the region called Pakhli, which is defined by Abul Fazal as comprising the whole hill territory between Kashmir in the east and the Indus in the west. To Pakhli belonged also the lower valley of the Kishen Ganga and the valleys of the streams which flow into the latter from the Kajnag and the mountains to the northwest of Kashmir.

The Jhelum gorge is the single outlet for the waters of the Valley and has been traditionally one of the most important gateways into it. Owing to the restricted terrain, however, communication along it has always been difficult and risky. The natural difficulties were considerably increased by the restless disposition of the Khasas who have controlled the gorge since ancient times. Even during the later years of the 19th century, Moorcroft and Lawrence describe the obstacles created by these rapacious hill tribes for travellers along this route.

Nevertheless, this valley was used on a considerable scale during ancient and medieval times. Hieun Tsiang and Au-Kang, coming from ancient Gandhara and Urasa, followed it on their way to Srinagar. It was well known to Alberuni. There are frequent references

to this route in Kalhana, Srivara and Jonaraja. Abul Fazal describes it in considerable detail in connection with the return trip of Akbar from Srinagar to Lahore by the Pakhli route. Jahangir, in his memorable style, has described the hazards and beauties of this route in *Tuzuk-i-Jahangiri*. It may however be mentioned that its importance, both strategic and commercial, was, in the ancient and medieval period, far smaller than that of the Pir Panjal or the Tosh Maidan routes. It was only in modern times that the western route attained its real prominence. This originated in the time of Afghan rule over Kashmir, when the route along the Jhelum to Muzaffarabad and thence through Hazara afforded the shortest and least exposed passage between Kashmir and Peshawar. Baron Hugel quite correctly notes a Kashmiri tradition that the Baramulla route was properly opened up only about eighty years before his own visit (1835) on the arrival of the Pathans. This important lifeline of the Valley has been clogged up since 1947 owing to the aggressive designs of Pakistan.

Apart from the main route which followed the Jhelum from Baramulla to Muzaffarabad, the gorge acted as a feeder for the Haji Pir route which connected the Valley with Poonch. This side route deviates from the main route at Uri and leads across the Haji Pir pass to Poonch. This pass, owing to its lower elevation of only about 2,600 metres (8,652 feet), is never completely closed by snow. Hence, it was much used by the inhabitants of the higher valleys during winter months till 1947, when the illegal occupation of the pass by Pakistan blocked this outlet.

3. ACROSS THE NORTHERN MOUNTAINS

The space relations along the northern mountains can be meaningfully studied under three subsections.

a) At the northwestern corner of this sector lie the ancient territories of Karnah and Drava. Karnah comprised the hill district which lies immediately to the west of Kamraj, that is, the portion of the Kishen Ganga valley above Muzaffarabad and several side valleys drained by the Karnah river and its tributaries. It was generally held by small chiefs, normally tributary to Kashmir. Abul Fazal refers to the fact that Karnah was made into a *pargana* of the *sarkar* of Kashmir and separated from Kamraj. The valley of the Kishen Ganga, above its junction with the Karnah river and as far as the holy site of Sardi, formed a separate tract named Drava which, according to Stein, is probably the Duranda mentioned by Kalhana. Abul Fazal refers to it in conjunction with Karnah.

This sector was on the whole unimportant in the

space relationship of the Kashmir Valley because across the watershed, to the west, lay areas which were both politically and economically unimportant. The Kashmir areas of Samala (Hamal), Uttra (Utter) and Lolaha (Lolab) were, no doubt, in contact with Karnah and Drava across the watershed, so much so that during early Mughal times both were treated as constituent parts of Kamraj. But owing to the low level of development on both sides of the watershed, no important routes were developed. Traditional routes however, followed till recently by the pilgrims to the famous shrine of Sharda, led past the village of Drang or to the west of it, over the Sitalvan pass, or to its east, through the valley of Kroras along the Madhumati stream.

These routes were not important in themselves but considering the fact that they linked up with the routes leading directly by the Kankatori or Saraswati river and over a high pass into Chilas on the Indus, they acquired significance as an important link in the chain which joined the Indus and the Jhelum valleys.

b) As has been noted earlier, the course of the Kishen Ganga lies for a long distance above Sardi through an almost inaccessible and uninhabited gorge. Hence, for almost fifty kilometres eastwards, we find no proper route across the mountain. Beyond this gorge lies an important line of communication which connected the Valley with the Dard lands—the region of Gurez, Gilgit, Hunza, Nagar, Ishkuman and Mastuj— each one of them sprawling along the valley of one or the other of the mountainous tributaries of the Indus. The Bandipur-Gurez road now crosses the range by the Tragbal or Razdiangan pass, nearly 3,660 metres (12,000 feet) high. But the route frequented in ancient times lay some thirteen kilometres further to the east along the Dudakutta pass.

From Dudakutta pass up to Zoji-la the mountains are formidable and have had in ancient and medieval times restricted communication across them. The only line along which communication was established lay between Tilel on the Kishen Ganga and Lahara or Lar in the Sindh valley through the Satsaran pass. This line of communication was most probably developed as a result of the joining of the two routes to the Gangabal lake, one from the Sindh valley and the other from the Kishen Ganga valley.

With the bulk of the Dard territories at present under illegal Pakistani occupation, this traditional link has unfortunately been broken beyond Gurez.

c) The lowest point along the watershed between the Indus and the Jhelum basins is situated close to the junction of Harmukh with the Nanga Parbat-Nun Kun range. This pass is known by its Ladakhi name of Zoji-la. It leads at **an elevation of 4,444 metres (11,300 feet)** from the valley of the Sindh, a tributary of the Jhelum, to a high valley draining into the Dras river and thence into the Indus. In ancient times the route along this pass was undoubtedly a most important highway. It connected Kashmir with Baltistan and Ladakh—the Bhuttaland or Tibet, the land of the people of the Mongoloid race.

Ancient chronicles distinguish between the Little and the Great Bhuttaland which may be considered to be the same as *Tibet-e-Buzurg* and *Tibet-e-Khurd* of the medieval chronicles. The word Ladakh is not known to these chroniclers and there is some confusion in the indiscriminate use of the word Tibet for Baltistan, Ladakh and Tibet proper. It would be useful to recognize the distinction as given by Jesuit missionary Disideri who recognized Baltistan as the first Tibet, Ladakh as the second Tibet and Tibet proper as the third Tibet.

Au-Kong was probably the first to refer distinctly to this route when speaking of the road which leads through the "Gate in the East" to Tou-fan or Tibet. Kalhana refers to it only once as the route of the Bhuttaland, *Bhuttarastradhvan*. Through it came, early in the 14th century, the Bhautta Rinchana, whose occupation of the Kashmiri throne led to the downfall of the rule of the Hindu dynasties in the Valley. About two centuries later, Mirza Hyder, with his small Mughal force, successfully fought his entrance into Kashmir through this gateway. Since independence, impulses of growth and development have been induced into Baltistan and Ladakh along this line of communication and these regions are being brought within the orbit of the national market.

4. ACROSS THE EASTERN MOUNTAINS

Across the eastern mountain range lies the long narrow valley of the Maru-wadwan, a tributary of the Chenab. Owing to its high elevation and rigorous climate the region has been scantily populated. It is not mentioned in the ancient chronicles. Abul Fazal however refers to it as one of the *parganas* of the *sarkar* of Kashmir and Mirza Hyder describes it in some detail in connection with the entry of the Mughal army into the Valley from the Kishtwar side in pursuit of rebels.

The routes across the eastern mountains in the northern sector have been of relatively little significance because across the watershed lay an area which was considered economically and politically unimportant. There is no mention in ancient and medieval chronicles of the Margan pass, which connects the Valley with Maruwardwan. In the southern sector, however, the Marbal or the Singhpur pass has played a considerable part in linking the Kashmir Valley with Kishtwar, which has been historically the refuge of defeated factions in the Valley. It is now proposed to build a metalled road on this route. This project, when completed, would further strengthen the links between the Valley and Kishtwar.

As a result of the exploratory probings into the space relations of Kashmir Valley, one comes up with a spatial mosaic of tremendous complexity—of a process of systems within systems, each opening up steadily in-

to the one above in the hierarchical order. Since economic development in the area is still in its early stages, the interregional linkages are still weak and the regional structure still fragile. Rapid rates of growth, both in the Valley and the surrounding regions of the country, combined with an imaginative approach towards pluralism in a democratic set-up within the republic alone can hasten the opening up of the semi-closed system through strengthening interdependence to national as well as regional advantage.

Glossary

Ab	Water
Abpashi	Irrigation
Bahil	Loamy soil
Bakarwals	Gujjar bakarwals, a transhumant group
Bund	A small, earthen dam or embankment
Dal	Lake
Dand	Cattle
Dazanlad	Clayey soil on the periphery of swamps
Dok	Grazing ground (Gujjar)
Dont	Hail
Drag	Famine
Duns	Longitudinal valleys in the Himalayas
Grishim	Summer
Grist	Agriculture
Gurti	Silty soil
Harud	Autumn
Hel	Manure
Kadal	Bridge
Kanah	Stone
Karewa	Lacustrine deposits
Kharzamin	Soil infested with salts
Kuhl	Water channel for irrigation
Lemb	Soil tract around a natural spring
Margs	Meadows
Nag	Spring of water
Nala	Stream; rivulet
Nambal	Swamp; swampy soil
Nur	Grazing ground
Pantsal	Mountain
Rab	Mud
Rad	Soils of the floating fields
Rai	A common disease of paddy crop caused by excessive manuring
Ront	Parched, clayey soil
Rud	Rain
Runan	Plant
Sek	Sand
Sekil	Sandy soil
Shath	Sandy soils on a river bank
Shin	Snow
Sont	Spring day
Sorth	Spring
Sheshur	Severe cold
Surhzamin	Excessively manured soil
Sut	Bank
Tahsil	A revenue subdivision within a district
Tand	Depleted soil on the periphery of a forested tract and reclaimed from it
Tap	Sunshine
Tats	Pebbly soils
Thara	Bush
Thathri	Grass
Tir	Sheep, a flock of sheep
Udar	Karewa
Van	Forest
Vitasta	Jhelum
Wahrat	Rainy season
Wand	Winter
Zabalzamin	Highly saturated soil due to irrigation
Zand	Mist

Abbreviations

Agr. Jour. India	*Agricultural Journal of India*
Annl. Assoc. Am. Geog.	*Annals of the Association of American Geographers*
ASSOC. Thesis	Associateship thesis of the Indian Agricultural Research Institute
Curr. Sc.	*Current Science*
Geog. Rev. Ind.	*Geographical Review of India*
Geol. Soc. Am. Bull.	Geoglogical Society of America, *Bulletin*
IARI	Indian Agricultural Research Institute
I.M.D.	India Meteorological Department
Ind. Jour. Ag. Sc.	*Indian Journal of Agricultural Science*
Ind. Jour. Met. Geophys.	*Indian Journal of Meteorology and Geophysics*
Int. Geol. Cong.	International Geological Congress
Mem. Ind. Met. Dept.	*Memoirs* of the India Meteorological Department
Mem. GSI	*Memoirs* of the Geological Survey of India
Pak. Jr. Sc.	*Pakistan Journal of Science*
Proc. Nat. Inst. Sc. Ind.	*Proceedings of the National Institute of Sciences of India* (now Indian National Academy of Science)
Pusa Ag. Res. Inst. Bull.	*Pusa Agricultural Research Institute Bulletin*
Quart. Jour. Roy. Met. Soc.	*Quarterly Journal of the Royal Meteorological Society*
Rec. GSI	*Records* of the Geological Survey of India
Res. Rept. Met. Dept.	Research Reports of the US Meteorological Department
SOI	Survey of India
SSAC	Soil Survey and Agricultural Chemistry Unit of the Indian Agricultural Research Institute

List of Maps and Diagrams

List of Tables

List of Illustrations

Contents

Chapter One

In the Womb of the Himalaya

... Formerly, since the beginning of the Kalpa, the
land in the womb of the *Himalaya* was filled with water
during the periods of the (first) six Manus (and formed)
the Lake of Sati (Satisaras).
... That (land is protected by *Nila*, the lord of all
Nagas, whose regal parasol is formed by the circular
pond (of the Nilakunda) with the *Vitasta's* newly rising
stream as its stick.
... There Gauri, though she has assumed the form of
the *Vitasta*, still keeps her wonted inclination. (For in
her river shape) she turns her face towards the ravine
(*Guha*).
... To protect, forsooth, the Nagas who came (to
seek shelter) afraid of Garuda, it has stretched out its
arms high, above in the guise of mountain-walls. ...
—Kalhana in *Rajatarangini* (First Book, 25, 28, 29, 31)

The Kashmir Valley is a longitudinal depression in the
great northwestern complex of the Himalayan ranges,
and thus constitutes an important relief feature of geographic significance. Carved out tectonically, the
Valley has a strong genetic relationship with the
Himalayan complex which exercises an all-pervading
influence on its geographical personality. Knowledge
of the Valley and of the surrounding mountain ramparts would remain incomplete without a comprehensive understanding of the entire complex of topography
of which it is an integral part. An investigation into
the structural and geomorphologic features of the
macro region therefore becomes imperative in view of
the dominating influence which this Himalayan complex exercises on the water and air circulation of the
highlands of Central Asia, on its climate and physiography and on the distribution of people and their
activities.

On a macro level, it is customary to divide the Himalayan mountain chain into four sections: the Punjab
Himalayas, the Kumaon Himalayas, the Nepal Himalayas, the Assam Himalayas.[1] The Punjab Himalayas
are separated from the Kumaon Himalayas by the
Sutlej defile which cuts across the Zaskar, the Great
Himalayan and the Lesser Himalayan ranges at almost
right angles.

The exact geographical limits of the northwestern
Himalayan complex would be difficult to define. It is
however to be noted that the complex is more or less
conterminous with the Punjab Himalayas, incorporat-
ing all land between the sources of the Sutlej on the
one hand and the Pamir on the other. It is necessary
to identify the essential geographical lineaments of the
larger frame in order to evolve a better understanding
of the position which Kashmir Valley occupies in the
entire complex.

There have been two major motives behind this
attempt. First, to recognize the links which the Jhelum
Valley possesses with the larger region that constitutes
the northwestern complex of mountain ranges; and
secondly, to develop a better understanding of its structural and physico-geographical determinants as mani-
festing themselves in the make-up of its personality.

EARLY REFERENCES

The northwestern Himalayan region, with its high
mountain ranges, lush meadows and snowclad peaks
has inspired generations of philosophers, poets and
mystics throughout our history. The region finds
reference in the historical and quasi-historical literature, ancient texts, chronicles, travel accounts and in
the folklore of India. It is mentioned in ancient
Indian,[2] Arab and Greek sources as well as in the iti-
neraries of the Greek, Chinese and Arab travellers or

pilgrims who entered India at different points of time. The Buddhist and the Jain texts of the 4th and the 5th centuries B.C. mention the various Himalayan rivers, glaciers and peaks. Among ancient texts, the Puranas are by far the richest source containing a plethora of information on the physical features of the northwestern Himalayan region.

A fairly accurate account of the principal mountain ranges of the north and the northwest appears in ancient Indian literature.[3] Accepting the identification of S.M. Ali, one can conclude that the Pamir vertex was known to the Puranics as Meru. The Puranas noted in *Srngavan*, *Sweta* and *Nila*, the three principal mountain ranges splaying out of the Meru to its north. To the south lay the three great ranges of *Nisadha*, *Himakuta* (also referred to as *Denakuta*) and *Himalaya* (or *Himavana*). The Puranics described the southern ranges in great detail while the northern ranges were only vaguely known to them and the description is highly sketchy.[4] In some of the Puranas, the Karakoram is mentioned as Krishnagiri (black mountains).[5] About the Kailasa[6] the popular belief is that it is the abode of Siva and Parvati.[7] As it had a number of lofty peaks, the range was described as the king of mountains. Ancients described the Sulaiman mountains as Anjana.[8]

By the close of the 19th century authentic geological and geographical accounts of the northwestern Himalayas begin to appear. Notable among the earlier accounts are those of Schlagintweit and Colonel Tanner.[9] The former believed that on the western side of the Indus the Himalaya and the Karakoram could not be separated into chains and that they formed one single mountain mass, which decreased in altitude towards the west—a view not at all valid now. Colonel Tanner, writing twenty years after Schlagintweit, described the area between the Indus and the Kunar at great length.[10] Richard Lydekker,[11] in his survey of the physiography of this region, also referred to the uniformity of elevation which prevails in the area to the northwest of the Indus.

PHYSICAL LAYOUT

The Valley of Kashmir has an intrinsic genetic relationship with the complex of mountain systems which splay out of the Pamir Knot in different directions. The mountain systems literally fuse into the Pamir vertex which holds a pivotal position in the frame of the northwestern complex. The Pamir, along with Hindu Kush, Karakoram, the Sarikol-Muztagh and the Pamir-Alay-Tien-Shan ranges forms the water parting between the two inland systems of drainage, one ending in the Aral Sea, and the other in the lagoons of Lob Nor. The Pamir complex is a congregation of diverse relief features of great complexity and not a mere plateau as the popular notion goes. Broadly speaking, it consists of two distinct divisions: an eastern half which has the character of an upland, and a western half studded with transverse mountain ranges running parallel to one another.

Among the mountain systems that bifurcate from the Pamir vertex are the Hindu Kush, Muztagh, Karakoram and the Ladakh and the Great Himalayan ranges on the south, southeast and the southwest; Pamir Alay, Trans-Alay, and Tien-Shan on the northeast; and the Kun Lun and the Aghil ranges on the east and southeast. Arranged in series of massive ranges these mountains are believed to have been formed at different stages during the Himalayan, and even Ataid, orogeny (Fig. 1.1).

Conventionally, the northwestern Himalayan complex is divided into four parallel zones differing from one another in their geomorphic, hydrographical and vegetational features.[12] These zones are:

i) Trans- or Tibetan Himalaya

ii) Great or Inner Himalaya

iii) Lesser Himalaya

iv) Sub-Himalaya, or the Outer Himalaya, known as the Siwaliks

The Trans-Himalaya on the Tibetan side lies behind the Great Himalayan range and, at many places, is pierced by the southward flowing rivers with their basins nestled at altitudes of 3,000 to 4,000 metres. Occupying a width of approximately 40 kilometres, it is made up of sedimentary formations highly fossiliferous and belonging to a period of time ranging from Palaeozoic to Eocene (Figs. 1.2; 1.3).

The Great Himalaya, with an average height of 6,000 metres and having numerous snowclad peaks, forms a single mountain chain of great importance.

The Lesser Himalaya consists of a series of ranges closely aligned to or bifurcating from the Great Himalaya with an elevation ranging between 3,700 and 4,500 metres and an average width of 60 to 80 kilometres. These ranges are constituted by formations belonging to the Purana (Eparchaean, or Cuddapah and Vindhyan), Palaeozoic and Mesozoic times. The Pir Panjal and the Dhaula Dhar ranges of the northwestern complex are aligned parallel to the Great Himalayan range up to Zoji-la and beyond to the north Kashmir range which separates the Jhelum from the Kishenganga.

TRENDS OF THE PRINCIPAL MOUNTAIN RANGES IN THE NORTH-WESTERN HIMALAYAN COMPLEX

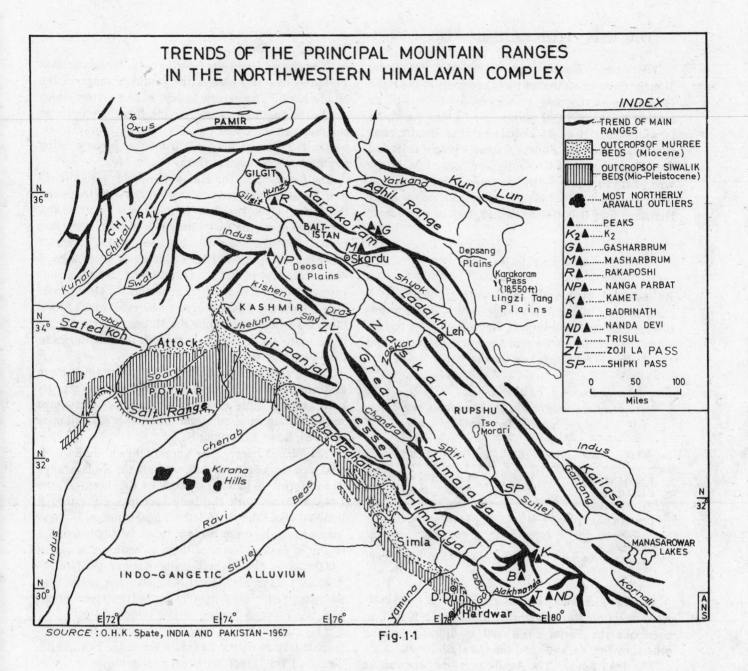

INDEX

- ⌇⌇⌇ TREND OF MAIN RANGES
- ░░░ OUTCROPS OF MURREE BEDS (Miocene)
- ▥▥▥ OUTCROPS OF SIWALIK BEDS (Mio-Pleistocene)
- ⬛ MOST NORTHERLY ARAVALLI OUTLIERS
- ▲ PEAKS
- K₂▲ K2
- G▲ GASHARBRUM
- MA MASHARBRUM
- R▲ RAKAPOSHI
- NPA NANGA PARBAT
- K▲ KAMET
- B▲ BADRINATH
- ND▲ NANDA DEVI
- T▲ TRISUL
- ZL ZOJI LA PASS
- SP SHIPKI PASS

0   50   100
Miles

SOURCE : O.H.K. Spate, INDIA AND PAKISTAN—1967

Fig.1·1

BLOCK SECTION OF KASHMIR HIMALAYAS

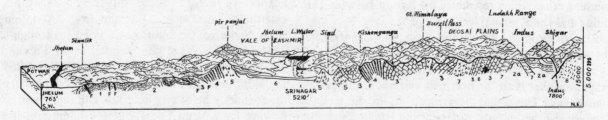

Fig.1·2 BLOCK SECTION OF KASHMIR HIMALAYAS (POTWAR TO LADAKH). LINE OF SECTION ON BEARING 38° FOR 690KM. FROM JHELUM TOWN TO INDUS BELOW SHYOK CONFLUENCE. GEOLOGY (BASED ON de TERRA) DIAGRAMMATIC : I, SIWALIKS; 2, MURREE; 2a, FLYSCH; 3, PERMO-CARBO. (THRUST ON TO 2), AND 'TETHYS' FORMATION (U·PERMIAN CRETACEOUS) IN NORTHEAST; 4, OLDER PALAEOZOIC; 5, YOUNGER PALAEO-ZOIC IGNEOUS; 6, KAREWAS BEDS; 7, CRET.– EOCENE ERUPTIVES; 8, GRANITES. F, MAJOR FAULTS AND THRUSTS.

SOURCE: Spate, O.H.K. AND Learmonth, A.T.A., INDIA AND PAKISTAN, 1967.

The lowly Siwalik hills constitute the Outer Himalayan zone on the northern periphery of the Indo-Ganga plains, forming a series of foothills with an average height of 1,000 metres only. This zone varies in width from 10 to 15 kilometres. The Siwalik zone is widest around the Potwar plateau where it is skirted by the salt range on the south, and narrowest in the area where the Ravi-Sutlej line forms a defile across it. At places the Siwalik hills are separated from the lesser Himalaya by flat-bottomed valleys, termed as "duns."

MOUNTAIN RANGES

As indicated earlier, the northwestern complex is a congregation of mountain ranges which act as water-divides between the divergent drainage systems consisting of the Indus on the one hand and the Oxus and the Yarkand (Zarafshan) on the other (Fig. 1.4).

TABLE I
Height of the snowline in the mountain ranges of the northwestern complex

Range	Latitude	Height of snowline
Kailasa range	34°	6,000-7,000 metres
Ladakh range	34°	7,000-7,250 metres
Zaskar range	34°	5,800-6,750 metres
Dhaola Dhar range	31°	7,000 metres

Courtesy: Burrard and Hayden, *A Sketch of the Geography and Geology of the Himalaya Mountains and Tibet*, first edition, p. 116.

The Kun Lun Shan. Running by and large in an east-west direction through northern Tibet the Kun Lun overlooks the Tarim basin and is drained, among others, by the Yarkand and the Qaratash rivers.

The Aghil Range. The Aghil range lies between the Kun Lun and the Karakoram ranges along the upper courses of the Yarkand river, in an area of extremely complex relief which resembles the terrain between the Indus and the Kunar rivers.

The Hindu Kush. The Hindu Kush, which represents the western continuation of the Karakoram, consists of two separate parallel ranges. Of these, the southern range is higher than the northern and has a number of high peaks. The Gilgit river which drains the trough between the two parallel ranges of the Hindu Kush for about 64 kilometres escapes through the southern range; the crests of the two ranges being 23 kilometres apart in the Gilgit basin. The Hunza, on the other hand, rises beyond the southern range and cuts through

it. The Kunar drains the interior of the trough for over 75 kilometres and pierces the southern range of the Hindu Kush. The narrow valleys of these rivers which pierce the southern range provide the only routes of communication. Otherwise, the range has only a few passes, the Darkot pass, 5,250 metres, perhaps being the most conspicuous of them.

The Karakoram. The Karakoram holds a significant position as it separates two great basins—the Indus and the Tarim. Geologists believe that the Karakoram and the Hindu Kush are two different sections of the same crustal fold. The fold which passes through western Tibet in a southeast-northwest direction forms a band around the Hunza and the Gilgit rivers off Chitral and enters Afghanistan from the northeast. The Shyok, Gilgit, Hunza and Kunar rivers drain the trough below the Karakoram range while the Nubra river rises in the Karakoram itself. All these streams are tributaries to the Indus (Fig. 1.6).

It is interesting to note that the Karakoram is more arid and less wooded than the Himalayan ranges. Its hard granitic strata and precipitous slopes discourage soil-formation, and whatever meagre precipitation is received, flows down rapidly.

The Kailasa Range. The Karakoram and the Sarikol-Muztagh merge towards the east into the Kailasa range which forms a parallel system to the north of the Ladakh range, with the Indus occupying the trough between the Kailasa and the Ladakh ranges.[13] Near Mansarowar lake the Kailasa range is studded with a cluster of peaks, several of them exceeding a height of 6,000 metres, the highest being Kailasa itself (6,714 metres).[14] East of Mansarowar lake the range runs uninterruptedly as a parallel trans-Himalayan range, with the Tsangpo flowing on its southern flank.

The Ladakh Range. Since it is the principal topographic feature of the Ladakh region, Godwin Austin described this range as the Ladakh range. West of Mansarowar lake the range follows the Indus, and its relation to the Indus river is of great geological significance. In fact, the Indus and the Ladakh range are essentially intertwined. For the first 290 kilometres from its source, the Indus flows along the trough north of the Ladakh range and parallel to it. For another 500 kilometres it flows along the southern flank of the Ladakh range, and then passes back to the north of the range shortly before its junction with the Shyok. After flowing for a stretch of about 160 kilometres it again cuts across the range for the third time.

The fact that there is a comparatively open trough on either flank of the Ladakh range, which is occupied by the Indus in its various reaches, should not over-

SECTION ACROSS KASHMIR HIMALAYAS:
Punjab Plains to Tarim Basin

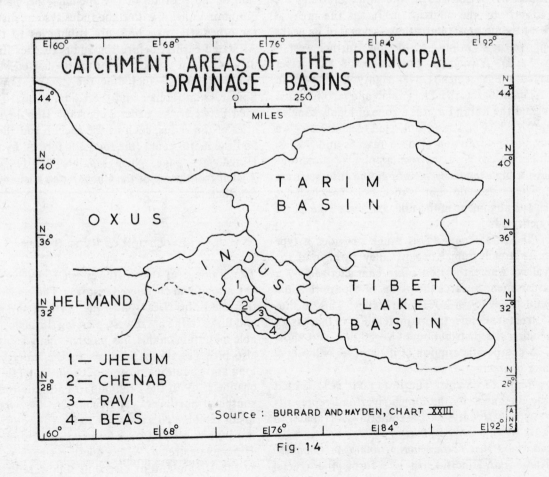

① PUNJAB PLAIN	⑤ N. KASHMIR RANGE	⑨ MASHERBRUM	⑬ YARKAND RIVER
② SIWALIK HILLS	⑥ GREAT HIMALAYA RANGE	⑩ K₂	⑭ KUENLUN RANGE
③ PIR PANJAL RANGE	⑦ LADAKH RANGE	⑪ OPRANG RIVER	⑮ TARIM PLAINS
④ KASHMIR VALLEY	⑧ INDUS RIVER	⑫ AGHIL RANGE	

SOURCE : BURRARD AND HYDEN (CHART-I)   Fig. 1·3

CATCHMENT AREAS OF THE PRINCIPAL DRAINAGE BASINS

TARIM BASIN

OXUS

INDUS

HELMAND

TIBET LAKE BASIN

1 — JHELUM
2 — CHENAB
3 — RAVI
4 — BEAS

Source : BURRARD AND HAYDEN, CHART XXIII

Fig. 1·4

shadow the fact that serious impediments occur all along in its way which have forced it to cut spectacular gorges. It is generally held that the two processes of upwarping and downcutting have been concurrent, that is, "the Ladakh range has grown since the Indus began to flow, and that like a tree trunk embraced by a creeper, it has in its expansions had grooves cut across it by the river."[15]

The Zaskar Range. The Zaskar range bifurcates from the Great Himalayan range to the north of Nanda Devi and a little east of Kamet. Running along a southeast-northwest axis, the Zaskar forms a parallel chain to the northeast of the Great Himalayan range and is pierced by the Sutlej and the Zaskar rivers.

The Great Himalayan range is a lofty mountain chain culminating in the Nanga Parbat and enclosing Kashmir Valley on the north, northwest and northeast. A detailed account of its layout and physical features will be more relevant in a forthcoming chapter.

The North Kashmir Range. Bifurcated from the Great Himalaya near the Zoji-La pass, the north Kashmir range constitutes the watershed between the Jhelum and the Kishenganga, the latter draining the angle formed by the bifurcation. It has the greatest altitude at the point of bifurcation—several of its peaks rising above the snowline—but declines further west.

The Lesser Himalayas. The zone of the lesser Himalayan ranges extends over eighty kilometres in width. Consisting of the Pir Panjal and a bifurcated chain called the Ratan Pir, it is a zone of highly tangled topography which has been subjected to severe erosion resulting in the formation of deep ravines and defiles. The ranges do not have any regular plan of directions and have a high tendency of bifurcating into separate ridges. They also do not show any concordance between the alignment of the hills and the strike of the component beds.

The Pir Panjal Range. This range provides a type case in its stretch from Khagan valley to beyond the Ravi valley, where the ridges are characterized by a steep escarpment towards the plains of the south and a long gentle slope towards Kashmir Valley. This "ortho-clinal" structure defines the major features of its character including the distribution of vegetation and snow cover. A detailed description of its features will follow in a later chapter.

The Ratan Pir Range. The Ratan Pir is separated from the Pir Panjal by the Punch river and represents the western extremity of the outermost Himalayan ranges.

Drainage of the Northwestern Himalayan Complex. The Karakoram-Hindu Kush line forms the crucial watershed between the three principal drainage basins of Central Asia—the Indus, the Tarim and the Amu (Fig. 1.5). There are, however, three upper headstreams of the Indus system which provide exceptions to this generalization: they are the headstreams of the Shyok, the Gilgit, and the Kunar. Barring these three cases, all other streams originating on the northern, northwestern and northeastern slopes of the Karakoram and the Hindu Kush ranges either flow towards the east into the Tarim basin or towards the west, as tributaries of the Amu Darya (Oxus). The area of divergence between the three systems lies somewhere along the line formed by the Sarikol-Aghil ranges, and certainly on the southern and southeastern flanks of the latter. It is from here that the Ab-i-Panja and Ab-i-Wakhan, the headstreams of the Amu are diverted to the west, the Tash Qurghan (Almaligh tributary of the Yarkand) flows to the east and the Hindu Kush feeders of the Indus, as represented by the upper streams of the Gilgit, Hunza and the Kunar systems, flow to the south.

The water-divide between the Amu, the Tarim and the Indus systems thus delineated leads to the recognition of the position of the Jhelum—the main river of Kashmir Valley—within the Indus system, distinct from the other streams which are tributaries to the Indus. As stated earlier, before the Indus reaches its point of debouchure at Attock, it carries the united waters of its minor tributaries including the Zaskar, Dras, Shyok, Shigar, Gilgit-Hunza and the Kabul rivers. The watershed between the other important Himalayan tributaries of the Indus, such as the Jhelum and the Chenab, and the mainstream (the Indus) is formed by the Great Himalayan range which separates the feeders of the Zaskar from those of the Chenab, the Kishenganga and the Jhelum.

EVOLUTION OF RIVER SYSTEMS

The drainage of the northwestern Himalayan complex has a long and chequered history. The remarkable fact that the Indus rises well to the north of the Himalayas and flows to the northwest, piercing through the formidable mountain chains, has puzzled many researchers. It also provides the basic clues to the unfolding of the long and circuitous process of evolution of the drainage channels. Both the Brahmaputra and the Indus have a southeast-northwest alignment in the trans-Himalayan region. This gives rise to the conjecture that perhaps the two rivers once formed part of a mighty trans-Himalayan stream. While questions, such as the source of this stream and its direction of flow, remain unresol-

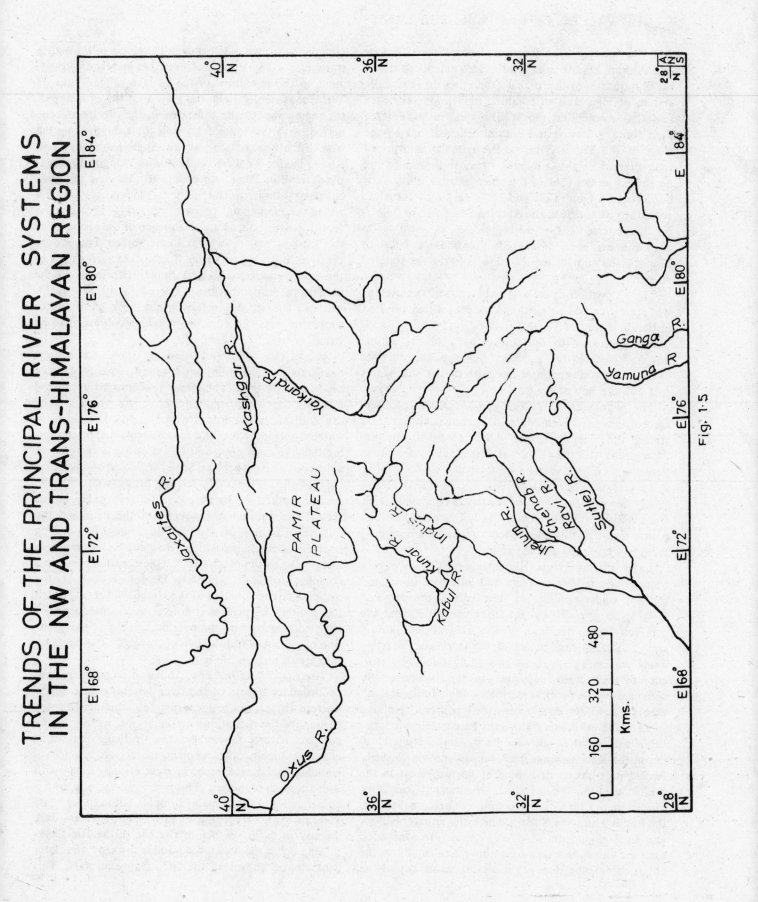

TRENDS OF THE PRINCIPAL RIVER SYSTEMS IN THE NW AND TRANS-HIMALAYAN REGION

Fig. 1·5

ved, the theory still holds good. Two scholars, Pascoe and Pilgrim, hypothesized on this idea independently in the first quarter of this century, building up the whole system of logic and marshalling tremendous evidence scattered throughout the Siwalik zone in support of their views.[16] Pascoe and Pilgrim believed that by the close of the Tertiary, before the Himalayas attained their present height, a mighty stream[17] flowed to the northwest at the foot of the emergent mountain mass bordering on Gondwanaland. It seems that the river continued its course to the Arabian Sea, perhaps following the course of the existing lower Indus. Pilgrim cites the evidence of the Siwalik boulder beds to support the northwesterly flow of the postulated stream.

The dislocation in the original layout of the streams was mainly caused by earth movements which resulted in the damming of Siwalik river beyond Kangra, and, in conjunction with the cutting back of the south-flowing rivers in the Rajmahal-Shillong water-divide, facilitated the diversion of drainage to the south and east into the Bay of Bengal.

The alignment of the Tsangpo-Mansarowar-Sutlej-Gartang-Indus line led Pascoe to envisage another great stream, the "Tibetan River," which flowed to the west throughout the length of the Himalayan zone from Pemakoi to Gilgit. Pascoe postulated it to be flowing northwestwards to the Oxus. Pascoe's Tibetan river was finally dismembered by the Himalayan upheaval which created disruptions in its way. It was suggested that its course in the northwestern sector might have been captured by the Sutlej and the Indus.

Later studies in the Himalayan region, especially those conducted by de Terra and Paterson, developed a new understanding of the whole problem of Himalayan rivers.[18] In fact, they contended that the pre-Pleistocene drainage of the Ladakh-Karakoram region flowed from northwest to southeast, possibly along the Tsangpo to Tibet or even beyond. The evidence of the Siwalik deposits was too incoherent to convince de Terra to subscribe to the "Indo-Brahm" theory which he hastily discarded without resolving some of the valid issues which the Pascoe-Pilgrim hypothesis attempted to answer. Partly, some explanation lies in the Kailasa range itself, whose uplift in the Sub-Recent past has created some of the problems in the evolution of the Indus system. Significantly, de Terra dismissed the idea of a structural connection between the Ladakh and the Kailasa which the apparent topographical alignments so often suggest. He contended that the Indus, whether seen above Leh or above the Gilgit confluence, does not really cut across any of the

Himalayan ranges—its bend and the course through a transverse valley being interpreted as merely an adjustment to the re-entrant of the Ladakh range. Thus de Terra consistently held the view that the drainage of the region was to the southeast in the pre-Pleistocene period; with the Indus following the trough along the base of the Karakoram-Ladakh ranges from Gilgit and thence having a course similar to the Tsangpo-Brahmaputra trend in Tibet. According to this view the critical separation between the Indus-Tsangpo systems is a recent phenomenon, perhaps occurring in the most recent Pleistocene, as a consequence of the upheaval of the Kailasa region, which finally forced Tsangpo to draw its headstreams from the southeastern slopes of the newly-emergent Kailasa range. The Indus in the process of dismemberment charted for itself a northwesterly course, still receiving the bulk of the water supply from its earlier affluents which continued to be tributary to it.

While the Indus adjusted to these stupendous developments, the Sutlej underwent an equally complex phase of evolution. The major problems arise from the fact that the Sutlej has an upper course which is quite dry and totally discordant with the present volume of water supply it carries. This may be explained by supposing that the river course in this stretch is a remnant of an earlier phase when the Sutlej served as an outlet for the so-called Tibetan River, as fitting well into the schema worked out by Pascoe. The river course, in this sector, lies between the courses of the Beas and the Giri, a tributary of the Yamuna, and the puzzling problem as Spate poses, is: "How the Sutlej has been inset between the other two." One explanation to this complex problem is offered by Davies who believes the Sutlej to be the youngest of the Himalayan rivers, which has assumed its present character as a consequence of the "collapse of the main Himalayan axis along the line of an old Gondwana fault-trough." The explanation seems to be fairly convincing.[19]

Drainage Pattern. The above discussion of the evolutionary history of the river systems of the northwestern Himalayan region brings out the fact that the rivers, like the mountains of the region, have a highly complex nature. Obviously, the drainage pattern is characteristically antecedent as the region has seen a simultaneous development of river systems along with the orogenic processes. The river systems are not a consequence of the Himalayan uplift but in many cases anterior to it. According to this view, the rivers were already in existence before the rise of the Himalayas flowing down the Tibetan landmass towards what later came to be known as the Indo-Gangetic plain. This

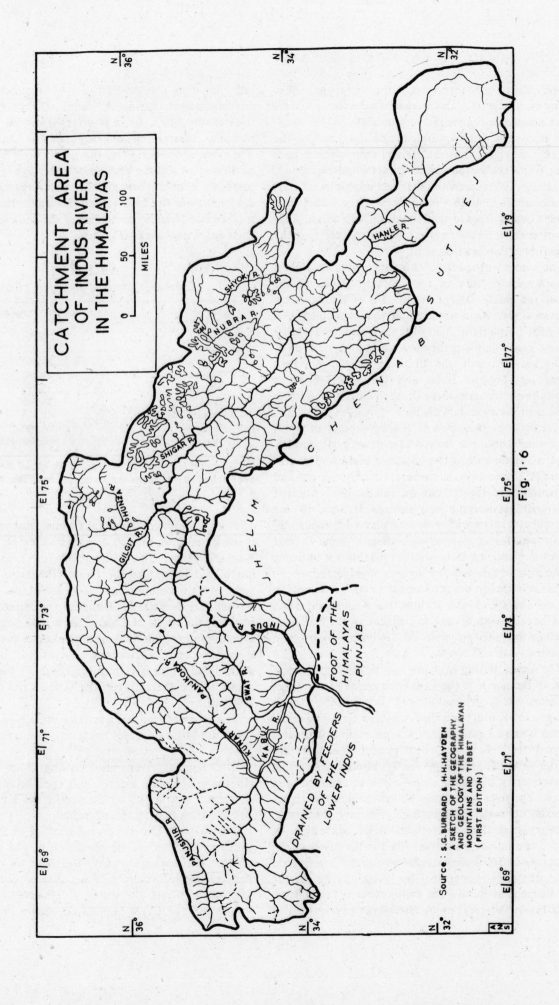

CATCHMENT AREA
OF INDUS RIVER
IN THE HIMALAYAS

MILES

0   50   100

SHYOK R.

NUBRA R.

HANLE R.

SHIGAR R.

HUNZA R.

HUNZA R.

GILGIT R.

DRAS R.

CHENAB

SUTLEJ

JHELUM

INDUS R.

PANJKORA R.

SWAT R.

KUNAR R.

KABUL R.

PANJSHIR R.

DRAINED BY FEEDERS
OF THE
LOWER INDUS

FOOT OF THE
HIMALAYAS
PUNJAB

E 69°   E 71°   E 73°   E 75°

N 36°

N 34°

N 32°

E 69°   E 71°   E 73°   E 75°   E 77°   E 79°

N 36°

N 34°

N 32°

S I Z A

Source : S.G.BURRARD & H.H.HAYDEN
A SKETCH OF THE GEOGRAPHY
AND GEOLOGY OF THE HIMALAYAN
MOUNTAINS AND TIBBET
(FIRST EDITION)

Fig. 1·6

pattern continued throughout the orogenic phase during which the Himalayan ranges were formed, with the consequence that with every upheaval of the land-mass transverse gorges were cut and deepened in the ranges. The rivers thus maintained their original beds intact while the bordering landmass lifted higher up. The Indus rivers provide the best examples of this process. In fact, both the Indus and the Sutlej flow through deep gorges in the Himalayas, often thousands of metres (3,000-5,000 metres) below the crest of the bordering precipices (Fig. 1.5).

The antecedent nature of this drainage is not only a characteristic feature of the southern slopes of the Himalayas but to a large extent also of the northern Tibetan slopes. One outcome of this phenomenon is seen in the mountain chain which is found not along its highest peaks but a great distance to the north of it. For great distances the drainage of the northern slopes—notably the Indus and the Sutlej—flows in longitudinal troughs through the Tibetan landmass parallel to the mountain chain.

Having been subjected to a long process of uplift and rejuvenation, the valleys have developed a compli-cated character with juxtaposition of senile and youth-ful traits. The valley surfaces are highly uneven and frequented by cataracts, rapids, and the like. Another important geomorphic development is seen in the predominant network of rectangular or "trapezoid" topographic features occurring between valleys. Former phases of glaciation have also left indubitable evidence in the form of lakes and recurrence of gravel terraces.[20]

It is intended to describe here the major rivers of the region—the Indus, the Jhelum, the Kishenganga and the Chenab—with a view to delineating the Valley of Kashmir on the principle of catchment basins and divides.

The Indus. Rising in the vicinity of the Mansarowar lake, to the north of the Ladakh range, the Indus takes a northwesterly course flowing through the trough between the Kailasa and the Ladakh ranges. The initial stream is known as the Senge Khambab up to Thangra. Beyond this place the river pierces the mountain barrier—the Ladakh range—and continues to flow in a northwesterly direction along the inner flank of the range. The river once again pierces the Ladakh range, receiving soon after its right bank tributary, the Shyok, from across the Karakoram and the Kailasa ranges. A third and another spectacular bend in the course of the river is seen 160 kilometres downstream from Skardu where the river cuts across the Ladakh range for the third time near Bunji. The Indus gorge between Bunji and Hazara is typical of the Himalayan rivers, the river

bed lying deep between 900 to 1,400 metres below the skirting mountain rim. At Bunji, the course of the river is due south, till it is diverted, by the mountain complex culminating at Nanga Parbat, to the west. The river again bends to the south near Sazin, west northwest of Chilas and passes through a long and tortuous course through the Himalayan range to debouch from the hills at Attock. Table II shows the major trans-Himalayan streams of the Indus along with their catchment areas (Fig. 1.6).

TABLE II
Catchment areas of the Indus river

Streams	Catchment area (sq. km)
Kabul	90,600
Shyok	33,410
Gilgit	20,464
Zaskar	20,464
Shinghi	17,870
Dras	12,769
Shigar	12,769
Indus	268,907
Jhelum	34,747

Courtesy: Hayden and Burrard, *A Sketch of the Geography and Geology of the Himalaya Mountains and Tibet*, first edition, p. 131.

The Kishenganga. As already noted, Kashmir Valley is separated from the Kishenganga valley by the north Kashmir range. The Kishenganga catchment in the north is delimited by the Great Himalayan range as some of its tributaries flow down the slopes of Nanga Parbat (8,126 metres). Rising in the mountain com-plex to the west of Dras and to the south of the Deosai plateau, the Kishenganga receives the waters of a number of tiny tributaries. At Shardi, it makes a sharp bend which is akin to the bends of the Indus at Bunji, of the Jhelum at Wular, and of the Chenab at Kishtwar.

The Kishenganga has a narrow and elongated basin the width in many places being only twenty kilometres or so.

The Kunhar river, also flowing from the same mountain complex, merges into the Jhelum south of its great bend at the confluence of the Kishenganga and the Jhelum near Muzaffarabad.

The Jhelum. The northern boundary of the Jhelum valley in Kashmir is thus delineated by the watershed of the Kishenganga valley, the crest of the north Kashmir range forming the water-divide. On the south and the northeast, the valley is delineated by the Pir Panjal and the Great Himalayan ranges respectively.

The Pir Panjal, in its own way, acts as a watershed between the catchment areas of the Punch, the Chenab and the Jhelum rivers. Thus the southern and the eastern slopes of the Pir Panjal are drained by the affluents of the Chenab. Towards the east, in the Amarnath region, the glaciers on the precipices of the Great Himalayan range separate the waters of Suru and Dras from the Sind and the Liddar rivers. Similarly, the Wadwan-Marau, which are affluents of the Chenab, rise from the Amarnath glacial region and are separated from the headstreams of the Liddar and the Sind by a ridge of the Great Himalaya (4,429 to 4,638 metres).

The Jhelum itself rises from the Pir Panjal range near Vernag. Initially, the river flows in a north-westerly direction, but at its exit from the Wular lake, it takes a southwesterly direction which it pursues as far as Baramulla where it finally leaves the valley in Kashmir, escaping through a gorge in the Pir Panjal range. This upper basin of the Jhelum lies in the trough between the Great Himalaya and the Pir Panjal ranges, popularly known as the Vale of Kashmir.

DELINEATION OF THE KASHMIR VALLEY

The above discussion of the physiographic features of the northwestern Himalayan complex lays down the very premise for the identification of Kashmir Valley as situated within the frame of the mountain systems which define clearly the watersheds and basins. As noted above, the essential elements in its identity emerge from the following facts:

i) A valley is defined by its drainage network and theoretically includes all land that lies within the two ridges from crest to crest which form the watershed and determine the layout of the drainage channels within the valley;

ii) the concept of "catchment basin" makes it imperative to include all the affluent streams which are tributary to the main stream holding the basal position in the drainage taxonomy of the valley;

iii) as an extension of the same logic and for the purpose of a rational definition, it would be necessary to distinguish and delink the affluent streams of the same river which sometimes do not contribute to the drainage of the valley, though they form an integral part of the larger catchment basin, of which the drainage of the valley is a component.

Within the frame of the above theoretical constructs an attempt has been made to delineate the Kashmir Valley, as located within the gamut of drainage channels of the northwestern Himalayan complex (Fig.1.7). The entire complex of the drainage systems has been given a definite hierarchal ordering, and the micro catchment basins have been desegregated from the meso and the micro basins. This necessarily involves a differentiation between the Jhelum system (the meso basin) and the Indus system (the macro basin) on the one hand, and the Jhelum valley in Kashmir and the Jhelum system lying beyond the valley on the other. Thus delineated, the valley includes all land lying within the water-divides formed by the Pir Panjal, the north Kashmir and the Great Himalayan ranges which encircle the great synclinal trough occupied by the Jhelum, the main channel of drainage. The narrow upland valleys of the Liddar, the Sind and the Pohru, and of the numerous other minor affluents, such as the Rambiara, which flow from the slopes of the bordering mountains and drain into the Jhelum within the tectonic valley of Kashmir, form an integral part of the valley delineated for the purpose of this study. The Kishenganga and the Kunhar rivers, which, on the other hand, join the Jhelum outside the Kashmir Valley are definitionally excluded from this discussion.

The valley has a typical oval shape, its length has a parallel axis to the general direction of the bordering mountain ranges. The transverse ranges of the surrounding mountain ramparts on the southeast and the northwest are located on an average distance of 220 kilometres when measured from crest to crest. The crests of the Pir Panjal and the Great Himalayan ranges, on the other hand, are 125 kilometres apart. The flat alluvial basin, however, measures only 150 kilometres from southeast to northwest and 42 kilometres from southwest to northeast. In altitude the flat plain varies from 1,500 to 1,800 metres above the mean sea level and, as the direction of the main stream suggests, the grain of the land is from southeast to northwest (Fig. 1.7).

In its administrative set-up the Valley consists of the three districts of Anantnag, Srinagar and Baramulla. While the boundaries of Anantnag and Srinagar districts correspond by and large with the limits of the Valley as delineated here, the district of Baramulla is not conterminous with the Valley. The anomaly arises from the fact that the entire catchment basins of the Kishenganga and the Pohru have been included in the district. Thus, while parts of Handwara, Sopore and Karnah tahsils of Baramulla have been included, the Uri tahsil lies beyond the purview of this discussion.

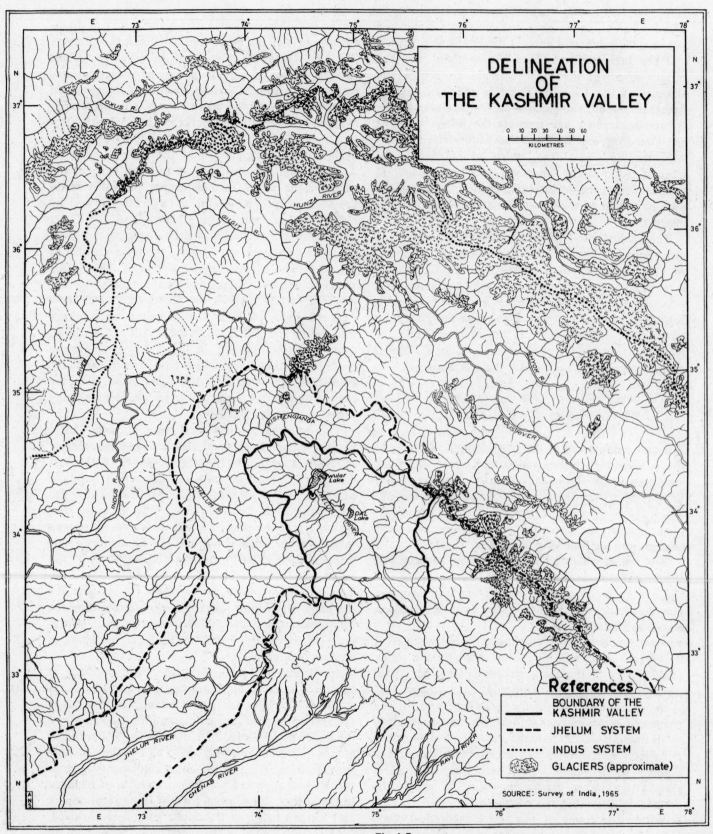

DELINEATION
OF
THE KASHMIR VALLEY

References

—— BOUNDARY OF THE
KASHMIR VALLEY

– – – JHELUM SYSTEM

········ INDUS SYSTEM

GLACIERS (approximate)

SOURCE: Survey of India, 1965

Fig. 1·7

NOTES AND REFERENCES

[1] Burrard and Hayden, *A Sketch of the Geography and Geology of the Himalaya Mauntains and Tibet*, first edition, p. 5, first recognized the present scheme of division of the Himalayan system, which has since been usually accepted by later workers in the field including Wadia, *of. Geology of India*, London, 1970, p. 9.

[2] The *Tirthayatra Digvijay* sections of the *Mahabharata*, the *Jambukhandavinirmanaparva* of the same epic, the *Kiskindhyakanda* of the *Ramayana*, the *Kurmayibhaga* section of the Puranas, *Bhuvanakosa*, the *Jambudipavarnana*, the *Brhatsamhita*, the *Parasatantra* and the *Atharvaparisista* are greatly helpful in the study of this section. Equally important from this point of view are the Buddhist *Nikayas*, *Jatakas* and the *Jaina Agama* texts. The two works known as the *Jambudivapannati* and the *Vividhatirthakalpa* are very useful from the geographical point of view.

[3] The *Mahabharata* (*Vanaparva*, Ch. 253) refers to *Himavanta* as the region lying to the north of Nepal. The *Himavanta* (Snowy), mentioned as the *Parvataraja* in an early Buddhist work (*Anguttara Nikaya* I, 152), *Himavanta* occurs in the *Atharvaveda* XII, I. II; vi. 95.3; 9.9. V, 4.2.8; 25.7; vi, 24.1; *Rgveda*, X, 121.4; *Taittirivasamhita*, V. 5. 11. l; *Vaisanevisamhita*, XXIV, 30; XXV, 12; *Aitareya Brahamana*, VIII, 14.3, is the only *Varsaparvata* which is placed within the geographical limits of *Bharatvarsa*. According to ancient geographers *Himavanta* was applied to the entire mountain range which stretches from Sulaiman mountain in the northwest along the entire northern boundary of India.

[4] S.M. Ali, *The Geography of the Puranas*, New Delhi, 1966, pp. 52-55. Ali has given the following identification of the Puranic mountains:

   i) *Srngavan* represents Kara Tan-Kirghiz-Ketman chain

   ii) *Sweta* represents Nura-Tan-Turkistan-Atbashi chain

   iii) *Nila* represents Zaravshan-Trans-Alay-Tien Shan chain

   iv) *Nisadha* represents Hindu Kush-Kun Lun range

   v) *Hemaka* represents Ladak-Kailasa-Trans-Himalayan chain

   vi) *Himavana* represents the Great Himalayan range (p. 53).

[5] *Vayupurana*, Ch. 36.

[6] The Puranic account of Kailasa leaves no doubt that it was treated only as a peak in the *Himakuta* mountain. "It is the existing Kailasa mountain and not the Kailasa chain (Ali, *op. cit.*, p. 57).

[7] Also, Singur Inscription of Yadava, *Mahadeva-raya*-E. 1, XXIII, pt. V, p. 194.

[8] Cf. *Bhagvata Purana*, IV, 5.22; V, 16.27, Ch. 14.31.

[9] Colonel Tanner, *General Report*, Survey of India, 1878-79, Schlagintweit, *Journal of the Asiatic Society of Benga'*, Vol. XXVI, 1857.

[10] Tanner described the area between the Indus and the Kunar in some detail which now has an historical value only.

[11] "A remarkable feature along the Indus valley, for the notice of which the writer is indebted to Colonel Tanner is that all the peaks over a considerable area reach to a nearly uniform height of about 6,400 metres, thus, this level indicates an old plain of moraine denudation, originally bordered by higher ground of which the peaks of Nanga Parbat and Rakaposhi reaching to over 7,200 metres to 7,450 metres are remnants."

[12] Notable contributions towards this understanding have been made by D.N. Wadia and W.D. West, "The Structure of the Himalayas," International Geological Congress, *Abstracts*, 22nd Session, India, 1964; and by A. Gansser, *Geology of the Himalayas*, London, 1964.

[13] One can hardly differ with Spate and Learmouth, *India and Pakistan*, third edition, 1967, p. 29, in their view that both "relationships and nomenclature of the ranges" in this area are a matter of dispute. In fact a good deal of confusion still remains. "It is almost as dangerous for the uninitiated to venture into Karakoram and Himalayan nomenclature as it would be to penetrate the mountains themselves," fn. p. 29.

[14] Burrard and Hayden, however, argue that the Kailasa range extends even beyond into Ladakh forming a parallel system between the Karakoram and the Ladakh ranges, and see its re-emergence beyond the Nubra in the Saltoro range. Their views are no more valid. *A Sketch of the Geography and Geology of the Himalaya Mountains and Tibet*, first edition, pp. 94-96.

[15] *Ibid.*, p. 94.

[16] E.H. Pascoe, "Early History of the Indus, Brahmaputra and Ganges," *Quarterly Journal of the Geological Society*, LXXV, 1919, pp. 138-159; G.E. Pilgrim, "History of the Drainage of Northern India," *Journal Roy. Asiatic Soc. of Bengal*, New Series, XV, 1919, pp. 81-99.

[17] Pascoe's "Indo-Brahm" and Pilgrim's "Siwalik River."

[18] H. de Terra and T.T. Paterson, *Studies on the Ice Age in India and Associated Human Cultures*, Washington, 1939. H. de Terra published the main results of these explorations in his earlier papers also, especially in "Physiographic Results of a Recent Survey in Little Tibet," *Geographical Review*, XXIV, 1934, pp. 12-41.

[19] L.M. Davies, "Geographical Changes in North-West India," *Proc. Sixth Pacific Science Congress*, Berkley, 1940, cf. O.H.K. Spate, *India and Pakistan*, 1957, *op. cit.* p. 33.

[20] R.S. Mittal, "Physiographical and Structural Evolution of the Himalaya," in B.C. Law (ed.), *Mountains and Rivers of India*, 1968, p. 49,

BIBLIOGRAPHICAL NOTE

Geologically, the northwestern Himalayan complex continues to be the most thoroughly known part of the Himalayas. The environment of the Valley has played a key role in arousing this extraordinary scientific interest—its attractive weather, majestic mountain ranges, scenic beauty and, no less significantly, its resourcefulness as a grand museum of geological and natural history, all acting as strong pulls. Barring the Valley itself, where the basal rocks lie buried under the alluvial deposits and the Karewas, the strata of the surrounding rim of mountains can be studied anywhere in ideally exposed sections.

Significant contributions in the early phase came from H.H, Godwin-Austin, "Geological Notes on part of the North-West Himalayas," *Quarterly Journal of the Geological Society*, Vol. XX, London, 1864; R. Lydekkar, "Notes on the Geology of the Pir Panjal and the Neighbouring Districts," *Recd. Geol. Survey of India*, 1876; "Notes on the Geology of Kashmir, Kishtwar and Pangi," *Rec. Goel. Surv. Ind.*, 1876; and "Geology of Ladakh and Neighbouring Districts," *Recd. Geol. Surv. India*, 1880. A valuable account of the geography and topography of Kashmir Valley and the surrounding regions is given in F. Drew, *The Territory of Jammu and Kashmir*, 1875; W. Lawrence, *The Geography of Kashmir Valley*; *The Gazetteer of Kashmir and Ladakh*, 1890, being exceptionally rich in information, and indispensable.

C.S. Middlemiss and H.S. Bion, *Kashmir, Records Geol. Surv. Ind.*, 1913, laid a special emphasis on the economic geology of the region.

An exceptionally rich assemblage of facts on the physical features of the northwestern Himalayan and trans-Himalayan region appears in H.H. Hayden and S.G. Burrard; *A Sketch of the Geography and Geology of the Himalaya Mountains and Tibet*, first edition; its richness in detail is impressive but organization of material leaves much to be desired. A second edition of the work appeared with A.M. Heron as one of the co-authors in 1933. For a critique of the work, see K. Mason's review in *The Himalayan Journal*, VII, 1935. New light on some of the tangled problems of the structural history of the Himalayas is shed in D.N. Wadia, "The Syntaxis of the North-West Himalayas," *Recd. Geol. Surv. Ind.* I. XV, 1931; H. de Terra, "A Scientific Study of the Eastern Karakoram and Zanskar-Himalaya," *Himalayan Journal*, 1933; and "Geological Studies in the North-West Himalayas between the Kashmir and Indus Valleys," Memoirs of the Connecticut Academy of Arts and Science, VIII, 1935.

On the evolution of Himalayan rivers, Pascoe and Pilgrim's notable contributions have been acknowledged above. While A.A. Michel's *The Indus Rivers*, London, New Haven, 1967, is essentially a work dealing with the utilization problems of Indus waters, it indirectly provides a useful insight into the drainage pattern of the Indus streams.

Among general works, Wadia's monumental work *Geology of India*, 1952, is extremely valuable; so is O.H.K. Spate's *India and Pakistan*, London, 1954, which continues to be the most outstanding work on India to date.

Chapter Two

The Corridors of Time

... Afterwards when the present period of the (Seventh) Manu Vaivasvata had arrived, the Prajapati *Kasyapa* caused the gods led by Druhina, Upendra and Rudra to descend, caused (the demon) Jalodbhava, who dwelt in that (lake), to be killed, and created the land known by the name of *Kasmir* in the space (previously occupied by) the Lake.—Kalhana in *Rajatarangini* (First Book, 26-27)

The familiar view of the Kashmir Valley as a synclinal trough with its flat plain covered with alluvial deposits of great thickness and bordered by Karewa uplands should not overlook its solid geology as evident in the structure of the surrounding mountain ranges which contribute the essential elements to the making of the Valley's geographical personality. In fact, the tectonic processes leading to the emergence of the bordering mountain systems are also intrinsically linked to the physical make-up and genesis of the Valley. An understanding of the structural outline and evolution of these mountain ramparts and of the alluvial-lacustrine deposits within the flat plain of the Valley is of great importance in clearing up some of the complicated issues pertaining to the physical geography of Kashmir Valley.

Besides being the repository of worn down rock materials and moisture from the encompassing mountain precipices, the Valley, as nature's vast open theatre, offers scope for the study of the complete succession of rock strata belonging to different geological periods from Palaeozoic onwards, which are exposed in the anticlinal ridges.

STRATIGRAPHICAL GEOLOGY (Fig. 2.1)

The stratigraphic and structural plan of the Kashmir Valley will be discussed here in chronological order and will be supplemented by a summary of the structural history. The schematic plan shown in Table III will facilitate understanding of the order in which the rock formations have been discussed.

Archaean. There is a fair representation of Archaean formations within the Himalayan ranges surrounding the Valley, though the crests of these ranges, which describe the catchment area of the basin, do not have any exposure of the Archaean strata in themselves. Moreover, the very origin and the Archaean affinity of these strata is disputed by geologists in view of the growing mass of evidence which invalidates earlier views on this question. The older view that the bulk of the Himalayan ranges, especially in their central axis, was composed of crystalline rocks, such as granites and gneisses, is no more tenable as the recently collected evidence attributes their origin to an alteration of the sedimentary strata. In fact, the stratum has an intrusive character and its relation to the old Archaean foundation is extremely doubtful, the intrusions having been made during the later geological periods in various parts of the region.[1] The only areas of interest within this region, where the gneissic intrusions frequently occur lie in the Pir Panjal range.

Cambrian. The Cambrian age in Kashmir is represented by the fossiliferous rocks occupying vast stretches of the mountain slopes in the Handwara tahsil of Baramulla district, north of the Jhelum. Often overlaying the Dogra slates, which are devoid of fossils, these rocks consist of soft quartzites, clays and colitic limestone containing trilobites. Besides the Handwara exposure, the fossiliferous Cambrian rocks are also visible in the Basmai anticline of the Sind valley, and in the Liddar valley.

Ordovician. It seems that the Palaeozoic rocks of the Kashmir region were deposited in an elongated ellipsoidal basin extending from Handwara in the northwest to the southeast extremity of Kashmir Valley. The best exposures of Ordovician rocks are found in the vicinity of the Cambrian strata in the Shamsh Abri anticline, near Trehgam (Handwara tahsil), in the

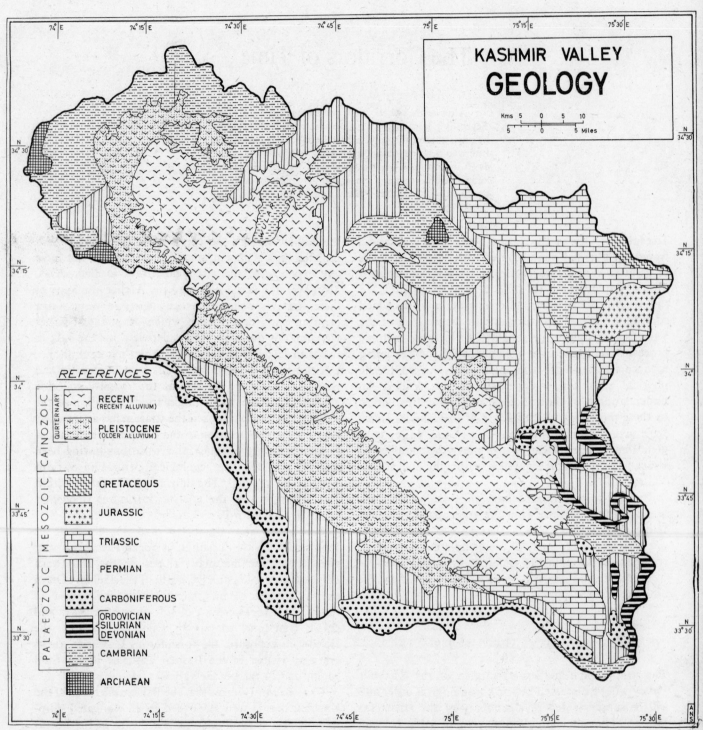

Fig. 2·1

TABLE III
Geological formations of the Kashmir Valley

Era	Period	Age	Formations	Localities
Cainozoic	Quaternary	Recent Pleistocene	Recent alluvium Older alluvium Karewa deposits river terraces	Jhelum river valley Karewa uplands bordering the Valley; river terraces in the upland valleys
	Tertiary	Eocene	Nummulitics, Ranikot series	Southwestern flank of the Pir Panjal range
Mesozoic		Cretaceous	Shales, agglomerates, agglomeratic conglomerates and volcanic series	Astor, Burzil, Dras, Ladakh
		Jurassic	Spiti shales, Kioto limestones	Banihal
		Triassic	Pir Panjal trap, triassic shales interbedded with limestone, dolomites	Sind valley, Liddar valley and northern slopes of Pir Panjal range
Palaeozoic		Permian	Zewan beds, *productus* shales, dark arenacious shales and limestones	Pir Panjal, upper Sind and Liddar valley
		Carboniferous	Panjal trap, agglomerates, limestones and shales	Pir Panjal range, Zaskar range, Banihal valley
		Devonian	Muth Quartzites	Liddar valley, Pir Panjal (southern flank)
		Silurian	Sandy shales, shaly sandstone and yellow limestone	Liddar valley (Anantnag)
		Ordovician	Quartzite, limestones, greywackes	Sind and Liddar valleys
		Cambrian	Soft quartzites, massive clays, limestone	Baramulla and Anantnag, Pir Panjal, Banihal valley
Archaean		Pre-Cambrian	Fundamental gneisses, intruded granites	Great Himalayan range, Pir Panjal

Modified from M.B. Pithawala, *An Introduction to Kashmir—Its Geology and Geography*, Karachi, 1953, pp. 13-14.

Liddar and Sind valleys.[2] The rock formations consist of arenaceous and ferruginous shales, quartzose greywackes and limestones.

Silurian. Like their predecessors the Silurian rocks are also exposed in Liddar valley in Anantnag, and the Shamsh Abri in Handwara. The Liddar valley outcrop occurs in a relatively thin layer of not more than thirty metres in thickness, but is fairly continuous and extends from Eishmakam in Liddar valley to Lutherwan in the Wadwan valley. Generally composed of arenaceous shales and impure limestones, the rocks are rich in fossils, especially of the *genera orthis*. The Shamsh Abri outcrop, on the other hand, has much greater thickness and consists of slates and greywackes but is largely unfossiliferous.

Devonian. The thick quartzite beds lying conformably on the Silurian strata on both the flanks of the anticlinal ridges in the Liddar valley in Wadwan,

Shamsh Abri and the Pir Panjal range, are assigned a Devonian origin. They are known to possess a stratigraphical resemblance to the Muth quartzites of the Spiti, believed to be Devonian in age. The quartzitic outcrops are massive, at places being 300-600 metres in thickness, but do not contain fossil remains, which creates difficulties in age determination.

The Cambro-Silurian fossiliferous sequence, as exposed in various parts of Kashmir, has a general complementarity in so far as the biostratigraphic evidence contained in it is concerned. But in specific cases even a tentative correlation poses a number of difficulties. The Lower Palaeozoic formations of Baramulla and Anantnag, for example, cannot be correlated on the basis of their fossil contents alone. This is mainly due to the fact that the fossiliferous layers in the two areas are not synchronous. S.K. Shah[3] has attempted a tentative correlation of the

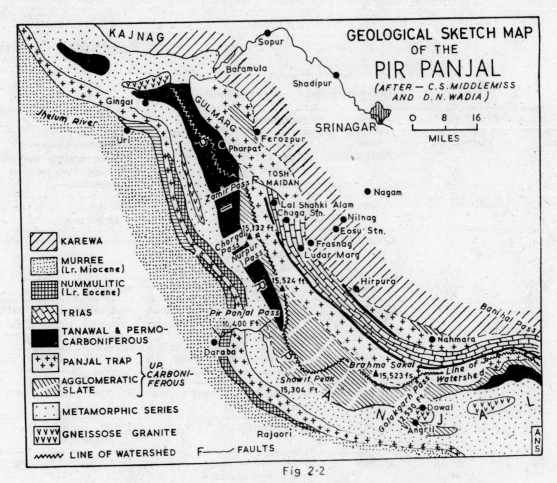

GEOLOGICAL SKETCH MAP
OF THE
PIR PANJAL
(AFTER — C.S. MIDDLEMISS
AND D.N. WADIA)

0   8   16
MILES

KAJNAG

Sopur
Baramula
Shadipur
Gingal
Jhelum River
Uri
GULMARG
Ferozpur
Pharpat
SRINAGAR
TOSH MAIDAN
Zamir Pass
Nagam
Lal Shahki Alam
Chaga Stn.
Nilnag
15,132 ft
Eosu Stn.
Chorgali Pass
Frasnag
Nurpur Pass
Ludar Marg
15,524 ft
Hirpura
Pir Panjal Pass
10,400 Ft.
Bani hal Pass
Daraba
Brahma Sakal
15,523 fs
Line of Watershed
Showit Peak
15,304 Ft.
Gojalgarh Pass
Nahmara
Rajaori
2530 ft
Dowal
Angril

KAREWA
MURREE (Lr. Miocene)
NUMMULITIC (Lr. Eocene)
TRIAS
TANAWAL & PERMO-CARBONIFEROUS
PANJAL TRAP } UP. CARBONI-FEROUS
AGGLOMERATIC SLATE
METAMORPHIC SERIES
GNEISSOSE GRANITE
LINE OF WATERSHED   F——— FAULTS

Fig 2·2

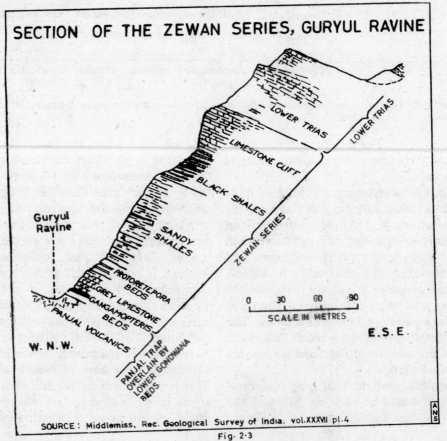

SECTION OF THE ZEWAN SERIES, GURYUL RAVINE

LOWER TRIAS
LOWER TRIAS
LIMESTONE CLIFF
BLACK SHALES
SANDY SHALES
ZEWAN SERIES
Guryul Ravine
PROTORETEPORA BEDS
GREY LIMESTONE
GANGAMOPTERIS BEDS
PANJAL VOLCANICS
PANJAL TRAP OVERLAIN BY LOWER GONDWANA BEDS

0   30   60   90
SCALE IN METRES

W. N. W.   E. S. E.

SOURCE : Middlemiss, Rec. Geological Survey of India. vol. XXXVII pl. 4

Fig. 2·3

TABLE IV
The Upper Palaeozoic sequence in Kashmir

	Characteristic fossils	Age
Zewan beds, (shales, limestones)	Danubites Pseudomonotis Protoretepora	Permian
Gangamopteris beds (shales, quartzites)	Glossopteris Gangamopteris	Lower Gondwana (Artinskian)
Panjal Trap, Panjal agglomeratic slates	Marine fossils of the Productus variety	Upper Carboniferous
Fenestella shales	Productus Fenestella, other obscure fossils	Middle Carboniferous
Syringothyris beds (limestones)	Syringothyris cuspidata	Lower Carboniferous
Muth Quartzites	Unfossiliferous	Devonian

Courtesy: S.K. Shah, in A. J. Jhingran (ed.), Himalayan Geology, Vol. II, Delhi, 1972, p. 477.

TABLE V
Tentative correlation of the Lower Palaeozoic sequences in Kashmir

			Anantnag district		Baramulla district (Shah 1968, 1971a)	Sind valley (Wadia, 1934)
Devonian	Middle	M	Muth quartzite	M	Muth quartzite	Muth quartzite
	Lower	A	Dipterus horizon	A		
Silurian		R	Stephanocrinus horizon	R		Silurian slate and greywacke
		G		H		
		A		A		
	Upper	N	Rafinesquina horizon	U		
Ordovician	Middle			M		
	Lower	S	Lihinwan			
		H		F		
		A		O	Orthis-leptaena zone	
		L		R		Older slate and phyllite
		E		M		
				A		
				T		
				I		
				O		
				N		
	Upper		Sandstone	TRAHAGAM	Conocorypheanomocare zone	
			Chhatargul	&		
				NUTUNUS		
Cambrian	Middle			F	Anomocare-Tonkinella zone	
			Mudstone	O		
	Lower			R	Solenopleura-Tonkinella zone	
				M		
				A		
				T		
				I		
				O		
				N		
				S		
			SAGIPURA FORMATION			
			LOLAB FORMATION			
			MARINAG FORMATION			

Source: S.K. Shah, "Stratigraphic Studies in Lower Palaeozoic Sequence of Anantnag District, Kashmir," Himalayan Geology, Vol. II, 1972, p. 477.

Lower Palaeozoic sequences in Kashmir and his scheme is reproduced in Table IV.

Carboniferous to Permian. The Carboniferous and Permian strata are fairly widely developed in various parts of the Valley. The general sequence of these formations as reconstructed from sections exposed at a number of sites in the Kashmir region, including Lehindajjar, Golabgarh pass of Pir Panjal, the Guryul ravine and in the Liddar valley anticline from Kotsu through Eishmakam to Pahalgam,[4] is illustrated in Table V (see also Figs. 2.2, 2.3 and 2.4).

The outcrops at Eishmakam and Kotsu in the Liddar valley anticline illustrate well the stratigraphical position of the lowermost carboniferous stratum. A thin layer of limestones, described as the *syringothyris* beds, is observed in all these localities as lying conformably over the Devonian quartzites of the muth variety. They are supposed to be fairly extensive, though concealed below the younger formations such as the Panjal trap and the Recent and Sub-Recent alluvium. Other outcrops of these beds have been noted in the Banihal and the Sind valleys. Barring localized outcrops, the *syringothyris* beds in both places lie buried under a thick cover of the Panjal volcanic series. The most characteristic fossil frequently occurring in these beds is the *syringothyris cuspidata*, regarded to be an index fossil of great importance.

Next in order of superimposition comes a series of quartzites and shales, entirely unfossiliferous and being only "passage beds" to the upper group of the fossiliferous shales and quartzites. The outcrops of the so-called *Fenestella* shales and quartzites are highly restricted, being traceable only in some parts of the Liddar anticline and at Banihal and Budil in the Pir Panjal. The shales vary from dark greyish to black sandy and contain a variety of fossils, notably of the brachiopod class including *Fenestella* and species of productus and corals. The relations of the shales series with the beds immediately above and below them are highly conformable.

The Upper Carboniferous in Kashmir saw an intensive phase of "igneous outbursts" covering vast areas of the region under 2,000 to 2,500 metres of fragmentary productus such as agglomerates and pyroclastics besides the lava flows. This short but eventful igneous phase is represented in the volcanic strata which lend themselves to a two-fold division—into an upper and a lower series. The lower series, consisting of pyroclastic slates, conglomerates and other agglomeratic products, are described as the "Panjal agglomeratic slates," named after their major development in the Pir Panjal range. The agglomeratic slates are overlain by a thick series

of bedded andesitic and basaltic traps, called Panjal traps. The volcanic series has a fairly impressive areal extent, being a major constituent in a large number of high peaks around the Jhelum valley from Shamsh Abri to Kolahoi. The series is mainly exposed in the Pir Panjal almost all along the range from the Kishenganga to the Ravi.

There is a general lack of uniformity in the stratigraphical position of the Panjal series as is evident from its lower and upper limits in various parts of Kashmir. The distribution pattern reveals that the volcanic phase ended up with the Lower Permian in the Vihi area and with the close of the Permian in the Liddar valley; but it continued up to the Upper Trias in the Guraiz region.

The stratigraphic position of the Panjal lava flows is clearly defined in the Vihi area by beds which directly overlie it.[5] These comprise a series of shales and quartzites which come next in order of position in this area and are described as *Gangamopteris* beds.[6] The fossil contents of these strata bring them in close affinity to the peninsular Gondwana and are assigned a period contemporaneous to Lower Gondwana in age. The main outcrops of these beds have been located both on the northeast slopes of Pir Panjal and the anticlinal ridges across the Jhelum valley, notably at seven places—Banihal and Gulabgarh passes, near Gulmarg, in Vihi, near Srinagar, Bijbiara and at Nagmarg close to the Wular lake. The beds generally have a diverse thickness, the Pir Panjal outcrops being the thickest.

Both the Gulabgarh and the Vihi horizons show clear contacts of the *Gangamopteris* beds with the overlying fossiliferous limestones of Permian times— the Zewan beds. Studded with a variety of fossils, notably of the brachiopod and polyzoa type, these beds comprise shales and limestone, and have a direct correspondence to the productus limestone of the Salt range and the productus shales of Spiti. When considered together, the whole succession of strata between the *Gangamopteris* beds and the lower Triassic beds is known as the "Zewan series."[7] (See Fig. 2.3.) Other outcrops of the series are found in the Pir Panjal and in the Sind and Liddar valleys.

Triassic. The Himalayan Triassic belt, which extends from Hazara to Nepal, shows impressive development within the mountain ranges of Kashmir. Composed of a voluminous series of limestones, slates and dolomites, the Trias are exposed in the Sind, Liddar, Wadwan, Guraiz and Tilel valleys and in the Pir Panjal precipices facing Jhelum valley. Unlike the Trias of Spiti, the strata in Kashmir are seldom rich in fossils, though an

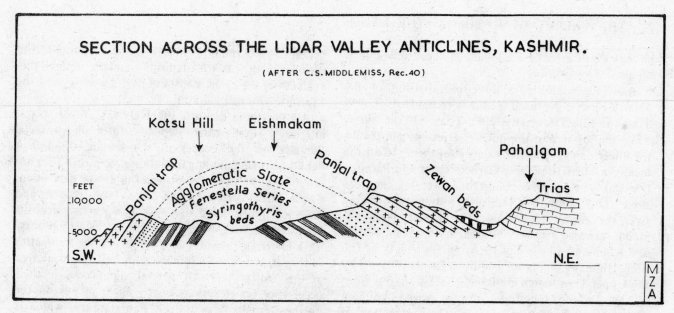

SECTION ACROSS THE LIDAR VALLEY ANTICLINES, KASHMIR.

(AFTER C.S. MIDDLEMISS, Rec.40)

FIG. 2·4

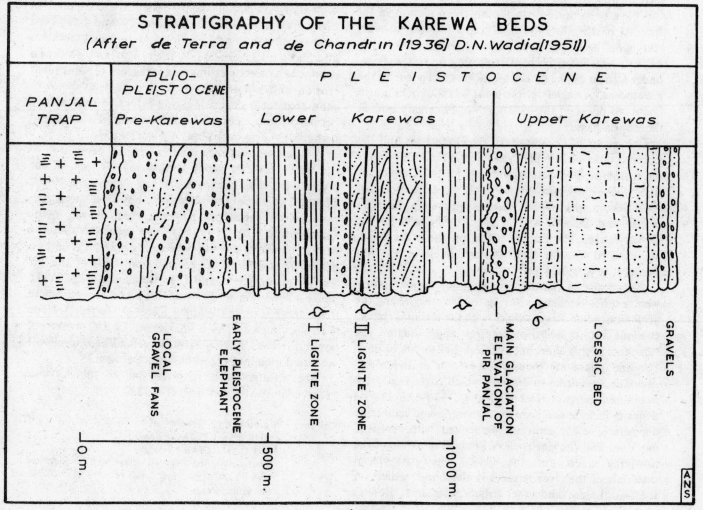

STRATIGRAPHY OF THE KAREWA BEDS

(After de Terra and de Chandrin [1936] D.N. Wadia [1951])

Fig. 2·5

abundance of *cephalopoda* fossils has been noted in a number of horizons.

Biostratigraphically, a three-fold division of the Triassic rocks of Kashmir is usually recognized—Lower Trias, Middle Trias and Upper Trias. Of the three, while the lower and the middle series contain fossils, the upper one is completely devoid of them. In all the localities where the Upper Carboniferous and Permian (Zewan) beds have been noticed, Lower Triassic beds are also noted for their exposure, resting conformably over the earlier formations. The Lower Trias are mainly exposed in the Vihi area, at Pastanah, Khrew and Khunmu and some of the tributary valleys of the Sind. In many places the middle strata are followed by the Upper Trias which are largely unfossiliferous [8]

The Triassic limestones are a prized building material and have been used in the construction of many noted monuments in Kashmir.

Jurassic. The Jurassic outcrops, characterized by their series of shales, limestones and sandstones, and infrequently containing cephalopods and lamellibranchs, have been noticed on the northern section of the Banihal pass in the Pir Panjal, often indistinguishably resting on the Upper Trias. The horizon is believed to be fairly extensive, perhaps stretching up to Gulmarg, under a cover of the glacial and Karewa deposits of the Pleistocene. A variety of the basal Jurassic rocks is also known to occur in the hills north of Sonamarg and at the Zoji-la pass.

Cretaceous to Eocene. Both the Cretaceous and the Eocene strata remain unrepresented in the hills bordering Kashmir. The isolated outcrops of the Cretaceous rocks have however been found in a number of localities in the Great Himalayan range between Burzil and Deosai, and in the Rupshu area of the Zaskar range. The Eocene strata, on the other hand, are exposed on the southwestern flank of the Pir Panjal over a wide area.

Pleistocene to Sub-Recent. Kashmir region underwent a series of changes during the Pleistocene and the geologically Sub-Recent times with far-reaching repercussions on its physical features and climate. The remnants of this short but eventful Pleistocene or post-Pliocene phase are found in the form of deposits—fluviatile, lacustrine or glacial—which cover vast areas in different parts of Kashmir Valley. These superficial deposits include the Karewas, fluviatile and lacustrine deposits of older alluvium embedded with terminal moraines and the glacial clays, younger alluvium of the low-lying tracts and the glacial and para-glacial materials of the river terraces in the upper valleys of the Sind, Liddar and other tributary streams. Besides

being a vitally important asset to the economy of the region, these surface deposits contain indubitable evidence of the cyclic phases of past glaciation and the associated human cultures.

Among these deposits the Karewas are of special interest.[9] These older deposits form flat-surfaced mounds on the border of the Jhelum flood-plain flanking the surrounding mountain precipices. They are reminiscent of an earlier phase of intensive deposition, whose initial platform has since been eroded and dissected into isolated uplands. The Karewa deposits are extensive roughly over an area thirteen to twenty-six kilometres in width and about eighty kilometres in length, thus covering more than half the total area of the Valley floor. Of special significance is their occurrence on elevations up to 3,800 metres on the northeastern flank of the Pir Panjal range, which is 2,130 metres above the bed of the river.

The horizons of the Karewa beds suggest that they were mainly deposited in two stages, mutually separated by a dry interval during which they were intensively eroded by sub-aerial agents. They are composed of blue, grey and buff silts and sands and have been intermixed with conglomerates and terminal moraines at almost all levels. While their aggregate thickness cannot be correctly estimated for reasons of subsequent erosion and upwarping, there is definite evidence to show that their deposition was extensive over a long period of time, perhaps beginning with Pliocene and going as far up as the upper Pleistocene.[10]

As the time sequence involved in the deposition of the entire Karewa series should suggest, not all the layers were equally exposed to the Pleistocene glacial phase. The glacial influences are, however, more pronounced on the upper Karewas than on the lower. Gansser and other geologists have suggested that the sandstone and gravel fans underlying the lower Karewa series are related to the erosion and uplift of the Pir Panjal in the south and the Himalayan range in the north. The lower series was folded and eroded before the transgression of the upper Karewas started.[11] H. de Terra estimated that a maximum of 800 metres of lower Karewas is certainly preserved, as beds of almost an equal amount of thickness were eroded.[12]

The stratigraphical arrangement of the Karewa series is illustrated below[13]: (Fig. 2.5).

Upper	Moraines and Terraces of FOURTH GLACIAL STAGE THIRD GLACIAL STAGE Sands, clays and "varved" clays with boulders and erratics and containing fossil remains of molluses and some plants

SECTION OF THE *PIR PANJAL* ACROSS THE N.E. SLOPES FROM NILNAG—TATAKUTI
(after : Middlemiss, Geological Survey of India Record XLi pt 2)

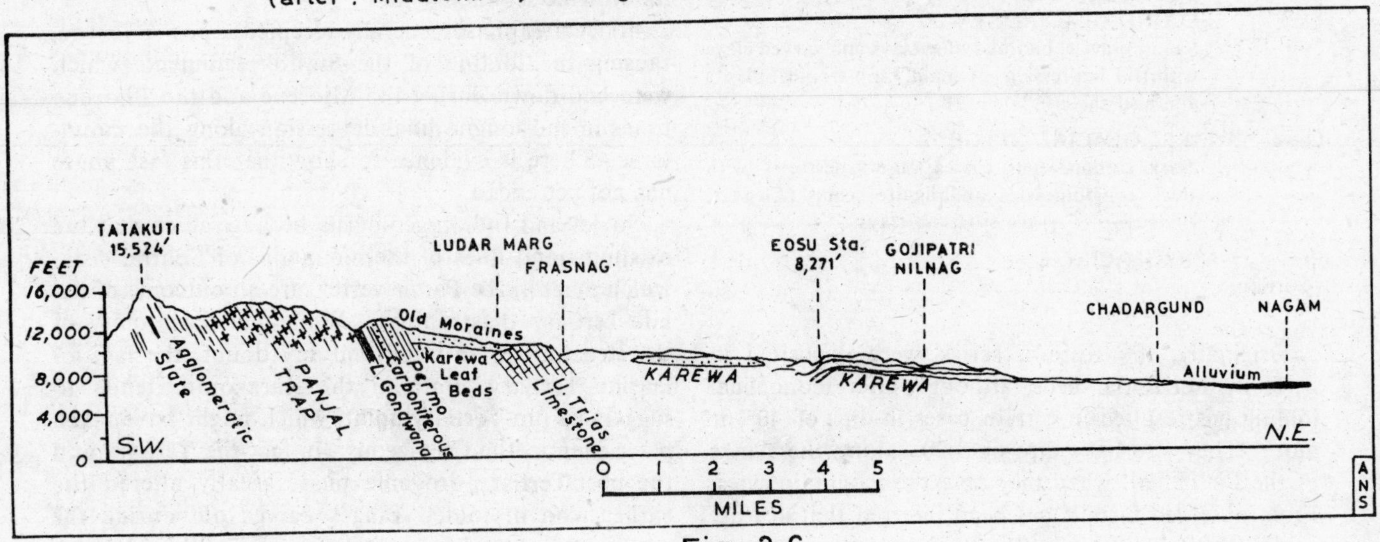

Fig. 2·6

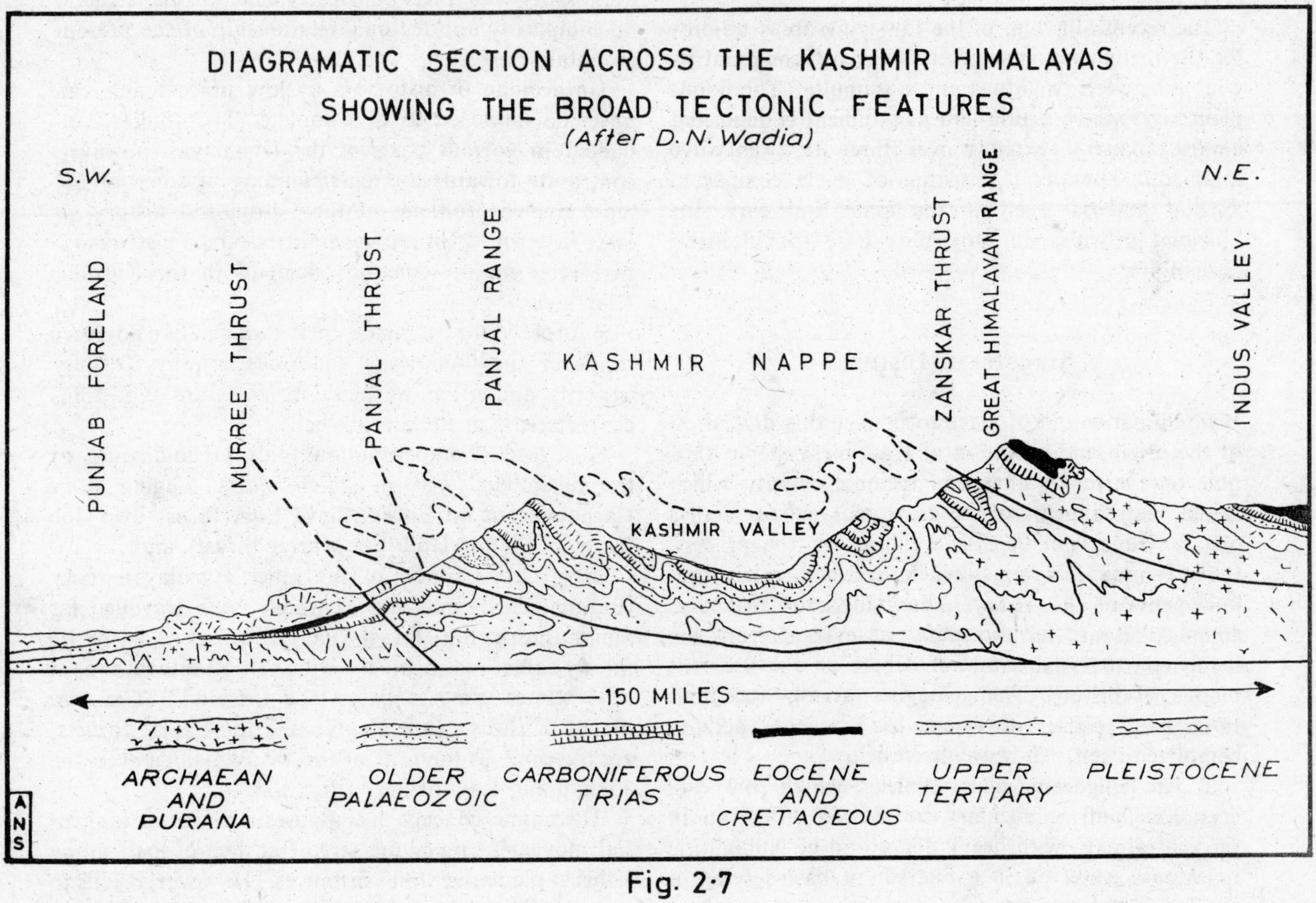

DIAGRAMATIC SECTION ACROSS THE KASHMIR HIMALAYAS
SHOWING THE BROAD TECTONIC FEATURES
(After D.N. Wadia)

Fig. 2·7

Basal boulder beds
SECOND GLACIAL STAGE
   Sands, gravels, buff and blue clays and varved clays
   with leaf impressions of mainly sub-tropical plants
   and also shells

Lower   FIRST GLACIAL STAGE
   Dark carboneceous shales and sandstones with
   thick conglomerates and lignite seams (*Elephas,*
   Rhinoceros, Cervus), silts and clays

Pre-   PREGLACIAL
Tertiary

Originally, the Karewa series were deposited in perfectly horizontal beds, although later monoclinal folding has resulted in certain cases in dips of 40° or more. They also have dips of 5-20° along the flanks of the Pir Panjal, when they abut the mountain sides. From observed facts it has been inferred that at least a part of the uplift of the Pir Panjal was preceded by the Karewa deposition phase at it has resulted in the placement of the Karewa layers at high altitudes[14] (Fig. 2.6).

The recent alluvium of the low-lying areas adjoining the Jhelum covers an extensive area throughout its course between Anantnag and Baramulla. The floodplain, over which a thin film of sediment is deposited almost annually, extends over three to twenty-five kilometres laterally. Consisting of finely compacted detrital material such as the loam and clay, the alluvium provides an important base for intensive agriculture.

STRUCTURAL HISTORY

It would not be out of place to preface this discussion of the origin and evolution of Kashmir Valley with a note on the major phases of tectonic activity which raised the sediments of the great geosynclinal Tethys Sea to Himalayan heights, building, in the process, the lofty mountain ranges which describe the structural lineaments of the Valley. Admittedly, the structural complexities are far too many, as evident from the highly controversial nature of debate on the different phases of history. The geologists usually recognize three main phases in which the orogenic activity completed itself. They are given below:

i) An Oligocene phase during which the old crystalline and sedimentary strata were lifted up in the central axis, with heavy deposition of Nummilitic limestones going on in a number of basins lying in areas such as Ladakh;

ii) a Miocene phase resulting in the upwarping of the Murree sediments; and

iii) A later phase, generally accepted as post-Pliocene, causing the folding of the Siwalik sediments which were laid down during the Miocene and the Pliocene times in the longitudinal depression along the mountains. There is evidence to show that this last phase has not yet ended.

Soviet and Indian geologists broadly agree that the existing trend lines of the mountains of Central Asia, which meet in the Pamir vertex, are an outcome of the late-Tertiary diastrophism. While the basic unity of the structural plan is beyond any doubt, the lack of marine Tertiary strata in the Karakoram tends to suggest its pre-Tertiary uplift, which might have taken place even in the Cretaceous. In fact the Tertiary and the post-Tertiary orogenic phase greatly altered the earlier plan of folded ranges carved out during the Altaid orogeny. Later developments, although they succeeded in transforming the schema of earlier architecture, drew heavily on their materials—an eventuality which has immensely added to the structural complexity and tectonic relationship of the present mountain ranges.

Unravelling of history is a slow process and can never be supposed to be complete. The studies conducted in various parts of the Himalayas, however, contribute towards an understanding of some of the most tangled problems of their structural history, at least in terms of broad generalities. Geologists recognize three major structural elements in the Kashmir Himalayas:

i) A foreland zone, made up of a tongue-like northern fringe of the Gondwana land overlain by Tertiary deposits and often warped into the Jura type folds characteristic of the Siwalik belt;

ii) a zone of autochthonous folds, predominantly of the recumbent type in which strata ranging from Carboniferous to Eocene have been thrust over the fringe of the foreland (the Murree thrust); and

iii) a nappe zone[15] of the inner Himalayan rocks (Purana schists and slates) which "has travelled far along a horizontal thrust (Panjal thrust) so as to lie fitfully sometimes against a wide belt of autochthon, at other times almost against the foreland." The two planes of thrusts (the Murree and the Panjal thrusts) are traceable at the foot of the Pir Panjal between the Jhelum and Ravi defiles. (Fig. 2.7).

The nappe concept presupposes a powerful tangential movement involving large transfers of load along a thrust-plane over long distances. However, it fails to explain fully the mechanism involved in such a dislocation; "and thrusting is not the only (one) involved, if only because such vast transfers of load as are implied by the Siwalik and Gangetic deposition, and the thrust movements themselves must have isostatic implications."[16] The evidence collected by de Terra on the uplift of the Pir Panjal since the Pleistocene,[17] by Garwood on the isostatic uplift caused by reducing load of glaciers, and by Wager on the isostatic adjustments made in the Tibetan landmass, caused by removal of surface material by vigorous river erosion, all weigh heavily in favour of a vertical uplift (a balance movement) in areas of heavy displacement of load.

ORIGIN OF THE KASHMIR VALLEY

Lying between the bordering anticlinal flexures, represented by the Pir Panjal and the Great Himalayan ranges, Kashmir Valley is undoubtedly a synclinal trough. The Valley owes its origin to differential uplift which forms depressions between the two mountain chains. The tectonic process, which has carved out this trough within the nappe zone of Kashmir Himalayas has analogy in the narrow, longitudinal valleys, such as Dehra "dun." In fact, according to Wadia, Kashmir Valley is "an exaggerated instance of a dun." But what an exaggeration it is, and certainly far more than a mere difference of scale.

The Valley has a peculiar physical personality. A distinctive feature is its asymmetrical extent; on the southern flank it rises gently from the floor to the crest of the Pir Panjal; the northern flank, on the other hand, is too narrow, and is marked by abrupt changes in gradient, accompanied with faceted spurs suggestive of a recent faulting. The original floor of the Valley lies buried under a thick mantle of superficial deposits which conceal all possible evidence on the course of events prior to Pleistocene. Unlike the Kashmir syncline, the valleys of the affluents of the Jhelum, which dissect the bordering mountains, possess important clues to the nature of mutual relationships in the past. Like the master stream, these upland affluents are antecedent and are characterized by a peculiar configuration. In most of the cases a deep U-shaped or I-shaped gorge is abruptly alternated with a broad V-shaped valley. Wadia attributes this to a declining rainfall which incapacitates the erosive power to erode the hard, crystalline valley sides, while the gorge goes on deepening by the corrosive work of the down-rushing snow-melt. Above the gorge lies the broad valley, where the detrital rock material easily lends itself to mechanical disintegration resulting in the emergence of an open V-shape.[18]

Being a depression in the mountains, the Valley has been receiving huge loads of worn down material from the bordering precipices. The superficial deposits laid down during the Pleistocene, such as sands, clays and silts of the Karewas, old deltaic fans and the like testify to the vast fluctuations of level in the past. Geological studies, such as those conducted by de Terra and Paterson in the Kashmir Himalayas, are helping to unravel the sequence of developments in its most recent past, whose broad outlines are now fairly well known.

It is believed that a subsequent stream flowed to the southeast, having a channel parallel to that of the longitudinal course of the Chenab. The Jhelum had captured it, but its southeasterly exit was later blocked by the uprising Pir Panjal, an eventuality which converted the Kashmir syncline into a veritable lake receiving all the drainage from the surrounding highlands but without an outlet. The detrital material deposited by the numerous streams raised the bed of the lake with the consequent overspilling through some channel. The evidence of the Pleistocene deposits suggests that the lake remained a scene of stupendous changes of level for quite some time: its bed deepening with the accentuation of the glacial process, and being alternately filled and drained as uplift blocked the outlet or erosion allowed drainage. The Pir Panjal continued to rise all through, with the Jhelum actively responding to its challenge, deepening its channel further and finally forming a way out of the mountain barrier which resulted in complete drainage of the lake.

Early geologists had accepted the lacustrine origin of the Karewas, thus upholding a strong mythological tradition of the existence of a vast lake occupying the entire floor of the Kashmir Valley in late geological times.[19] R.D. Oldham, however, contested this view, ruling out the lacustrine origin of the Karewas. Extensive evidence collected by later workers, such as de Terra and Paterson, Gansser, Wager and others, corroborates the views of early observers on this question, making Oldham's position absolutely indefensible.[20]

GLACIATION—PLEISTOCENE AND RECENT

The surface features of Kashmir Valley and the bordering mountains contain positive proof of glaciation. The extensively scattered evidence is seen in

i) the Karewas which have layers of terminal moraines embedded with them at many places, and buff coloured sands and laminated clays at others,

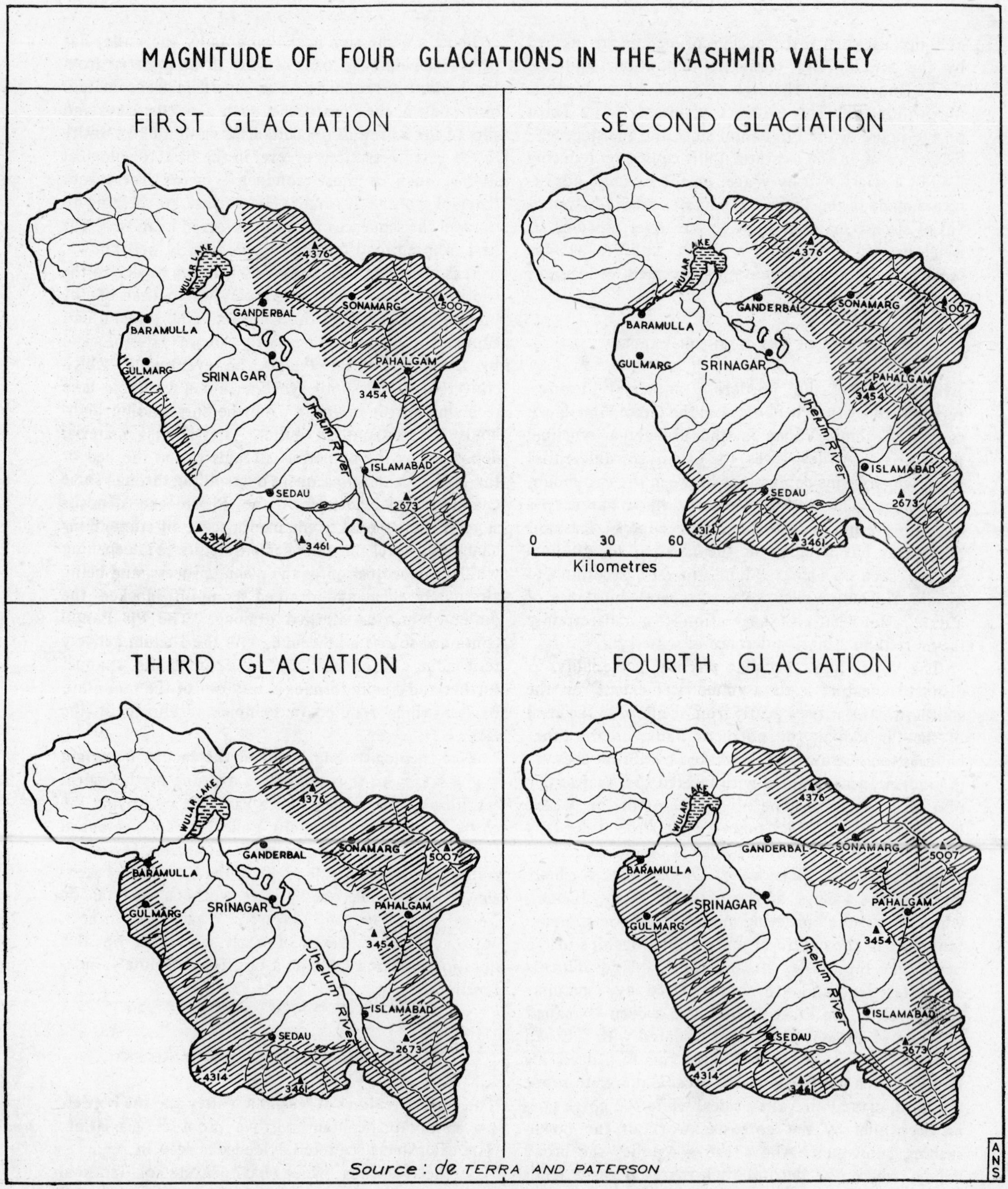
MAGNITUDE OF FOUR GLACIATIONS IN THE KASHMIR VALLEY
FIRST GLACIATION
SECOND GLACIATION
THIRD GLACIATION
FOURTH GLACIATION
WULAR LAKE
4376
5007
SONAMARG
GANDERBAL
BARAMULLA
GULMARG
SRINAGAR
PAHALGAM
3454
Jhelum River
ISLAMABAD
SEDAU
2673
4314
3461
0 30 60
Kilometres
Source : de TERRA AND PATERSON
ANS

Fig. 2·8

supposed to have been deposited during the interglacial periods;

ii) the Pir Panjal range, notably its northeastern face covered extensively with moraine materials;

iii) the terraces built by the affluents of the Jhelum in their upper valleys, particularly the Liddar, Sind and their tributaries, which have been formed of moraine beds mixed with fluvio-glacial deposits;

iv) the hard rock surfaces which have been converted into well-grooved *roche moutonnees*, a common phenomenon in all river valleys; and

v) polished rock surfaces, rock grooving, striation marks and perched blocks, so typical of the glaciated regions occurring abundantly.

These features bear witness to an intensive glaciation which affected the region in the Pleistocene and the Sub-Recent periods. It has been noted that the present glaciers in the mountain ranges of the northwestern Himalayan region, although in themselves being the largest anywhere outside the polar areas, are but the relics of their mighty predecessors. It seems certain, as suggested by the geological investigations of Dainelli, Grinlinton, de Terra and Paterson, that the Kashmir region underwent four glacial phases which were alternated by interglacial periods with warmer conditions and intensive fluvial activity

(Fig. 2.8). The cyclic nature of glaciation is indicated by the series of terminal moraines and other drift materials which were laid down during the successive Ice Ages. The evidence on these glacial phases collected by de Terra and Paterson is very rich and establishes the general glacial sequence in Kashmir Valley as recorded in the Karewa beds[21]:

First Interglacial	Lower Karewas deposition (C. 600m.), lake beds, fluvial inwash and aeolian drift,
Second Glaciation	Karewas gravel (C. 120m.), glacio-fluvial outwash fans,
Second Interglacial	Upper Karewas (C. 60m.), "topmost beds of aeolian and fluvial origin; lower beds lacustrine; also fluvial outwash (partly varved)."

As noted earlier the evidences of folding, faulting and tilting contained in the Karewas testify on the concomitant uplift which was going on in the Pir Panjal all through the Pleistocene time and perhaps even to the Recent. These diverse processes have added immensely to the already existing complexities of the Valley's geomorphological evolution in the Recent past.

NOTES AND REFERENCES

[1] Wadia, *Geology of India*, op. cit, pp. 89-91.

[2] The Ordovician origin of the Liddar valley outcrops is however doubtful, *ibid*, p. 159.

[3] S.K. Shah, "Stratigraphic Studies on Lower Palaeozoic Sequence of Anantnag District, Kashmir," A.J. Jhingran (ed.), *Himalayan Geology*, Vol. II, Delhi, 1972, p. 477.

[4] The stratigraphic sequence in Table V is based on information in C.S. Middlemiss, *Recd. Geol. Surv. Ind.*, Vols. XXXVII and XL; D.N. Wadia, *Geol. of Ind.*, op. cit., pp. 162-163, 218-221, 224 and 226, which has been reconstructed here in order to promote understanding of the Upper Palaeozoic formations of the Kashmir region.

[5] The stratigraphical position of the *Gangamopteris* beds is, however, not so clear elsewhere. They lie "above the volcanics at Khunmu and Golabgrah pass, below them at Nagmarg and Bren, or intercalated with them in one or two places." (Krishnan, *Geology of India and Burma*, Madras, 1968, p. 302). The Golabgarh section, therefore, cannot be considered as illustrative of the stratigraphic arrangement of the Lower Gondwana rocks in Kashmir on a universal basis.

[6] The beds have been named after the common seed-fern *Gangamopteris*, as the rocks have impressions of its leaves fully preserved on them.

[7] The term "Zewan series" has. . .been amplified to receive the entire succession of beds between the *Gangamopteris* and the lower Triassic beds. The base of the Zewan series is argillaceous in composition. . .the upper part is calcareous, the limestone strata are preponderant. (Cf. Wadia, *Geol. of India*, op. cit., pp. 225-226.)

[8] The Guraiz area is an exception, however. Here the Lower and the Middle Trias are missing and the Panjal trap conformably passes on directly to the Upper Trias.

[9] Godwin Austin (op. cit., 1864) was the first to recognize the significance of these enormous deposits to an understanding of the later geological history of the Himalayas. The evidence of the Karewa series was extensively used by Dainelli (1922) in reconstructing the different stages in the structural evolution of the Pir Panjal. It was the work of de Terra and Paterson (1939) that really unravelled the massive evidence of the Karewa deposits and enlisted it in support of their interpretation of the climatic changes and the evolution of human cultures in northwestern India during the Pleistocene period.

[10] Wadia believes that the base of the Karewas touches "as low a horizon as the *Dhok Pattan* stage of the Middle Siwaliks . . .", which is generally regarded as contemporaneous with Pliocene. (Cf. Wadia, *Geol. of Ind.*, op. cit., p. 383.)

[11] A. Gansser, *Geology of the Himalayas*, London, 1964, p. 50.

[12]de Terra and Paterson, *op. cit.*

[13]Wadia, *op. cit.*, p. 384; Krishnan, *op. cit.* p. 505.

[14]Wadia, *op. cit.* p. 384.

[15]The zone of "overfolds of the recumbent type, severed by reversed faults that have passed into thrust-planes, along which large slices of the mountains have moved bodily southwards . " Wadia, *op. cit.*, p. 418; cf. Pilgrim and West, "Structure of the Simla Rocks," *Mem. G.S.I.*, Vol. LIII, 1928; Wadia, *Rec. G.S.I.*, Vol. LXV, pt. 2, 1931; and Vol. LXVIII; pt. 2, 1934; Auden, *Rec. G.S.I.*, Vol. LXVII, pt. 4, 1934.

[16]Spate and Learmonth, *India and Pakistan*, 1967, pp. 34-35.

[17]de Terra believes that the Pir Panjal has been upheaved to the extent of 1,830 metres (6,000 ft) since the middle of the Pleistocene, (de Terra and Paterson, *op. cit.*).

[18]Wadia, *Geology of India, op. cit.*, p. 16.

[19]The lake legend is universally accepted in Kashmir. According to mythological tradition "a Shakti manifestation of Siva called Sati appeared in the form of water. This Shakti is also named as Parvati and the place where it appeared came to be known as Satisaras, the place where the Shakti Sati took the shape of a tarn or lake. . .Kashyap the grandson of Brahma, had come to know of the evil deeds of a *raksas* (demon) called Jalodbhava (water-born). So he sought the help of Brahma, Vishnu and Siva. . . .Vishnu assuming the form of a *Varaha* struck the mountains at Varahamula (modern Baramulla) with his tail and cut up the remaining obstacles with his teeth. The waters of the lake rushed out. . . ." (G.M.D. Sufi, *Kashir: Being a History of Kashmir*, Lahore, 1948, Vol. I, pp. 9-10.)

Equally interesting is Kalhana's version of the lake legend: "Formerly since the beginning of the Kalpa, the land in the womb of the Himalaya was filled with water during the periods of the (first) six Manus (and formed) the Lake of Sati (Satisaras).

"Afterwards when the present period of the (seventh) Manu *Vaivasvata* had arrived, the Prajapati Kasyapa caused the gods led by Druhina, Upendra and Rudra to descend, caused (the demon) *Jalodbhava*, who dwelt in that (lake), to be killed, and created the land known by the name of Kasmir in the space (previously occupied by) the lake." (M.A. Stein, *Kalhana's Rajatarangini*, 1961 Reprint, Vol. I, First Book, p. 5.)

[20]R.D. Oldham, *Rec. G.S.I.*, Vol. XXXII, p. 152, *op. cit.*, Burrard and Hayden, *op. cit.*, first edition, p. 169. Oldham's finality on this question is amusing: ". . .the Karewas are of fluviatile and not of lacustrine origin, and there was never at any time a materially larger lake than at the present day."

[21]de Terra, *op. cit.*, p. 224.

BIBLIOGRAPHICAL NOTE

The references given at the end of Chapter One are equally relevant here also.

Among the pioneering studies Lydekker's work on the stratigraphy of Kashmir has already been acknowledged in the bibliographical note to Chapter One; for the results of his geological survey in the 1880s, which is now of historical interest only, see *Mem. G.S.I.*, Vol. XXII, 1883. His contribution came in that initial phase of confusion in Himalayan geology which preceded the later clarity. The later workers, such as Middlemiss, helped in solving some of the fundamental problems. Of great value, in this respect, were his studies of the "Silurian-Trias Sequence of Southeast Kashmir," *Recd. G.S.I.*, Vol. XL, pt. 3, 1910; and another study on the geology of Pir Panjal, *Recd. G.S.I.*, Vol. XLI, pt. 2, 1911. This understanding was further augmented by Wadia's field studies. Notably among these are: "Cambrian-Trias Sequence of Northwest Kashmir," *Recd. G.S.I.*, Vol. LXVIII, pt. 2, 1934; "Permo-Carboniferous in the Tertiary Zone of Kashmir Himalayas," *Recd. G.S.I.*, LXXII, pt. 2, 1937; "Geology of Poonch and Adjoining Areas," *Mem. G.S.I.*, Vol. LI, pt. 2, 1928.

Wadia's *Geology of India*, (third revised edition, London, 1961) gives a masterly synthesis of the work done on the geology of Kashmir Valley and adjoining mountains. M.S. Krishnan's *The Geology of India and Burma* (Madras, fourth edition, 1960) is a work of almost equal importance although less rigorous. New light on the geology of the Himalayas was shed by Gansser in *Geology of the Himalayas* (London, 1964) and A.J. Jhingran, *Himalayan Geology* (Delhi, 1972).

A team of the G.S.I. geologists is known to be engaged in geological work of a fundamental nature in Kashmir these days. The results of this work are, however, not yet available for use in academic studies.

On Himalayan orogeny, useful material is available in Krishnan's "Structural and Tectonic History of India," *Mem. G.S.I.*, Vol. LXXXI, 1953; H. de Terra, "Himalayan and Alpine Orogenies," Report of XVth *Intn. Geol. Cong.*, Vol. II, 1936, pp. 859-872; Wadia, "Syntaxis of the N.W. Himalaya," *Recd. G.S.I.*, Vol. LXV, pt. 2, 1931; H.H. Hayden, "Relationship of the Himalaya to the Indo-Gangetic Plain and the Peninsula," *Recd. G.S.I.*, Vol. XLIII, pt. 2, 1913; J.B. Auden, "Traverses in the Himalayas," *Recd. G.S.I.*, Vol. LXIX, pt. 2, 1935; and J.W. Gregory, *Structure of Asia* (London, 1924). Other stray papers from de Terra, particularly "Physiographic Results of Recent Survey in Little Tibet," *Geographical Review*, 1937, pp. 46-52, are also of basic value.

H. de Terra and Paterson's *Studies on the Ice Age in India and Associated Human Cultures* (Washington, 1939), continues to be a fundamental work of reference on problems of Pleistocene glaciation as well as Ice Age deposits of Kashmir. Earlier contributions of R.D. Oldham, "Glaciation of the Sind Valley, Kashmir," *Recd. G.S.I.*, Vol. XXXI, pt. 3, 1904; and of J.L. Grinlinton, "Glaciation of the Liddar Valley, Kashmir," *Mem. G.S.I.*, Vol. XLIX, pt. 2, 1928, are still of some value. Wadia's work on the Ice Age deposits of Kashmir, (*Proc. Nat. Inst. Sc. Ind.*, 7, 1941; *Report of the XVIIIth Intn, Geol. Cong.*, London, 1948) and other associated problems is undoubtedly required reading.

Chapter Three

The Face of the Land

... Kashmir where loveliness dwells and an enchant-
ment steals over the senses.—Jawaharlal Nehru
... It cannot be only because of its magnificent woods,
the pure limpidity of its lakes, the splendour of its
snowy mountain tops, or the happy murmur of its
myriad brooks sounding in the cool soft air.—M.
Foucher (cf. *Discovery of India*, p. 555)

Geomorphologically, Kashmir Valley holds a unique
position in the Himalayas in so far as it possesses an
extensive body of evidence on the evolution of its
surface features. Nestled in the young folded mountain
ranges still in the process of uplift, the Valley's
geomorphic evolution has a striking recency. Having
been the scene of operation of the complementary
processes of deposition and subareal erosion simulta-
neously, the surface features of the Valley show an
inextricable juxtaposition of both. Both these processes have been accelerated or slowed down sporadi-
cally in response to the tremendous variation in level
in the recent past. To this have been added the ever-
puzzling complexities of the Pleistocene glacial phase
as contributed by alternations of glacial and fluviatile
activity. These past processes have left indubitable
imprints on the surface features of the Valley.

As noted earlier, the valley is surrounded by an
unbroken ring of mountains which give it the character
of an enclosed vale. While the Pir Panjal forms quite
a formidable barrier on the south and southwest,
separating it from the Jammu region, the Great Himalayan and the north Kashmir ranges shut it off from
the frost-bitten plateau-deserts of Ladakh and Baltistan lying within the towering ranges of the black and
bare mountains to the northeast and northwest. Seen
from the crest of the Pir Panjal, the Valley offers the
view of a huge green bowl with its lakes and winding
rivers set within the frame of the snowclad mountain
ramparts which add incredibly to its scenic beauty.

The surface features of Kashmir Valley can be properly studied within the frame of the following three
broad divisions[1]: The contrasts in altitude are depicted
in Fig.3.1.

i) The northern and northeastern slopes and the
foothills of the Pir Panjal range;

ii) the slopes and foothills of the Great Himalayan
and the north Kashmir ranges; and

iii) the Valley floor.

Features of the Pir Panjal Range. The northern
flank of the Pir Panjal, along with its complex of
Karewa-studded foothills and deeply eroded slopes, is
a relief feature of great geographic significance. The
Pir Panjal is a lofty mountain chain with many of its
peaks rising above the perennial snowline. Some of
them rising above 3,500 metres and are capped with
extensive glaciers which project their tongues down
the slopes. The highest of the peaks, Tatakuti and
Barhma Sakal, rise above 4,500 metres.

The lithological complexity of the Pir Panjal has
already been noted. Equally marked are its geomorphological complexities. A succession of folding and
faulting has resulted in the emergence of sharply
defined ridges with spectacular slopes contrasted by
low-lying depressions entrenched in between. Over and
above it are the intertwined impacts of the Pleistocene
and Sub-Recent uplift and recurrent glaciation which
have added to its distinctive characteristics. The
vigorous subareal erosion which has continued since
the emergence of the mountain range has created neat
valleys and narrow gorges.[2] Undoubtedly, the dissection has been of a high order. Its northern face is
flanked by enormous Karewa beds, which have been
continually raised up, tilted and folded along with the
upheaving range. The Pir Panjal descends through a
long gentle slope towards the Valley of Kashmir, as
opposed to its sharp escarpment-like ascent from the
plains of Jammu. The gentle and graded nature of the
slope on the northern flank makes it ideally suited to
the accumulation of snow. Practically all Pir Panjal
glaciers rest on the northern slopes. In contrast to the
glaciers in Karakoram and the other Himalayan ranges,

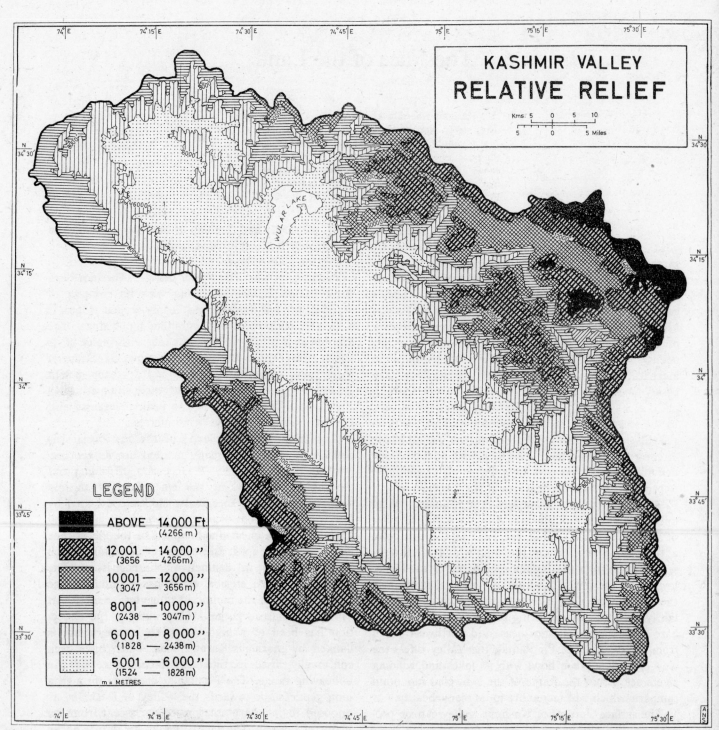

KASHMIR VALLEY
RELATIVE RELIEF

Kms. 5 0 5 10
5 0 5 Miles

WULAR LAKE

LEGEND

	ABOVE 14000 Ft. (4266 m)
	12001 — 14000 " (3656 — 4266m)
	10001 — 12000 " (3047 — 3656m)
	8001 — 10000 " (2438 — 3047m)
	6001 — 8000 " (1828 — 2438m)
	5001 — 6000 " (1524 — 1828m)

m = METRES

Fig. 3·1

they are tiny and rarely have valley tongues.

Two distinct sections are usually recognized in the Pir Panjal range, as is evident from its alignment into two different axes. In its east-west axis the range extends for over forty-eight kilometres, ultimately culminating in the Rupri ridge. The headstreams of all the important left bank affluents of the Jhelum, such as the Bring, Sandran, Vishav and Rembiara, rise in this precipitous ridge. The other section of the range, having a north-northwest-south-southeast axis, runs for about sixty-four kilometres up to the Jhelum gorge at Baramulla. As noted earlier, the Pir Panjal is more imposing in its east-west axis, which in the Rupri promontory is studded with a number of peaks, most conspicuous among which is Barhma Sakal, 4,704 metres (15,440 ft). Other peaks in the range are Jatakuti 4743 metres (15,560 ft); Parasing 4,583 metres (15,040 ft); Kousarnag 4,436 metres (14,555 ft); Nabapir 4,287 metres (14,068 ft); Kankut 4,107 metres (13,480 ft); Aheratop 3,974 metres (13,043 ft); and Sundartop 3,877 metres (12,725 ft).

The Pir Panjal is the main barrier between the plains of India and Kashmir Valley; the passes of this range assume special significance. Of these, the Pir Panjal (3,491m), Budail Pir (4,261m) and the Banihal passes (3,224m) have been the most frequented.[3] The Banihal marks a low passage in the range and offers a natural line of communication into the Valley. The recently constructed tunnel at Banihal has made it largely independent of the hazards of weather, keeping the road open throughout the year. Moving from east to west, the following passes offer routes of communication across the Pir Panjal range into Kashmir Valley.

i) Halan Pass (3,189m)
ii) Banihal Pass (3,224m)
iii) Didamgali Pass (3,809m)
iv) Phutian Pansal Gali (3,123m)
v) Budil Pir Pass (4,261m) close to the Dhakiar peak (4,568m) and at a point where the range realigns itself to the north and the northwest
vi) Rupri Pass (4,099m)
vii) Darhal Pass (3,946m)
viii) Khabi-ki-Gali (3,979m)
ix) Pir Panjal Pass (3,491m)
x) Naba Pir Pass (4,250m) also known as Tangtala Pass
xi) Chhoti Gali (4,296m) overlooked by the snowy peak Tatakuti (4,657m)
xii) Nurpur Gali (4,093m) to the south of the Toshmaidan
xiii) Toshmaidan Pass (4,091m) also known as Chinamarg Pass connecting Toshmaidan with the Punch area
xiv) Jamianwali Gali (4,088m)
xv) Chor Panjal Pass (3,964m) and
xvi) Haji Pir Pass (2,607m).

Features of the Great Himalayan Slopes. The Great Himalayan range, which encloses the Kashmir Valley on the east-northeast and north-northwest, is a massive topographic barrier, offering stupendous difficulties in cross-communication. The northern affluents of the Jhelum which manage to pierce it point up the only routes to communication to lands beyond. Ladakh, for example, is reached only by a tortuous route along the sinuous Sind valley and after crossing the Zoji-la at an altitude of 3,526 metres. The range extends uninterruptedly for over 150 kilometres from west to east and has a maximum width of 40 kilometres, which nowhere decreases below 20 kilometres. Its precipitous and snowclad ridges overlook the valleys of Kishenganga to the north and of Kashmir to the south. At a point near Zoji-la the range takes a bend towards the southwest, and is often described as the north Kashmir range.[4] It is in this stretch that the range forms the water-divide between the Jhelum river in Kashmir Valley and the Kishenganga, the affluents of the latter washing its northwestern slopes.[5] The range which rises to great heights, has some of its highest peaks in this stretch. Notable among them are Harmukh, 4,876 metres (16,872 ft); Shutiyan, 4,371 metres (14,341 ft); Kutbal, 4,344 metres (14,257 ft); Viji, 3,622 metres (12,111 ft); Kainagrad, 3,639 metres (11,942 ft); Marinag, 3,599 metres (11,814 ft); and Rangtop, 3,487 metres (11, 443 ft). As suggested by the altitude of these peaks the north Kashmir range declines steadily towards the west and the southwest.

The Harmukh precipice is a vast snow waste. The peak is covered by a snow field of great thickness and feeds the Madhumati and the Erin systems which flow into the Wular lake. While cross-communication has its own hazards, the range is negotiable at a number of passes, most of them between 3,000-4,000 metres high. Notable among them are Waril Gali (4,291m); Viji Gali (4,246m); Kuljan Gali (4,246m); Gosai Gali (3,501m); Nao Gali (3,334m); Sonapind Gali (3,047m); Puta Kham Gali (2,972m); Pharkhiam-Ki Gali (2,940m); and Rangwar Gali (3,738m).

To the northwest of Baramulla the Kazinag ridge of the north Kashmir range describes the western boundary of Kashmir Valley. To the east of Harmukh the range coalesces with the Great Himalayan range near Zoji-la.

Of the three mountain chains girdling the Valley, the Great Himalayan range is by far the most imposing. This is evident from the altitude of its peaks, the highest one being Kolahoi 5,425 metres (17,799 ft); Tatakuti in the Pir Panjal lies at 4,743 metres, and Harmukh (north Kashmir range) at 4,876 metres, and the average height of its crest, which occupies more area above 3,650 metres (12,000 ft) than either of the two ranges. Other conspicuous peaks are Sheshnag, 5,096 metres; Kotsal Saribal, 4,882 metres; Niltup, 4,423 metres; Hoksar, 4,298 metres; Wandar Dur, 4,333 metres; Maorinag, 4,431 metres; and Agas Mundi, 4,196 metres. The Zoji-la lies at a point where the eastern and the northern mountain ranges intertwine into a complex mass. A striking feature of the Great Himalayan range is the asymmetrical development of slopes on the two flanks in sharp contrast to the gentle slope towards Ladakh, the descent from the Zoji-la to the Kashmir Valley is very steep. Zoji-la is a remarkable feature in more than one sense. Burrard believes it to be a relic of an ancient river which carved out a defile within the mountain precipices with towering peaks on either flank—it is much lower in altitude than the table-land lying to the east.[6] The Himalayan range forming the eastern boundary of the Valley branches off from the main chain close to the peak near Amarnath, 5,003 metres (16,421 ft) east-southeast of Zoji-la. Between the eastern and the western branches of the Liddar, above Pahalgam, south of Amarnath, lies the huge snow field of Kolahoi—the peak rising to 5,425 metres (17,799 ft). The Kolahoi feeds the headstreams of the Liddar and the Sind on either flanks. In its southern extremity the mountain chain coalesces with the Pir Panjal not far from the Banihal pass.

The range is traversed by a number of passes all lying above 3,500 metres as a rule. The significance of the Zoji-la has already been noted; others are Gulol Gali, 4,405 metres; Sargali, 4,131 metres; Zajimarg, 4,036 metres; Putwalmarg, 3,992 metres; Shilsar, 4,141 metres; Drinyansar, 4,327 metres; Sinthan, 3,788 metres; Singpur Gali, 3,571 metres; and Kun Gali, 3,973 metres.

The drainage of the Great Himalayan range is antecedent, beyond any doubt, with remarkable development of terraces on either flank of the stream channels. These narrow upland valleys offer interesting contrasts in cultural features and human geography.

The Valley Floor. Like all sedimentary basins the Valley has a queer combination of depositional and erosional features. The low-lying areas which are either waterlogged or subjected to recurrent inundation go on receiving layer after layer of fine silt and coarse gravel. The numerous affluents of the Jhelum which fall down the slopes of the bordering mountains bring tons of detrital material to the Valley floor, building levees and deltaic fans over extensive areas at their confluences. The heaps of deposits, consisting

of boulders, sand and silt, in the deltas of the Sind and the Liddar rivers deserve special mention.

The alluvial flats of the Valley are bordered by the Karewa deposits whose denuded tops offer sharp contrast to the aggradational features of the low-lying tracts. The dry and bare surfaces of these table-lands have been subjected to intensive sub-aerial erosion ever since their emergence. In fact, the prolonged fluvial action has reduced them to a highly dissected mass with a confusing network of ravines and intertwined gullies.

The Karewa formations cover a wide area on the southern periphery of the Valley all along its longitudinal extent. The Karewa series differ vastly in their surface characteristics and are divisible into two main types—the sloping Karewas and the flat-topped Karewas. The former, however, are the dominant type. Their gently sloping surfaces towards the Valley floor have been cut into deep ravines, ranging from 50 to 150 metres in depth. The level-topped Karewas are few and farther apart. They are found mainly in three places: in Pampur, the Karewa upland rising to seventy-five metres above the Valley floor; in Payech, ninety-six metres above the general level; and near Anantnag, seventy-five metres above the surrounding area. Along the edge of the hills from Shupian to Sopore the sloping Karewa beds have been dissected into a multitude of steep-sided ravines, giving the landscape a typical look of immaturity.

Below the 1,828 metres contour, Kashmir Valley has a distinctive homogeneity in level, as evident from the line of the Jhelum, which is a "placid" stream all along. The spatial variations in slope can, however, be brought out by a rigorous morphometric analysis only.

MORPHOMETRIC ANALYSIS

The morphological features of Kashmir Valley can best be appreciated by identifying the geomorphic units with homogeneous slope characteristics. While such an exercise is of paramount importance in an understanding of the surface profile, the very complexity of the relief and associated features makes morphometric analysis fairly difficult. The relief map contains a plethora of information in a simplified way, yet it is difficult to draw meaningful conclusions from it without developing some understanding of the essential features of landscape, such as the degree of slope and the volume of change occurring in it over a unit of area.

The present slope characteristics have evolved

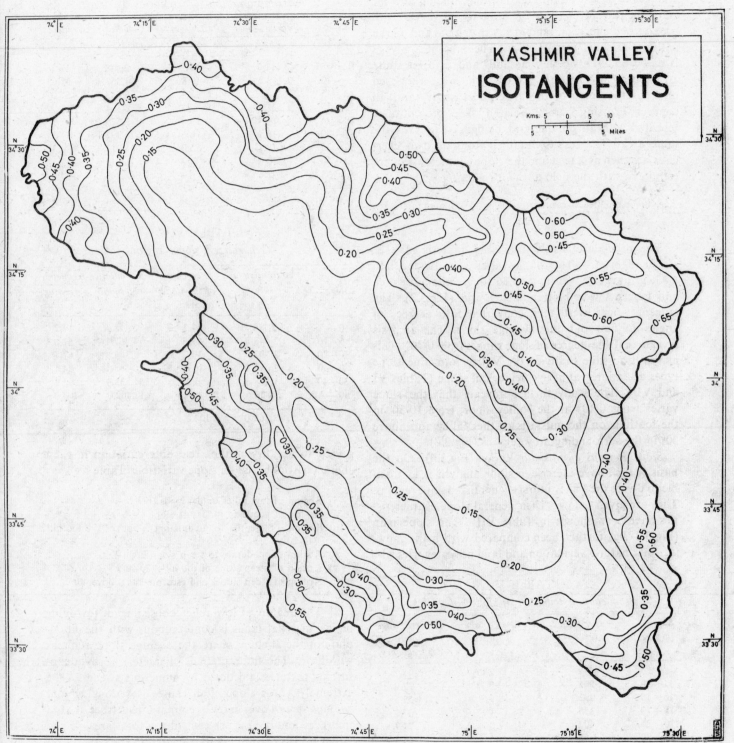

Fig. 3·2

through a sequence of events including spectacular changes in base level through faulting, folding and the consequent rejuvenation of drainage channels with pronounced effects on land forms in general and on the patterns of slope in particular. The present analysis[7] is based on Wentworth's method[8] and involves quite an elaborate procedure. A square grid is superimposed on a contour map of the area under study, and all contour crossings are tabulated. The procedure is repeated with an oblique grid being spread over the same area. The results obtained from the two exercises are then averaged and the slope characteristics are estimated with the help of the formula[9]:

$$\frac{\text{Average number of contour crossings} \times \text{contour interval}}{3361}$$

The procedure involved in this analysis may be stated in brief.[10] The whole valley was divided into 1,036 grids each covering a 10.36 square kilometre area and tangents were plotted in each grid (Fig.3.2). The tangent values were then converted into degrees of angles to find out the average slope. The analysis reveals that the degree of slope ranges from 0-40°. This makes it possible to divide the Valley into nine slope types at an interval of five degrees of slope (Tables VI and VII). The study further reveals that the slope varies from 0-10° in the Valley floor, from 10-30° in the foothills on the outskirts of the Valley and above 30° in the surrounding hilly regions (Fig.3.3).

Slope Regions of Kashmir Valley (Fig.3.4). On the basis of the above exercise in slope analysis it is possible to divide the Valley into six generalized slope regions. They are given below. Their general slope characteristics have been shown in Table VIII. The slope map (Fig.3.4) has further been compared with maps showing soils, natural vegetation and land use categories with

TABLE VI
Frequency distribution of slope categories

Slope (degrees)	Frequency (grids)	Percentage of total	Percentage cumulative frequency
< 5	178	17.2	17.2
5—10	205	19.8	37.0
10—15	192	18.5	55.5
15—20	128	12.4	67.9
20—25	102	9.8	77.7
25—30	68	6.6	84.3
30—35	52	5.0	89.3
35—40	37	3.6	97.1
7 40	30	2.9	100.0
	1,036	100.0	—

TABLE VII
Distribution of slope categories by area

Slope (degrees)	Area in square kms	Percentage of the Valley area	Cumulative frequency square kms	percentage
Below 5	2,118.3	17.2	2,118.3	17.2
5—10	2,448 8	19.8	4,567.1	37.0
10—15	2,276.6	18.4	6,843.7	55.0
15—20	1,521.1	12.3	8,364.8	67.9
20—25	1,211.4	9.8	9,576.2	77.7
25—30	818.9	6.6	10,395.1	84.3
30—35	618.1	5.0	11,013.2	89.3
35—40	520 2	4.2	11,533.4	93.5
Above 40	828 6	6.7	12,362.0	100.0
	12,362	100.0	—	—

TABLE VIII
Generalized slopes regions

Slope categories	Area in square kms	Percentage of the Valley area	Cumulative frequency net square kms	percentage
0— 5	2,118.3	17.2	2,118.3	17.2
5—10	2,448.8	19.8	4,567.1	37.0
10—20	3,797.7	30.7	8,364.8	67.7
20—30	2,030.3	16.4	10,395.1	84.1
30—40	1,138.3	9.2	11,533.4	93.3
40—Above	828.6	6.7	12,362.0	100.0
	12,362.0	100.0	—	—

a view to identifying the areal differentiation in these characteristics based on slope variation (Table IX).

   i) Region of low relief or flat lands (below 5°)
   ii) Region of gentle to moderate slope (5-10°)
   iii) Region of gentle to undulating slope of the foothills (10-20°)
   iv) Region of moderate to steep slop (20-30°)
   v) Region of steep slope of the hills (30-40°)
   vi) Region of steep slopes and escarpments (above 40°)

i) The region of low relief consisting of low-lying plains and flat lands is conterminous with the flood-plain of the Jhelum where the average slope remains within 5°. The flood-plain is characterized by depositional features laid down by numerous streams. The extremely gentle slope often causes waterlogging and swamps spread over extensive areas. This tract of land embraces about 17.2 per cent of the total area of the Valley and is predominantly devoted to the cultivation of rice in the kharif season and wheat over drier parts in the rabi season. It is an area of level plain, by and large, but the alluvial levees with pronounced slope are also not uncommon and have been skilfully

Fig. 3.3

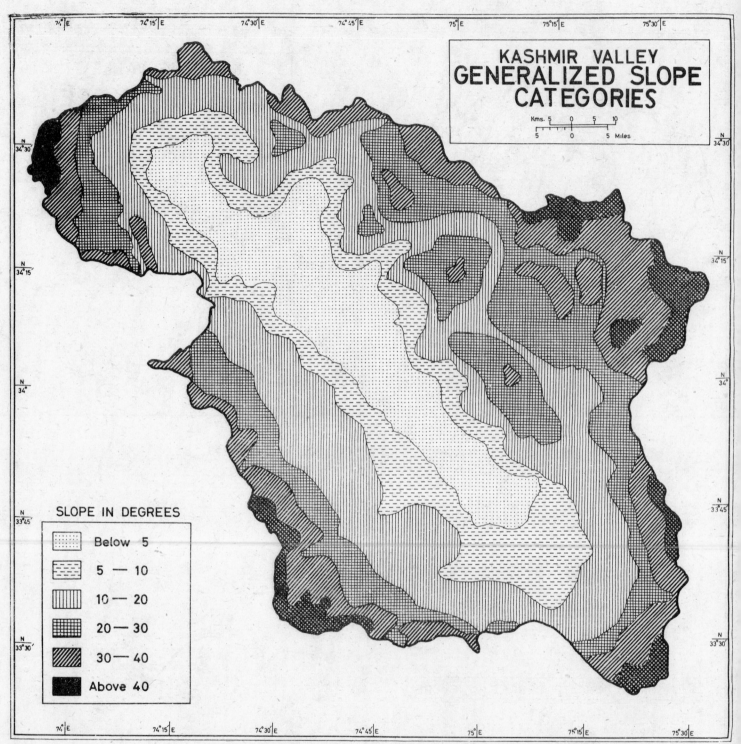

Fig. 3.4

TABLE IX

Relationship of slope categories with other physical factors

Slope region	Percentage area	Slope (in degrees)	Soils	Natural vegetation	Main land use type	
					kharif	rabi
1. Flat lands	17.2	0- 5	Alluvial (Recent)	Open	Rice	—
2. Gentle to moderate	19.8	5-10	Alluvial (Old)	Mixed	Rice, Maize	Wheat, Barley
3. Gentle to undulating	30.7	10-20	Alluvial Old to Coarse soil	Dense	Maize	—
4. Moderate to steep	16.4	20-30	Thin soil cover	Grasses and trees	No cultivation	
5. Steep slope of hills	9.2	30-40	Rocky exposure	Mixed	No cultivation	
6. Steep slopes and escarpments	6.7	40	Rocky exposure and snow cover	Open and grasses	No cultivation	

terraced for paddy cultivation. The level nature of terrain also rules out erosion, though silting is a serious menace all along the lower course of the Jhelum in the Valley. Jhelum floods have often drowned the paddy crop under a thick layer of sediment.

ii) The gentle to moderate slope (5°-10°) is mostly found in the higher parts of the Valley and along the Karewa lands. A heavy subsoil, coarse-textured surface soil, further becoming heavier with depth, and less moisture retaining capacity are the distinctive characteristics of this area. Largely given to subsistence farming, the lower parts are suited to rice while the upper parts are devoted to maize. This region covers about 19.8 per cent of the total area of the Valley. With increasing steepness, soil erosion assumes serious proportions, especially in the Karewa lands where a high percentage of the cultivable land lies as waste. In fact, the proper use of Karewa lands is constrained by a number of factors including coarse and highly permeable soils and lack of irrigation.

iii) The region with a gentle to undulating slope (10-20°) embraces about 30.7 per cent of the total area of the Valley. Being a transition zone between the hills and the Valley floor it displays an intermingling of the land use characteristics of both. While a good proportion of area is given to crops, an equally sizable area lies under forests or is used as grazing land. Areas characterized by less steep slopes are normally preferred for cultivation, which gives way to grazing as the angle of slope finally rules it out. Higher up, the forest seems to be the only conceivable land use.

iv) The region of moderate to steep slope extends over 16.4 per cent of the total area of the Valley. With increasing altitude the forest becomes sparse, leaving summer grazing as the only option. Grazing lands attract nomadic tribesmen with their herds of sheep and goats from far and near.

v) The region high up the hills with an angle of

slope between 30° and 40°, is too steep to be put to any productive use. The slopes facing the river beds are, however, occasionally used for grazing purposes. The land is devoid of any vegetational cover except a variety of poor grasses which do not invite much grazing activity.

vi) As the altitude and the gradient further increase, land remains covered with perennial snow. But the snow fields feed all the rivers and are the ultimate source of all life in Kashmir Valley.

DRAINAGE NETWORK

The Jhelum and a host of streams that drain the bordering mountain slopes together constitute the drainage network of Kashmir Valley. They include the fairly developed systems of the Sind, Rembiara, Liddar and the Pohru rivers as well as tiny rivulets such as the Sandran, Erin and the Viji. Set within the frame of the disparate geomorphic and geological locales, the Kashmir fluvial systems have distinctive characteristics of their own. They have evolved in the course of a chequered history marked by stupendous changes in level, rejuvenating at one time, and at others becoming sluggish, or even choking their channels with their own debris with consequent diversions and the ever-threatening process of mutual piracy. Admittedly, the hydrographic complexity is of a high order, yet in order to promote understanding the following drainage basins may be identified (Fig. 3.5):

a) Right bank drainage basins: (i) Sandran; (ii) Bring; (iii) Arapat Kol; (iv) Liddar; (v) Arapal; (vi) Harwan; (vii) Sind; (viii) Erin; (ix) Madhumati; (x) Pohru; and (xi) Viji-Dakil.

b) Left bank drainage basins: (xii) Vishav; (xiii) Rembiara-Sasara; (xiv) Romushi; (xv) Dudh-

KASHMIR VALLEY
DRAINAGE BASINS

Kms. 5   0   5   10
5   0   5 Miles

DRAINAGE BASINS
1—SANDRAN RIVER
2—BRING RIVER
3—ARAPAT KOL RIVER
4—LIDDAR RIVER
5—ARAPAL RIVER
6—HARWAN RIVER
7—SIND RIVER
8—ERIN RIVER
9—MADMATI RIVER
10—POHRU RIVER
11—VIJI-DAKIL RIVER
12—VISHAV RIVER
13—REMBIARA RIVER
14—ROMOSHI RIVER
15—DUDHGANGA RIVER
16—SUKHNAG RIVER
17—NINGAL RIVER

LEGEND
—— BOUNDARY OF KASHMIR VALLEY
----- DRAINAGE BASINS
(FIGURES INDICATE DRAINAGE DENSITY PER SQ. Km. BASIN-WISE)

Fig. 3·5

ganga-Shaliganga; (xvi) Sukhnag-Firozepura; and (xvii) Ningal

The Sandran. The Sandran rises in the Pir Panjal, below the Kakut peak. From its source to a point close to Vernag, the river passes through a deeply carved channel, studded with big boulders. Below Vernag its wide sandy bed is aligned parallel to that of the Jhelum —southeast-northwest. As it debouches into the plain, the river sheds its load, and divides itself into a number of channels which later unite to form a main stream. The Sandran has a perennial flow of water only in its lower reach of about eight kilometres before its merger with the Bring. The combined waters of the Bring, Sandran and the Arapat Kol merge with the Jhelum a little above Khanabal, near Anantnag. The Sandran has a small catchment area, extensive over only 291 square kilometres. From source to confluence with the Bring, it has a total length of fifty-one kilometres only.

The Bring. The headstreams of the Bring catch the snow-melt from over a wide area in the Pir Panjal close to the source of the Sandran. After the Anlan and the Razparyin unite above the village of Wangom the river after the confluence is called the Bring. The stream then takes a west-northwest course flowing for some twenty-five kilometres up to south of Anantnag where it unites with the Sandran.

The Arapat Kol. Before merging with the Sandran, the Bring receives the waters of the mountain torrent known as Arapat Kol. It has a small catchment area below the Niltup and Astanbal peaks in the Great Himalayan range and drains the Kutihar valley.

The Liddar. In Liddar the Jhelum has the first of its major right bank tributaries. It has a long and picturesque valley which is surpassed only by that of the Sind. Rising at the base of the Kolahoi and the Sheshnag snow fields, its two main upper streams—the West and the East Liddar—unite at Pahalgam. The western branch, after having received the Liddarwat, an upland torrent from Tarsar, flows for thirty kilometres before its merger with the East Liddar. The latter collects the snow-melt from the Sheshnag and traverses a course of a little over twenty-four kilometres before reaching Pahalgam.

Below Pahalgam the Liddar passes through a narrow valley, studded with massive boulders and overlooked by dense forests, till it debouches into a wide alluvial fan. At the head of its delta, the main stream divides itself into a number of channels, braiding being a common characteristic of all the rivers in the Valley, which fan out to form a wide alluvial plain and merge with the Jhelum between Khanabal and Gur.

Between Pahalgam and Gur the Liddar falls from 2,129 metres to 1,591 metres or about 14 metres in 1 kilometre (or 1 in 71). The gradient between the source and the confluence is, however, far more steep; taken from the main headstream of the West Liddar to Gur the fall is 49 metres in 1 kilometre or 1 in 20 (Fig. 3.6).

The Arapal. The Liddar and the Sind hold between themselves the entire drainage of the southern and southwestern slopes of the Great Himalayan range, leaving little scope for any other stream to survive. The two tiny streams—the Arapal and the Harwan—are tightly interposed between the two major affluents of the Jhelum in an outer fringe of the ridges skirted by the Pambagai and the Nao Gul heights. The Arapal, besides getting its water supply from the famous Arapal Nag spring, also drains the Wustarwan before its confluence with the Jhelum above Awantipura.

The Harwan. All drainage from the slopes of Harawar, Burzakut. Mahadeo and Sarbal escapes into the Dal lake through the Harwan and a number of other mountain torrents. Some of the feeders of the Harwan originate as high up as the glacial tract west of Tarsar (3,781m).

The Sind. The Sind, with a course of about 100 kilometres and a basin area exceeding 1,556 square kilometres, is perhaps the most well developed side valley of the Jhelum.[11] Its uppermost feeders rise below the lofty peaks near Zoji-la, as a number of other headstreams join from the Amarnath, Kolahoi and Panjtarni snow fields. At Sonamarg, the gushing torrent flows through a narrow channel with deeply incised caves in the bordering rocks on either bank. Further down, the river bed deepens more and more to assume the character of a gorge below the steep banks fringed with virgin stands of silver fir, junipers and birch. Below Kangan, the valley widens out, although the incising tongue of the arable reaches as far up as Wangat (1,989m) in the Wangat valley, and Gund (2,437m) in the Sind valley. The Sind receives the Kanaknaz or Wangat on its right bank a little above Dragti-yung. Flowing on the northern flank of a boldly projected ridge culminating in Harawar (3,449m) the river makes a knee-bend above Ganderbal before entering into a wide flood-plain. As the river sheds its load, its own channels choke with debris and the mainstream bifurcates into a number of channels over an extensive deltaic core. One of the branches escapes into the Anchar lake while the others merge with Jhelum near Shadipur.

Up to Kangan the Sind falls 3,433 metres in about 69 kilometres or 50 metres in 1 kilometre

LONGITUDINAL PROFILES

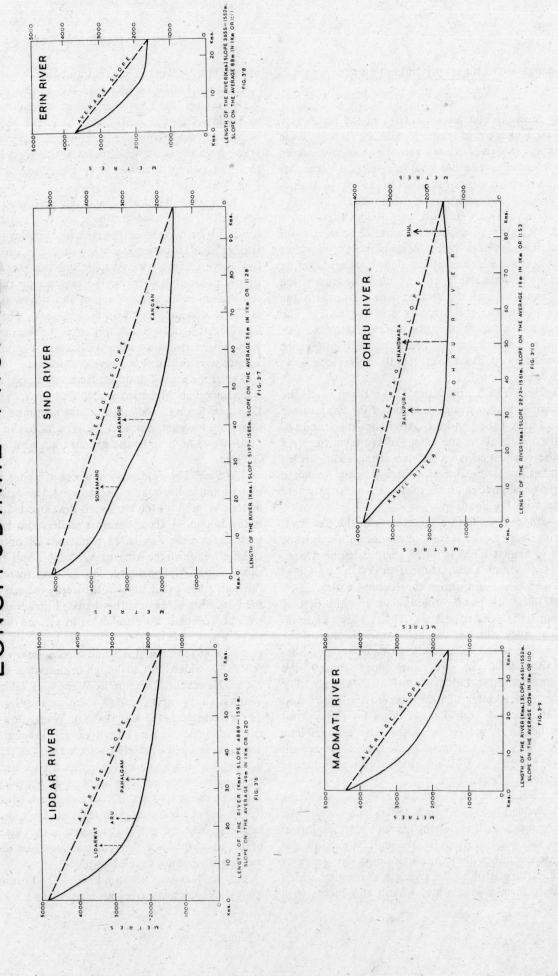

ERIN RIVER

LENGTH OF THE RIVER(Kms.) SLOPE 3055–1552m.
SLOPE ON THE AVERAGE 88m IN 1Km OR 1:11

FIG. 3·8

SIND RIVER

KANGAN

GAGANGIR

SONAMARG

AVERAGE SLOPE

LENGTH OF THE RIVER (Kms.) SLOPE 5197–1585m. SLOPE ON THE AVERAGE 36m IN 1Km OR 1:28

FIG. 3·7

LIDDAR RIVER

AVERAGE SLOPE

PAHALGAM

ARU

LIDARWAT

LENGTH OF THE RIVER (Kms.) SLOPE 4889–1591 m.
SLOPE ON THE AVERAGE 49m IN 1Km OR 1:20

FIG. 3·6

POHRU RIVER

SIUL

AVERAGE SLOPE

CHANDWARA

RAINPURA

POHRU RIVER

KAMIL RIVER

LENGTH OF THE RIVER (Kms.) SLOPE 2832–1561m. SLOPE ON THE AVERAGE 19m IN 1Km OR 1:53

FIG. 3·10

MADMATI RIVER

AVERAGE SLOPE

LENGTH OF THE RIVER (Kms.) SLOPE 4451–1552m.
SLOPE ON THE AVERAGE 103m IN 1Km OR 1:10

FIG. 3·9

(1 in 20). From Kangan to Shadipur the gradient is gentle—6 metres in 1 kilometre (Fig. 3.7).

The Erin. Both the Erin and the Madhumati belong to a larger group of tiny streams which feed the Wular lake. The Erin rises from the western flank of the Harmukh. After pursuing a course of about twenty-four kilometres through a neatly cascaded valley, it falls into the Wular, south of Bandipur. The stream serves as an important artery of transport for timber. The Erin is characterized by a steep gradient; it falls eighty-eight metres in one kilometre or 1 in 11 (Fig. 3.8).

The Madhumati. Farther north, the Madhumati, or Bod Kol, drains the northern slopes of the Harmukh precipice with its feeder streams spread over a vast area between Nagmarg in the west and Sarbal Nag in the east. From a point a little above Bunakut, the valley starts opening up laterally, forming an alluvial triangle which lends itself to intensive exploitation. The Madhumati empties itself into the Wular lake near Bandipur after traversing a course of thirty-nine kilometres. Like the Erin, the Madhumati also falls steeply, the average fall being 103m in 1 km or 1 in 10 (Fig. 3.9).

The Pohru. The Pohru, with its network of confluent streams perhaps ideally dendritic in pattern, occupies the northwestern corner of Kashmir Valley. Consisting of a number of sizable tributaries, such as the Lolab, Kahmil, Talar and the Mawar, the Pohru has a series of palm-leaf shaped valleys with their interesting mosaic of land uses. Almost all tributaries have their origin at high elevations in the crest of the north Kashmir range which divides the waters of the Pohru from the Kishenganga system.

The Lolab,[12] perhaps the most fascinating and picturesque of the Himalayan valleys in Kashmir, has its sources in the Nagmarg and Bagalsar heights, north of Wular. Below Khumarial, it receives the tribute of an upland affluent flowing from Kalarosh and takes a southerly bend to merge with the Pohru, a little below Rainpura. The mainstream of the Lolab has a length of twenty-three kilometres only.

At almost the same point where the Lolab flows into the Pohru, the Kahmil joins from the west. It drains a wider plain and has a longer course, with a general southwest-northeast trend. The headstreams of the Kahmil draw their water from a series of ridges between the Shamsh Abri in the west and the Phishaitong in the north. A little above Handwara, the Pohru receives the waters of its winding tributary Talar on its right bank, while the Mawar joins seventeen kilometres downstream. The Mawar drains the northern flank of the Kazinag range and passing through Lingayat merges with the Pohru below Khohanu. From its confluence with the Lolab and the Kahmil, the Pohru flows for fifty-six kilometres before its merger into the Jhelum, below Achhibal. The Pohru is a highly tortuous stream all through, though meandering is most marked between the confluence of the Talar and the Mawar. This is largely due to the level nature of the plain with a gentle slope. From Rainpura, near the confluence of the Kahmil and the Lolab to its merger with the Jhelum, the Pohru falls over twenty-three metres in fifty-four kilometres (or 0.42m in 1 km; 1 in 2,381); between Handwara and Siul, above a distance of about thirty kilometres, the fall is only four metres (Fig. 3.10).

The Viji. The Viji, a tiny stream flowing from the northern slopes of the ridges culminating in Viji peak (12,111), merges with the Jhelum just below Dobagh, close to the confluence of the Pohru. The Dakil joins the Jhelum, five kilometres downstream at Ludur. The Viji and the Dakil together drain a basin area of about 140 square kilometres.

The Vishav. The source of the Vishav lies in the southeastern corner of Kashmir Valley, close to that of the Jhelum. The river drains the entire northern face of the Pir Panjal between Sundartop and Budil Pir and thus has an extensive catchment area which reduces the upper Jhelum to a tiny rivulet. In fact, the Jhelum draws heavily on Vishav feeders in the initial stage. While passing through the volcanic strata in the Pir Panjal range, the Vishav forms the famous cataracts of Ahrabal. Near Dani Hunzpur the Vishav receives a lateral stream from the side of the Sundartop, the united stream forming a wide sandy bed occupied by a number of braided channels. It merges with the Jhelum about twelve kilometres below Kulgam. One of the bifurcated channels of the Vishav, however, continues farther north, merging into the Rembiara near Nyaiyun not far from the latter's confluence with the Jhelum.

The Vishav falls from 3,975 to 1,568 metres or 41 metres in 1 kilometre (1 in 24). The fall in the lower reach between Kulgam and the confluence is, however, very gentle—1 in 77 (Fig. 3.11).

The Rembiara. The Rembiara rises in the Rupri ridge of the Pir Panjal, its main feeders originating from Rupri peak and the Bhag Sar lake, on the one hand, and the Pir Panjal and the Naba Pir passes on the other. Above Shupiyan the river divides itself into a large number of channels, two of them being well marked and called Rembiara and the Sasara. While the Rembiara merges with the Jhelum near Nyaiyun, the Sasara loses itself into the marshy land west of Awantipura before finally merging with the Jhelum. The Rembiara alone has a course of sixty kilometres; the Sasara branch flows for another forty kilometres.

LONGITUDINAL PROFILES

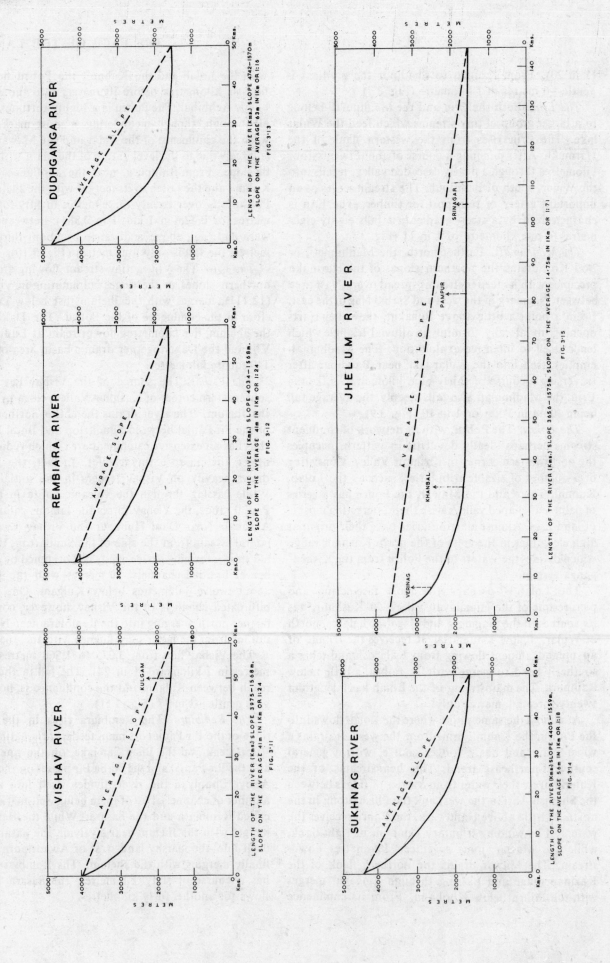

DUDHGANGA RIVER — FIG. 3·13
LENGTH OF THE RIVER (Kms.) SLOPE 4742–1570m
SLOPE ON THE AVERAGE 63m IN 1Km OR 1:16

REMBIARA RIVER — FIG. 3·12
LENGTH OF THE RIVER (Kms.) SLOPE 4034–1568m.
SLOPE ON THE AVERAGE 41m IN 1Km OR 1:24

VISHAV RIVER — FIG. 3·11
LENGTH OF THE RIVER (Kms.) SLOPE 3975–1568m.
SLOPE ON THE AVERAGE 41m IN 1Km OR 1:24
KULGAM

JHELUM RIVER — FIG. 3·15
LENGTH OF THE RIVER (Kms.) SLOPE 3656–1575m. SLOPE ON THE AVERAGE 14·75m IN 1Km OR 1:71
VERINAG   KHANBAL   PAMPUR   SRINAGAR

SUKHNAG RIVER — FIG. 3·14
LENGTH OF THE RIVER (Kms.) SLOPE 4405–1559m.
SLOPE ON THE AVERAGE 56m IN 1Km OR 1:18

AVERAGE SLOPE

METRES

From its source to the confluence the Rembiara registers a fall of 2,466 metres or 41 metres in 1 kilometre (1 in 24) which is similar to the gradient of the Vishav (Fig. 3.12).

The Romushi. The headstreams of the Romushi (also known as Ramshi or Kachgul) draw their waters from the snowy peak of Kharmarg (4,603m) near Naba Pir pass in the Pir Panjal. The upper torrents unite near Pakharpur to give rise to a sizable stream which passes through a wide sandy bed in the Karewa slopes. The Romushi merges with the Jhelum near Wudipur, below Awantipura. In all, it traverses a course of fifty-one kilometres and its bed below Pakharpur has an average gradient of sixteen metres in one kilometre or 1 in 62.

The Dudhganga. Rising below the Tatakuti peak in the Pir Panjal range, the Dudhganga flows north-north-east to finally merge in the marshy land west of Srinagar. Near Bagh Sahib Ram the Shaliganga joins the Dudhganga before the united stream loses itself into the *nambal*, a few kilometres below. A good amount of the discharge from the river is never allowed to pass into the Jhelum as it is diverted towards the west into marshy land. The Dudhganga traverses a course of fifty kilometres and has an average gradient of sixty-three metres in one kilometre or 1 in 16 (Fig. 3.13).

The Sukhnag. The slopes of the Pir Panjal range between the Nurpur and the Chinamarg passes are drained by a multitude of torrents unifying themselves into the Sukhnag and the Firozepura. Between themselves the two streams take care of the drainage of Toshmaidan and Gulmarg respectively. Descending from the mountains the Sukhnag passes through a sand choked bed across the Karewas, finally merging into the marshes of Rakh Aral, west of Hokarsar. The Firozepura empties itself through myriad channels into the Haigam Jhil and the Sultanpurich Rakh. Both the marshes are connected by a spill-channel constructed to drain out the floodwater.

With a total length of just over fifty-one kilometres the Sukhnag has a fall of fifty-six metres in one kilometre or 1 in 18 (Fig. 3.14).

The Ningal. The Ningal is the last major stream in the Kashmir Valley which joins the Jhelum on the left bank. The upper feeders of the Ningal rise below the Khan Pathri (3,809m) and Apharwat (4,141m) peaks of the Pir Panjal above Khelanmarg. Flowing for about thirty-eight kilometres in a northeasterly direction, the Ningal pours itself into the Jhelum immediately after the latter's debouchure from the Wular lake.

The Jhelum. The Jhelum in the Kashmir Valley is much of a drama. It owes both its strength and weakness to the river systems affluent to it. The river crawls through a basin which is not of its making. Its essential dilemma lies in its incapacity to transport the load delivered to it by its affluents and gets bogged down with it instead.

Although an upper channel has a small catchment area, close to that of the Sandran and the Bring, over the slopes of the Pir Panjal, the main source of the Jhelum is in a spring at Vernag. After issuing from this pool of water the rivulet immediately finds itself in a flat plain. It flows to the northwest, gradually swelling as it goes on receiving the discharges of its tributaries on either bank. After receiving the Liddar below Khanabal, the Jhelum is a sizable stream, flowing gently between stable banks of deep soil, and serving as a great artery of transport. However, during floods the river overflows its natural banks and damages the embankments constructed to contain the unusual discharge. While the essentially aggradational role of the river is largely responsible for the recurrent floods, man has also contributed to its devastating effects. The expansion of the city of Srinagar in historic times and its unimaginative beautification deprived the river of many of its outlets into the Dal and other lakes, with the consequence that all floodwater carried by the Jhelum was forced to pass through a narrow waterway across the city. The situation was amended much later when an elaborate network of spill-channels was constructed to divert the floodwaters from a point above Srinagar to a series of swamps—the nambal, as the Kashmiris call it—west of the city through which the water is ultimately drained into the Wular. The artificial embankments had robbed the drainage of the Pir Panjal of its natural outlets into the Jhelum, "which is above the level of the country on its left bank," and converted an extensive area into marshy land.[13]

Below Srinagar the river flows northwest for about forty-five kilometres to empty itself into the great Wular lake. The major problem of the Wular is that it is silting up, perhaps at a very fast rate. After its debouchure from the Wular the Jhelum takes a southwesterly direction to Baramulla and forces out its way through a gorge across the mountains.

All along its course in the Kashmir Valley the Jhelum is characterized by two main features: (a) a sluggish flow (meriting to be described as a "sleeping lion," and (b) a highly tortuous course. Both arise from the highly level nature of the Valley floor. In its course from Khanabal to the Wular, the fall of the river is 18 metres in 113 kilometres or 1 in 6,250 (Fig. 3.15). The river makes some of the finest meanders over this stretch and lays down a good deal of its suspended load along its banks. The alluvial deposits

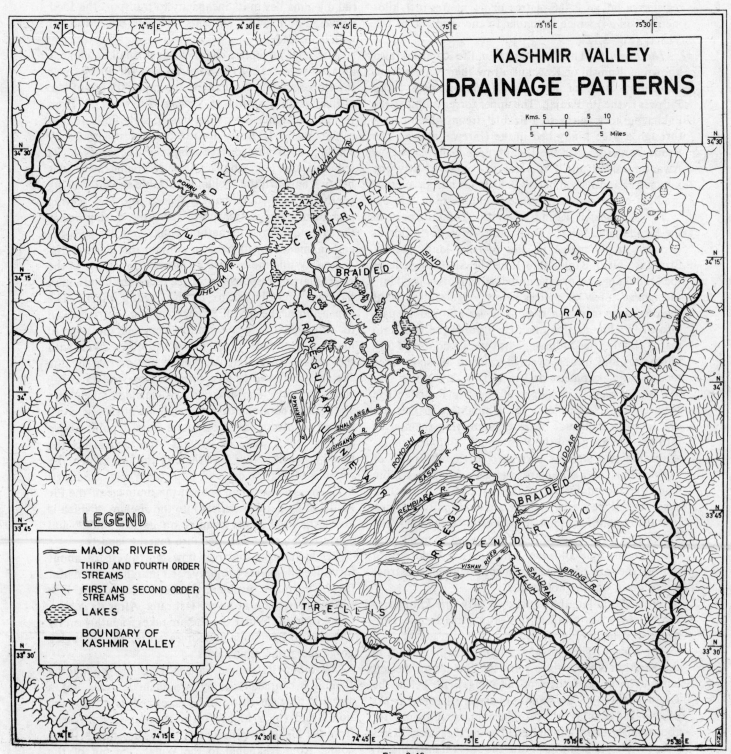

KASHMIR VALLEY
DRAINAGE PATTERNS

Kms. 5   0   5   10
5   0   5 Miles

LEGEND

〰 MAJOR RIVERS
THIRD AND FOURTH ORDER
STREAMS
FIRST AND SECOND ORDER
STREAMS
LAKES
BOUNDARY OF
KASHMIR VALLEY

Fig. 3·16

of the Valley offer the best scope for such undercutting and deposition on the outside and the inside of the bends, which have grown into big meander loops. The Srinagar lakes, as one would tend to agree, may be regarded as the "enlarged old oxbows and abandoned courses of the Jhelum." This is certainly not true for the Wular, whose connections with the original deluge of Kashmir seem to be quite intimate.[14]

The tortuousity of the course of a meandering stream is the outcome of both topographic and hydraulic factors and is expressed by a ratio called the index of sinuosity.[15] The index of hydraulic sinuosity may be expressed as

$$HSI = \frac{CI - VI}{CI - I} \times 100$$

where CI and VI denote channel and valley indexes respectively and may be computed by finding out the ratio between the channel length (CL), the valley length (VL) and the straight-line distance between the two given points on the stream. Thus CI and VI may be expressed as

$$CI = \frac{CL}{SL}, \qquad VI = \frac{VL}{SL}$$

where SL expresses straight-line distance between two points.

The hydraulic sinuosity of the Jhelum has been computed for three different reaches of the river—Khanabal-Wudipur, Wudipur-Srinagar and Srinagar-Wular (Table X).

Drainage Pattern. (Fig 3.16.) The river systems of the Kashmir Valley have disparate drainage patterns—the fluvial processes being dependent on the quantum of slope and the nature of rock material which differ from region to region. The drainage of the Great Himalayan slopes is dendritic, though in certain areas it tends to be linear and even irregular. Perhaps the best example of a dendriform is seen in the Pohru river system which makes a huge banyan tree-like canopy with its trunk attached to the Jhelum near Sopore. Another notable feature of the drainage of the northern arm of the Valley is its antecedence; typical examples of this are seen in the Sind and the Liddar river valleys. There are at least two localities in which the streams seem to have typical diverging and converging trends. Around Kolahoi one notices the radial nature of the drainage, while the bowl of the Wular lake stresses the centripetal character of the rivers.

The drainage of the Pir Panjal offers a sharp contrast to that of the Great Himalayan slopes. The northern flank of the Pir Panjal range is less extensive in width and does not seem to promote the lateral development of stream channels—the short lateral course of the Vishav being the only exception. The streams come down the mountains in parallel and often irregular lines. In the upper reaches they have a dendritic pattern, lower down, their courses are aligned parallel to each other. As the streams cut across the Karewa beds, they develop braided channels, braiding and constant shifting of channels being caused by rapid deposition of sand and gravel in the stream beds. This inter-

TABLE X
Jhelum river sinuosity indexes

Reach	CL km	VL km	Straight line length km	CI	VI	HSI	Standard sinuosity index	Gradient m/km
Khanabal-Wudipur	34	29	23	1.48	1.26	46	1.18	0.03
Wudipur-Srinagar	34	26	19	1.79	1.37	53	1.31	0.32
Srinagar-Wular	45	37	30	1.50	1.23	54	1.22	0.13

Table X reveals that in the Khanabal-Wudipur reach only forty-six per cent of the Jhelum's sinuosity is due to hydraulic factors, the rest is to be attributed to topographic factors. As opposed to this, in the other two reaches—Wudipur-Srinagar and Srinagar-Wular—HSI (hydraulic sinuosity index) has higher values of fifty-three and fifty-four respectively, thus reflecting a diminished role of the topographic factors in engendering sinuosity. It is further evident that the river is more sinuous in the Wudipur-Srinagar reach than in either of the other two reaches. While the overall gradient is low everywhere, it is relatively high in this section.

twined nature of the stream channels is most marked in the cases of the Dudhganga, Sukhnag and the Firozepura. The latter river undoubtedly offers an interesting case. Soon after its debouchure from the hills, the Firozepura Nala splits itself into a myriad channels, which bifurcate and reunite to create a maze of drainage channels (Fig. 3.17). Seen from Firozepura the lower reaches of the river channels look like its headstreams collecting water from over a wide catchment area and uniting into a main stream a little above this village. The uplift of the Pir Panjal range during the Pleistocene and the later tilting and folding of the

FEROZEPURA RIVER
DRAINAGE PATTERN

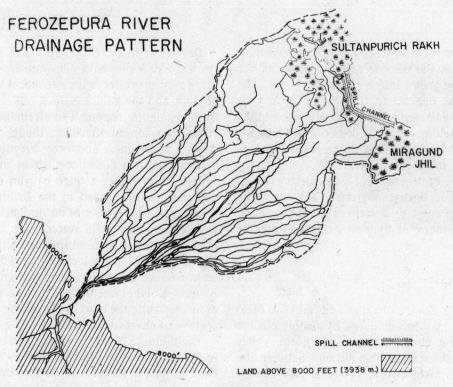

SULTANPURICH RAKH

SPILL CHANNEL

MIRAGUND JHIL

8000

8000

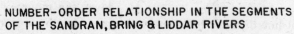

SPILL CHANNEL ⬛⬛⬛⬛⬛

LAND ABOVE 8000 FEET (3938 m.) ▨▨▨

FIG. 3·17

NUMBER-ORDER RELATIONSHIP IN THE SEGMENTS
OF THE SANDRAN, BRING & LIDDAR RIVERS

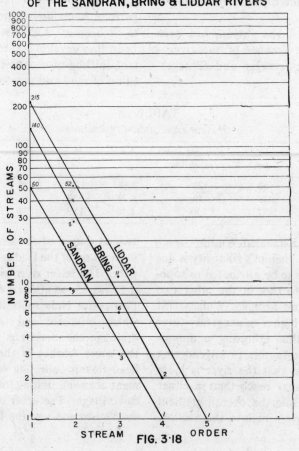

NUMBER OF STREAMS

SANDRAN

BRING

LIDDAR

STREAM   FIG. 3·18   ORDER

Karewa beds have all added to the complexity of the drainage along the southern flank of the Valley.

NETWORK ANALYSIS

Like all other networks, the streams also have their own peculiarities which are determined by a set of physical factors, such as structure, altitude, gradient and climate. They change in time and bring about a consequential change in the form of landscape with far-reaching repercussions on the hydrological processes. The intricacies of this relationship between the form and the process can best be appreciated by employing the tools of morphometric analysis. Such an exercise may yield a good deal of useful data pertaining to the drainage character and the intrinsic relationship between the area of the catchment basins of each of the component streams and the discharge of the trunk stream. Besides promoting an understanding of the dynamics of the entire system, these data have great relevance in planning for a rational utilization of the water resources of the Valley.

Stream Orders. Each channel segment in a stream system has a definite position in an hierarchal order of magnitude. Following Strahler,[16] all "fingertip" channels of the headstreams have been recognized as first order streams. The merger of the two first order streams gives rise to a second order segment; the union of second order streams creates a segment of the third order. The network thus goes on integrating itself up to the highest order. Tables XI-XXVIII show the number of stream segments with their cumulative length in each order of magnitude for all the seventeen basins and the corresponding values for the aggregative Jhelum basin in Kashmir Valley. The relative domi-

TABLE XI
Sandran river drainage basin characteristics

Stream order	Number of stream segments	Bifurcation ratio (Rb)	Length of segments in each order and as % of the cumulative length		Mean length of segments (km)
			Length km	%	
1	50		35.00	42.68	0.70
		5.55			
2	9		6.00	7.32	0.67
		3.00			
3	3		6.00	7.32	2.00
		3.00			
4	1		35.00	42.68	35.00
	Total 63	Average 3.85	Cumulative length 82		

TABLE XII
Bring river drainage basin characteristics

Stream order	Number of stream segments	Bifurcation ratio (Rb)	Length of segments in each order and as % of the cumulative length		Mean length of segments (km)
			Length km	%	
1	140		215.00	67.82	1.53
		5.00			
2	28		58.00	18.29	2.07
		4.66			
3	6		31.00	9.79	5.16
		3.00			
4	2		13.00	4.10	6.50
	Total 176	Average 4.22	Cumulative length 317		

TABLE XIII
Arapat Kol river drainage basin characteristics

Strem order	Number of stream segments	Bifurcation ratio (Rb)	Length of segments in each order and as % of the cumulative length		Mean length of segments (km)
			Length km	%	
1	72		147.00	57.65	2.04
		4.00			
2	18		52.00	20.39	2.89
		3.60			
3	5		32.00	12.55	6.40
		5.00			
4	1		24.00	9.41	24.00
	Total 96	Average 4.20	Cumulative length 255.00		

nance of the stream segments of the different orders can be judged from their respective share in the cumulative length of streams. As evident from the tables, a striking feature of most of the basins is the dominance of the streams of the first and the second orders. The cumulative percentage of the stream segments of the first two orders is the highest in the Sind river basin—89.43 per cent—and the lowest in the Sandran river basin—50.0 per cent. This proportion is above 80 in as many as 8 basins; it is above 70 per cent in another 7 basins. Thus, the streams of the first two orders together account for three-fourths to nine-tenths of the cumulative channel lengths. The lower order stream segments are, however, randomly distributed and there seems to be no direct relationship between the area of the drainage basin and such streams.

Lying in the upper parts of the mountains, the streams of the first two orders generally flow only intermittently, flushing out the instant flood from the rain

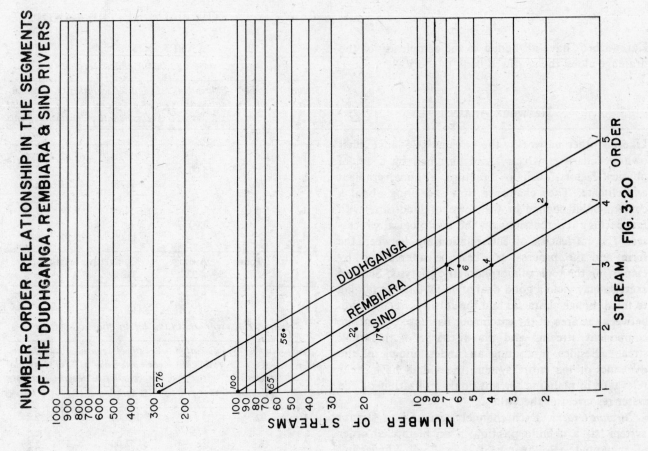

NUMBER-ORDER RELATIONSHIP IN THE SEGMENTS OF THE DUDHGANGA, REMBIARA & SIND RIVERS

FIG. 3·20

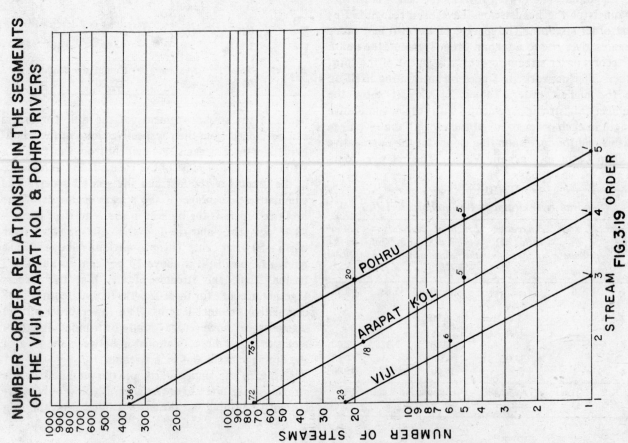

NUMBER-ORDER RELATIONSHIP IN THE SEGMENTS OF THE VIJI, ARAPAT KOL & POHRU RIVERS

FIG. 3·19

or the snow-melt to the third and fourth order streams. Their delivery role is however fundamental as they determine the volume of water that would flow down the higher order streams. The delivery system is such that while the streams of the first two orders are ephemeral those of the third and the fourth order flow perennially. The volume of water supply and its seasonal variation in the lower segments of streams is in any case of critical significance in chalking out strategies for their purposeful utilization.

The stream orders lead to the identification of another significant characteristic of the drainage channels, that is, the bifurcation ratio between successive orders. This ratio may be symbolically expressed as

$$Rb = \frac{Nu}{Nu + 1}$$

and constitutes an important parameter in drainage analysis.[17] The bifurcation ratios of the various river basins at each level of hierarchy are given in Tables XI-XXVIII. The Kashmir streams display an interesting range of variation in their bifurcation characteristics. In the Sind river basin, for example, there are about five times as many first order segments as second order; just eight times as many second order segments as third order; and three and a half times as many third order segments as fourth order. The Liddar basin, on the other hand, has four times as many first order segments as second order; four and three-fourths times as many second order streams as third order; and five and a half times as many third order streams as fourth order. The averages of the bifurcation ratio, however, do not markedly differ from basin to basin—

TABLE XIV
Liddar river drainage basin characteristics

Stream order	Number of stream segments	Bifurcation ratio (Rb)	Length of segments in each order and as % of the cumulative length		Mean length of segments (km)
			Length km	%	
1	215		412.00	60.68	1.91
		4.09			
2	52		152.00	22.39	2.92
		4.72			
3	11		58.00	8.55	5.27
		5.50			
4	2		25.00	3.68	12.50
		2.00			
5	1		32.00	4.70	32.00
Total 281		Average 4.07	Cumulative length 679.00		

TABLE XV
Arapal river drainage basin characteristics

Stream order	Number of stream segments	Bifurcation ratio (Rb)	Length of segments in each order and as % of the cumulative length		Mean length of segments (km)
			Length km	%	
1	89		234.00	65.92	2.63
		4.05			
2	22		64.00	18.03	2.91
		3.66			
3	6		32.00	9.01	5.33
		3.00			
4	2		25.00	7.04	12.50
Total 119		Average 3.57	Cumulative length 355.00		

TABLE XVI
Harwan river drainage basin characteristics

Stream order	Number of stream segments	Bifurcation ratio (Rb)	Length of segments in each order and as % of the cumulative length		Mean length of segments (km)
			Length km	%	
1	73		89.00	61.81	1.22
		3.84			
2	19		24.00	16.66	1.26
		3.16			
3	6		9.00	6.25	1.50
		2.00			
4	3		12.00	8.33	4.00
		3.00			
5	1		10.00	6.95	10.00
Total 102		Average 3.00	Cumulative length 144.00		

the highest average value is found in the Madhumati river basin, and the lowest in the Harwan river basin. It is interesting to note that both of these are minor basins. The average values for the Liddar, Sind and the Pohru are almost identical—4.1, 4.6 and 4.4 respectively. These may be compared with the corresponding value for the aggregative Jhelum basin which is 4.9.

Studies conducted in various river basins of the world reveal that the bifurcation ratio tends to be by and large constant under homogeneous physical conditions. Horton noted that the number of stream segments of different orders is likely to form a geometric series.[18] This *law of stream numbers* expressed as Nu = Rb (k—u) has been tested in the case of Kashmir streams. The number of stream segments in each order has been plotted against the relevant order with a view

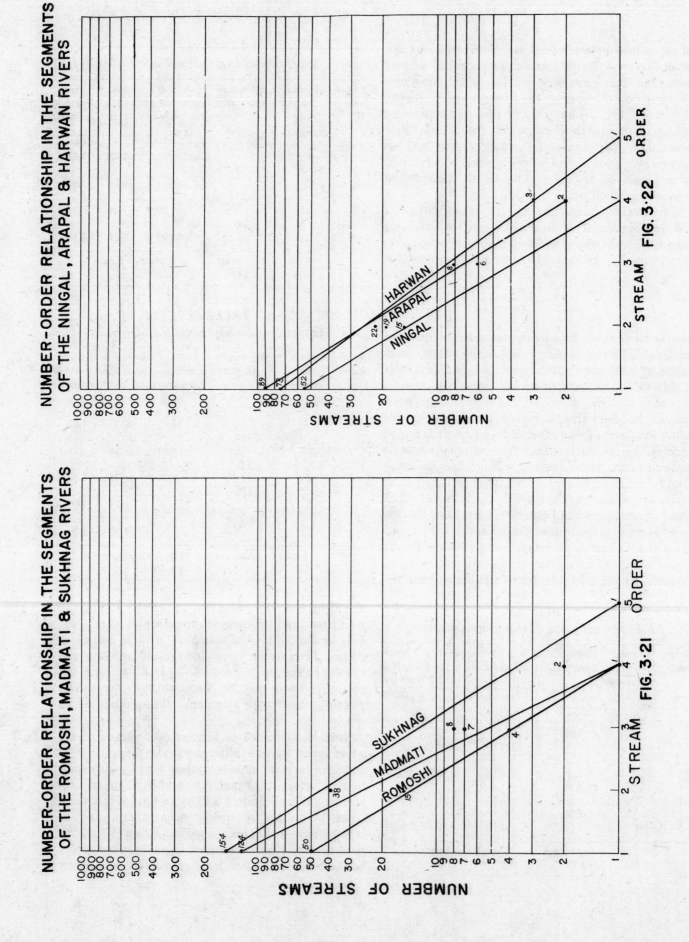

NUMBER–ORDER RELATIONSHIP IN THE SEGMENTS
OF THE NINGAL, ARAPAL & HARWAN RIVERS

FIG. 3·22

NUMBER–ORDER RELATIONSHIP IN THE SEGMENTS
OF THE ROMOSHI, MADMATI & SUKHNAG RIVERS

FIG. 3·21

TABLE XVII
Sind river drainage basin characteristics

Stream order	Number of stream segments	Bifurcation ratio (Rb)	Length of segments in each order and as % of the cumulative length		Mean length of segments (km)
			Length km	%	
1	276		512.00	66.85	1.86
		4.93			
2	56		173.00	22.58	3.09
		8.00			
3	7		33.00	4.31	4.71
		3.50			
4	2		24.00	3.13	12.00
		2.00			
5	1		24.00	3.13	24.00
Total 342		Average 4.60	Cumulative length 766.00		

TABLE XVIII
Erin river drainage basin characteristics

Stream order	Number of stream segments	Bifurcation ratio (Rb)	Length of segments in each order and as % of the cumulative length		Mean length of segments (km)
			Length km	%	
1	71		134.00	63.80	1.75
		4.23			
2	17		38.00	18 00	2.23
		3.40			
3	5		19.00	9.00	3.80
		2.50			
4	1		6.00	2.80	3.00
		2.00			
5	1		13.00	6.40	13.00
Total 96		Average 3.03	Cumulative length 210		

TABLE XIX
Madhumati river drainage basin characteristics

Stream order	Number of stream segments	Bifurcation ratio (Rb)	Length of segments in each order and as % of the cumulative length		Mean length of segments (km)
			Length km	%	
1	124		288.00	72.54	2.32
		4.96			
2	25		51.00	12.84	2.04
		3.57			
3	7		32.00	8.06	4.57
		7.00			
4	1		26.00	6.52	26 00
Total 157		Average 5.17	Cumulative length 397.00		

to checking whether they produce a straight line regression of negative exponential form or not. Figs. 3.18-3.23 show the nature of sequence as displayed by number-order data. The following main points are borne out:

i) that the points form almost perfect straight lines in the case of the Romushi, Dudhganga, Pohru and the Bring;

ii) that departures from a straight line are very small in the case of the Jhelum, Liddar, Viji, Arapat Kol, Rembiara, Sukhnag; and

iii) that they are very large in the case of Sind and the Vishav. It may be noted that the number-order relationship in the Dudhganga river basin approaches closest to Horton's Law. Here the average value of Rb is 4.02 and the numbers of stream segments are 1, 4, 17, 65.

The inequalities observed in the number-order relationship in the Kashmir basins may be attributed to the variations in configuration and to chance factors.

Stream Lengths. Tables XI-XXVIII further reveal that there is a specific relationship between the stream lengths and order. The first order streams have the shortest mean lengths in all the basins except in the Madhumati. Their mean length increases with each successive order, although no constant length ratio is observed in the different fluvial systems as suggested by Horton.[19]

Drainage Density. The drainage density, viewed as the length of river channels per square kilometre, is an important concept in quantitative hydrography. It may be symbolically stated as

$$D = \frac{\Sigma Lk}{Ak}$$

where D denotes drainage density in kilometres per square kilometre, ΣLk expresses the sum of the lengths of all channels, and the total basin area is represented by Ak.

The drainage density shows the level of dissection a landscape has reached at the hands of the fluvial systems. The density values for all streams and for the perennial ones have been computed separately in order to take note of the variations between them. It may be noted (Table XXIX) that the drainage density is the highest in the Madhumati river basin—0.83 km of channel for every square kilometre of surface area; it is the lowest in the Sandran river basin. There are ten basins with one-half to two-thirds of a kilometre of channels for every square kilometre. These inequalities may largely be attributed to differences in structure, rock texture and the vegetation cover. In fact, the low

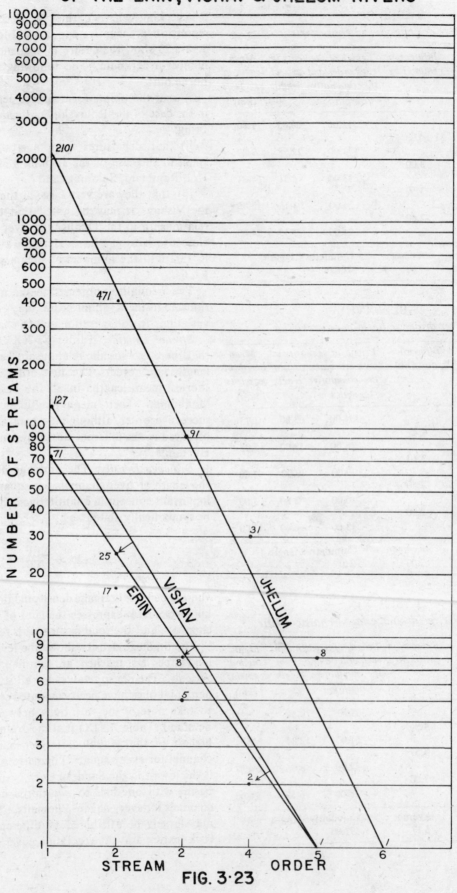

NUMBER-ORDER RELATIONSHIP IN THE SEGMENTS
OF THE ERIN, VISHAV & JHELUM RIVERS

FIG. 3·23

TABLE XX
Pohru river drainage basin characteristics

Stream order	Number of stream segments	Bifurcation ratio (Rb)	Length of segments in each order and as % of the cumulative length		Mean length of segments (km)
			Length km	%	
1	369		627.00	55.48	1.67
		4.92			
2	75		284.00	25.13	3.78
		3.75			
3	20		138.00	12.21	6.90
		4.00			
4	5		44.00	3.89	8.80
		5.00			
5	1		37.00	3.27	37.00
	Total 470	Average 4.41	Cumulative length 1,130		

TABLE XXI
Viji and Dakil river drainage basin characteristics

Stream order	Number of stream segments	Bifurcation ratio (Rb)	Length of segments in each order and as % of the cumulative length		Mean length of segments (km)
			Length km	%	
1	23		52.00	54.16	2.26
		3.83			
2	6		32.00	33.34	5.33
		6.00			
3	1		12.00	12.50	12.00
	Total 30	Average 4.91	Cumulative length 96		

TABLE XXII
Vishav river drainage basin characteristics

Stream order	Number of stream segments	Bifurcation ratio (Rb)	Length of segments in each order and as % of the cumulative length		Mean length of segments (km)
			Length km	%	
1	127		269.00	60.04	2.12
		5.08			
2	25		73.00	16.29	2.92
		3.12			
3	8		48.00	10.71	6.00
		4.00			
4	2		25.00	5.58	12.50
		2.00			
5	1		33.00	7.38	33.00
	Total 163	Average 3.55	Cumulative length 448.00		

TABLE XXIII
Rembiara river drainage basin characteristics

Stream order	Number of stream segments	Bifurcation ratio (Rb)	Length of segments in each order and as % of the cumulative length		Mean length of segments (km)
			Length km	%	
1	100		184.00	49.32	1.84
		4.54			
2	22		67.00	17.96	3.05
		3.66			
3	6		51.00	13.69	8.50
		3.00			
4	2		71.00	19.03	35.50
	Total 130	Average 3.73	Cumulative length 373.00		

TABLE XXIV
Romushi river drainage basin characteristics

Stream order	Number of stream segments	Bifurcation ratio (Rb)	Length of segments in each order and as % of the cumulative length		Mean length of segments (km)
			Length km	%	
1	50		154.00	58.77	3.08
		3.33			
2	15		51.00	19.46	3.40
		3.75			
3	4		33.00	12.59	8.25
		4.00			
4	1		24.00	9.18	24.00
	Total 70	Average 3.69	Cumulative length 262.00		

An attempt has been made to depict by isolines the spatial variations in drainage density for the entire Kashmir Valley. Fig. 3.24 reveals that the density is high in the Erin and the Madhumati catchment basins, it is fairly high in the Bring and the Sandran river basins and moderately high in the Pohru, Sind, Liddar, Rembiara and the Vishav river basins. The density figures for the perennial rivers (Fig. 3.25) reveal an inverse relationship with the altitude. An exception to this general rule is, however, observed in the Liddar-Sind catchment area which has a higher length of perennial streams per unit area. No substantive variation in the drainage density is observed in the different geomorphic regions of the Valley—the respective values for the uplands, the Karewas and the Valley floor being 0.7, 0.6 and 0.45 kilometre of channel for every square kilometre.

The actual number of channels within a square kilometre is often taken as an index of topographic texture. The uniformly low values, as evident from Fig. 3.27, are suggestive of a coarse texture, a characteristic of immature landscapes.

values of density per unit area for the entire Kashmir basin are themselves attributable to the hard resistant rock material, massive topography and the dense vegetation cover.

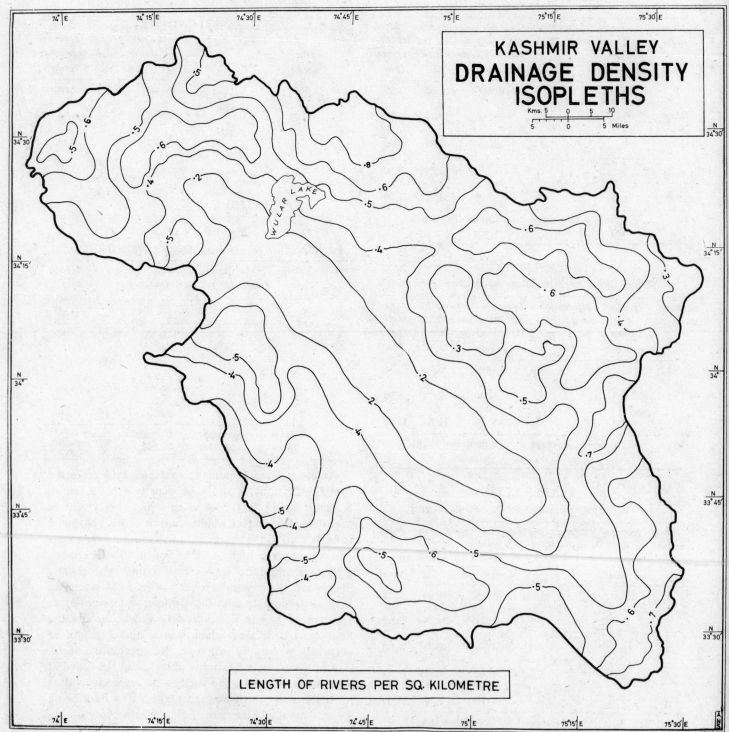

KASHMIR VALLEY
DRAINAGE DENSITY
ISOPLETHS

LENGTH OF RIVERS PER SQ. KILOMETRE

Fig. 3·24

TABLE XXV
Dudhganga river drainage basin characteristics

Stream order	Number of stream segments	Bifurcation ratio (Rb)	Length of segments in each order and as % of the cumulative length		Mean length of segments (km)
			Length km	%	
1	65		126.00	53.40	1.94
		3.82			
2	17		57.00	24.18	3.41
		4.25			
3	4		32.00	13.58	8.00
		4.00			
4	1		21.00	8.89	21.00
	Total 87	Average 4.02	Cumulative length 236.00		

TABLE XXVII
Ningal river drainage basin characteristics

Stream order	Number of stream segments	Bifurcation ratio (Rb)	Length of segments in each order and as % of the cumulative length		Mean length of segments (km)
			Length km	%	
1	52		115.0	49.57	2.21
		3.48			
2	15		51.0	21.99	3.40
		1.88			
3	8		34.0	14.66	4.25
		8.00			
4	1		32.00	13.78	32.00
	Total 76	Average 4.45	Cumulative length 232.00		

TABLE XXVI
Sukhnag river drainage basin characteristics

Stream order	Number of stream segments	Bifurcation ratio (Rb)	Length of segments in each order and as % of the cumulative length		Mean length of segments (km)
			Length km	%	
1	154		207.00	50.35	1.34
		4.05			
2	38		89.00	21.42	2.34
		4.75			
3	8		48.00	11.69	6.00
		4.0			
4	2		54.00	13.28	27.00
		2.0			
5	1		13.00	3.26	13.00
	Total 203	Average 3.70	Cumulative length 411.00		

TABLE XXVIII
Jhelum river drainage basin characteristics

Stream order	Number of stream segments	Bifurcation ratio (Rb)	Length of segments in each order and as % of the cumulative length		Mean length of segments (km)
			Length km	%	
1	2101		3848	58.02	1.83
		4.46			
2	471		1324	19.96	2.81
		5.18			
3	91		687	10.35	7.55
		2.94			
4	31		468	7.05	15.10
		3.88			
5	8		177	2.66	22.12
		8.00			
6	1		128	1.93	128.00
	Total 2,703	Average 4.89	Cumulative length 6,632.00		

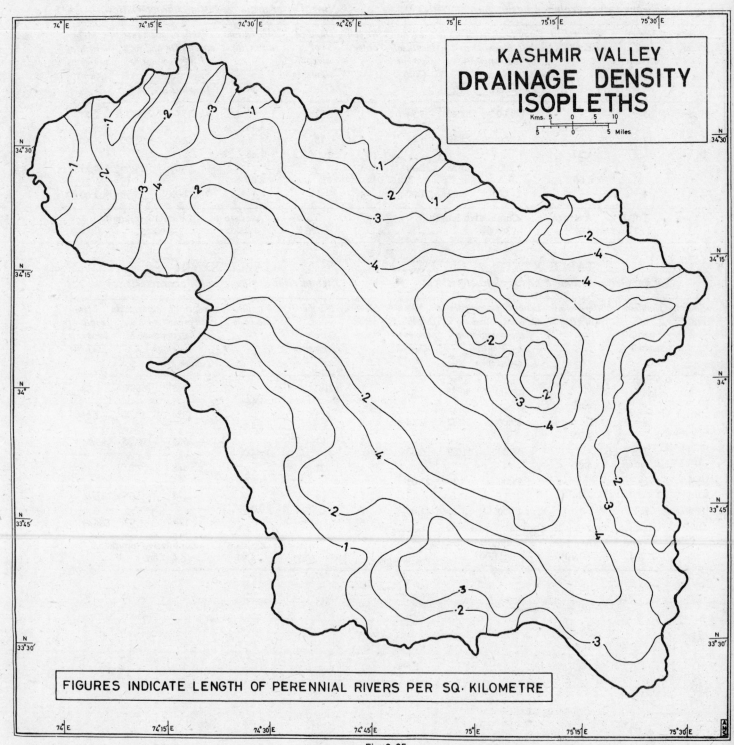

KASHMIR VALLEY
DRAINAGE DENSITY
ISOPLETHS

FIGURES INDICATE LENGTH OF PERENNIAL RIVERS PER SQ. KILOMETRE

Fig. 3·25

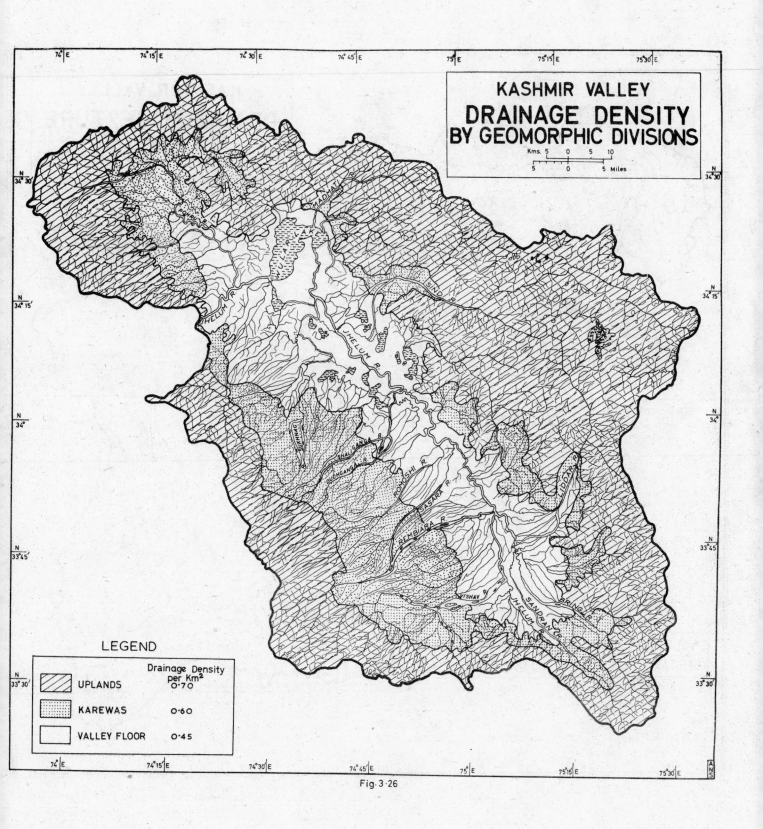

KASHMIR VALLEY
**DRAINAGE DENSITY
BY GEOMORPHIC DIVISIONS**

Kms. 5   0   5   10

5   0   5 Miles

LEGEND

	Drainage Density per Km²
UPLANDS	0·70
KAREWAS	0·60
VALLEY FLOOR	0·45

Fig. 3·26

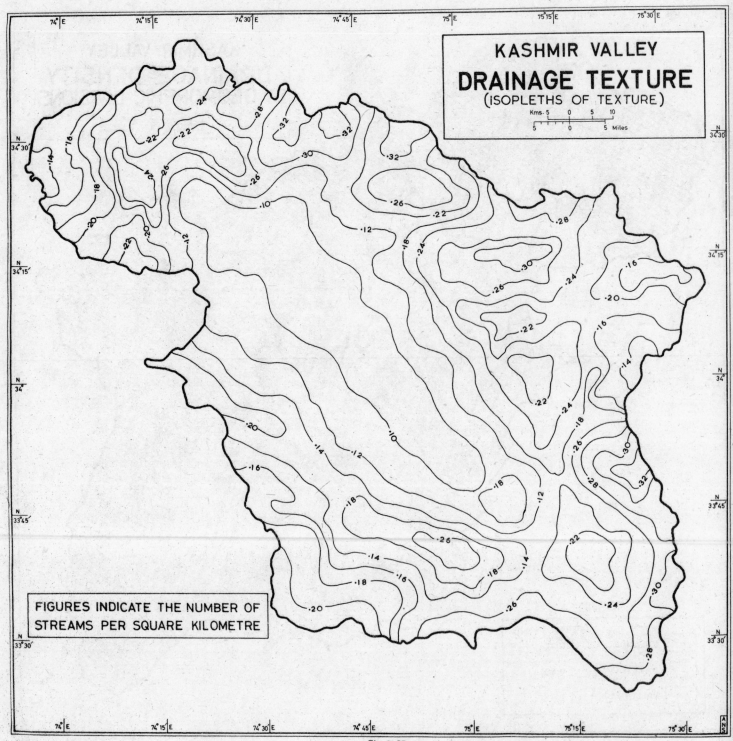

KASHMIR VALLEY
DRAINAGE TEXTURE
(ISOPLETHS OF TEXTURE)

FIGURES INDICATE THE NUMBER OF
STREAMS PER SQUARE KILOMETRE

Fig. 3·27

TABLE XXIX
Drainage characteristics of the Kashmir river basins

S. No.	Drainage basin	Area in square kilometres	Drainage length km	Number of streams Nu	Density $\Sigma Lk/Ak$	Texture Nu/Ak
1	Sandran	258	82	63	0.32	0.25
2	Bring	595	317	176	0.53	0.29
3	Arapat Kol	362	255	96	0.70	0.26
4	Liddar	1243	679	281	0.54	0.23
5	Arapal	571	355	119	0.62	0.21
6	Harwan	395	144	102	0.36	0.23
7	Sind	1556	766	342	0.43	0.22
8	Erin	321	210	96	0.66	0.29
9	Madhumati	476	397	157	0.83	0.33
10	Pohru	1936	1130	470	0.58	0.24
11	Viji Dakil	143	96	30	0.67	0.21
12	Vishav	828	448	163	0.54	0.19
13	Rembiara	751	373	130	0.48	0.17
14	Romushi	459	262	70	0.57	0.15
15	Dudhganga	580	236	87	0.41	0.15
16	Sukhnag	932	411	203	0.44	0.22
17	Ningal	538	232	76	0.43	0.14
	Jhelum	12,262	6,697	2,704	0.55	0.22

NOTES AND REFERENCES

[1]de Terra and Paterson recognize the following physical units: (a) Convex arches of the foothills of the Pir Panjal; (b) the Kashmir Valley basin; and (c) the southern slope of the main Himalayan range.
Cit. Studies on the Ice Age in India and Associated Human Cultures, Washington, 1939, p. 7.

[2]S.G. Burrard, *et al*, *A Sketch of the Geography and Geology of the Himalayan Mountains and Tibbet*, op.cit., p. 88.

[3]The significance of these routes of communication between India and Kashmir in the historic perspective has been brought out among others by M.A. Stein, (*Notes on Ancient Topography of the Pir Pantsal Route*, 1895, and Moonis Raza "Traditional Routes into the Kashmir Valley," JNU, Centre for the Study of Regional Development (mimeographed).

[4]Wadia thinks that the north Kashmir range is "an offshoot of the Zaskar range which forms the northeastern border of the Valley." (*Geology of India*, op. cit., p. 14). The Himalayan nomenclature is still a matter of dispute.

[5]Burrard, *op.cit.*, pp. 88-89.

[6]*Ibid.*, p. 79, " . . . such a depression elsewhere would have been sufficiently deep to open a passage for the drainage of the table-land . . ." Strachey, "Himalaya," *Ency. Brit.*, Vol. XI.

[7]Various methods have been evolved to measure the average slope:

i) S. Finsterwalder (1960) used a method of average slope determination which involved measurement of total length of all contours, contour intervals and the total area of the unit of space under consideration. The formula which, however, entailed much statistical work, is given below:

$$\text{Sine of degrees of average slope} = \frac{\text{Total length of contours} \times \text{contour interval}}{\text{Total Area}}$$

ii) Another method was used by G.S. Smith ("The Relative Relief of Ohio," *Geographical Review*, Vol. XXV, 1935, pp. 272-284) who introduced the term "relative relief" only to ascertain the amplitude of available relief to relate the altitude of the highest and the lowest points of any particular area. One obvious shortcoming in this method was that the resultant map presented amplitudes of maximum relief distances which may be either between two points on opposite ends of a diagonal of any square. Smith suggested that squares with extreme points farther apart should be subdivided, but obviously this would destroy the symmetry of the map.

iii) Other methods have been developed by Raisz and Henry, "An Average Slope Map of Southern New England," *Geographical Review*, Vol. XXVII, 1937, pp. 467-472; A.H. Robinson, "A Method for Producing Shaded Relief from Aereal Slope Data," *Surveying and Mapping*, Vol. VIII, 1948, pp. 157-160; A.N. Strahler, "Quantitative Slope Analysis," *Bulletin of the Geographical Society of America*, Vol. LVII, 1956, New York, pp. 571-596; A.A. Miller, "The Dissection and Analysis of Maps," Presidential Address, 1948, to the Institute of British Geographers, *Transactions of the Institute*, Publication No. 14, London, 1949, p. 3; J.L. Rich, "A Geographical Method of Determining the Average Inclination of a Land Surface from a Contour Map," *Transactions of the Illinois Academy of Sciences*, Vol. IX, 1916, pp. 110-115.

[8]C.K. Wentworth, "A Simplified Method of Determining the Average Slope of Land Surfaces," *American Journal of Science*, Vol. XX, 1930.

[9]Cf. F.J. Monkhouse and H.R. Wilkinson, *Maps and Diagrams*, 1971, p. 134. The denominator 3361 is a constant value in the formula.

[10]The present exercise in slope analysis as well as the forthcoming drainage analysis are based on Quarter Inch SOI sheets and are admittedly rudimentary in nature. They may be treated as an expression of a desire rather than its fulfilment.

[11]Lawrence gives a picturesque account of the side Valleys of Kashmir which have interesting altitudinal zonation of agricultural land use and natural vegetation. " . . . at the mouth of the valley there is the wide delta of fertile soil on which the rice with its varying colours, plane trees, mulberries and willows grow luxuriantly; a little higher up the land is terraced and rice still grows, and the slopes are ablaze with the uniline blooms of a wild indigo, till at about 7,000 feet the plane tree gives place to the walnut and the rice to the millets . . . . Then further up the Valley the river, already a roaring torrent, becomes a veritable waterfall dashing down between lofty cliffs, whose bases are fringed with maples and horse chestnuts, white and pink, and the millets are replaced by the buckwheat and Tibetan barley. Soon after this the useful birch tree appears and then come grass and glaciers—the country of the shepherds." (W.R. Lawrence, *The Valley of Kashmir*, p. 17.)

[12]Iqbal's fondness for the Lolab valley is well known. Its luxuriant forests, the music of its myriad rivulets foaming down from the mountains and the serene calm of the snowy heights seem to have contributed immensely to the exquisite richness of Iqbal's poetry.

[13]Lawrence, *The Valley of Kashmir, op. cit.*, pp. 19-20.

[14]Whether the Wular is also an abandoned old meander of the Jhelum is highly doubtful (cf. Spate, *op.cit.*, pp. 432-433).

[15]J.E. Mueller, "An Introduction to the Hydraulic and the Topographic Sinuosity Indexes," *Annals Assoc. Am. Geog.*, Vol. LVIII, 1968, pp. 371-385. Mueller's insistence on including the role of the topographic factors in the computation of sinuosity indexes is remarkable, as it gives a new dimension to the concept of sinuosity.

[16]A.N. Strahler, *Physical Geography*, Wiley, Toppan, 1969, pp. 483-496; also see the Bibliographical Note below.

[17]*Ibid.*, p. 484.

[18]Horton's law of stream numbers may be stated as follows: "The numbers of stream segments of successively lower orders in a given basin tend to form a geometric series, beginning with a single segment of the highest order and increasing according to a constant bifurcation ratio" (cf. Strahler, *op. cit.*, p. 484).

[19]Like his law of stream numbers, Horton's law of stream lengths also has a mathematical expression in an exponential regression equation.

BIBLIOGRAPHICAL NOTE

The pioneering works of early writers, such as Drew, Lawrence, Bates, Heyden, Burrard and others, cited above are equally good on geomorphology and drainage. So is the work of de Terra and Paterson who made the most significant contribution towards understanding the geomorphological and fluvial processes in the Kashmir Valley. Very little original work has been done on these aspects since the publication of their main work. Excepting the geologists who in their basic effort of documenting the geological record also took cognizance of the broad surface features, no systematic work of an analytical nature on the geomorphology of Kashmir has yet been attempted. S.C. Bose's "Morpho-ecology in and around Pir Panjal" (*Geographical Review of India*, Vol. XXIII, 4, 1961, pp. 55-67) seems to be the only study in which methodical fieldwork has enriched theory.

The Indian geomorphologist is, however, not much inclined to the use of quantitative methods in the analysis of land forms or fluvial processes. The contributions of S.K. Pal, "Quantitative Geomorphology of the Drainage Basins in the Himalayas" (*Geographical Review of India*, XXX, 1973, pp. 81-101) and M. Taher, "Fluvial Processes and Geomorphology of the Brahmaputra Plain," (*Geographical Review of India*, XXXVI, 1974, pp. 38-44) are noted exceptions. These works have only an indirect relevance to the study of the river systems of the western Himalayas and Kashmir Valley.

On methods, major contributions of Wentworth, Finsterwalder, Smith, Raisz and Henry, Robinson, Strahler, Miller and Rich have been cited in the notes. These may, however, be read with the following:

W. Penck, *Morphological Analysis of Landforms*, London, 1953.

A.E. Scheddegger, "Mathematical Models of Slope Development," *Geol. Soc. Am. Bull.*, 1961, pp. 37-50.

R J. Chorley, "The Application of Statistical Methods to Geomorphology," in G.H. Dury (ed.), *Essays in Geomorphology*, New York, 1966, pp. 275-387.

A.N. Strahler, "Quantitative Drainage Basins," *Geol. Soc. Am. Bull.*, Vol. LXX, 1959.

R.E. Horton, "Erosional Development of Streams and their Drainage Basins, Hydrophysical Approach to Quantitative Morphology," *Geol. Soc. Am. Bull.*, Vol. LVI, 1945, pp. 275-370.

Chapter Four

The Symphony of Weather

Heat there is, but hot 'tis not
Cold there is, but cold 'tis not. —Sufi, *Kashir*, I, 6

One of the powerful expressions of Kashmir's personality is observable in its weather. Undoubtedly, for many a visitor Kashmir is another name for bracing weather, whose clemency is one of the main attractions, along with the bewildering scenic beauty. Besides altitude, the surrounding mountains with their snowclad peaks exert an overriding influence on the local weather making processes. They protect the Valley from the blasting cold of the north as well as the scorching heat of the south and contribute significantly to its notable temperate character. This, however, does not nullify the fact of its continental climate, though it certainly distinguishes the Valley climate from the extreme continental quality of the climate of the plains of north India, south of the Pir Panjal. A mild summer, a not too vigorous winter and an absence of a regular rainy season are the three distinctive features of the climatic regime of the Kashmir Valley.

The role of the Himalayas as a major determinant in the climate of Kashmir Valley can hardly be over-emphasized. The southern arm of the mountains certainly acts as an effective barrier to the summer monsoon—the chief bearer of moisture in the subcontinent. The summer rainfall of the Valley clearly reflects this shadow-effect. The Great Himalayas, however, exercise little obstructive influence on the influx of the westerly troughs which frequent the Valley from the west and the northwest during winter.

The location of the Valley at a high altitude in the northwestern nook of the subcontinent, and enclosed within high mountain ranges, gives it a distinctive character with its own climatic peculiarities. Within the Valley, interesting variations in weather are witnessed, largely owing to the variations in altitude and aspect.[1] This diversity is well observed in the side valleys of Kashmir and in such parameters of weather as radiation, annual and daily ranges of temperature, humidity, snowyness and rainyness. Despite the fact that all visitors to Kashmir, particularly to its upper

valleys, such as the Sind, Liddar and the Lolab, are well aware of these contrasts, the climatic diversity remains largely notional. An analysis of its attributional components is inhibited by the sheer lack of meteorological data.[2]

MECHANISMS OF KASHMIR WEATHER

The genesis of Kashmir weather is intrinsically linked with the mechanisms of weather in the Indian subcontinent in general. It is intended here to give a general survey of the working of the meteorological phenomena that create Indian weather in different parts of the year.

The winter weather in the subcontinent is dominated by deep, dynamic, sub-tropical type anticyclones. To the north of the Himalayas there prevails a shallower thermal high with its centre in the lake Baikal region. This arrangement of pressure systems gives rise to a low-level flow of dry continental air from the north in the winter months. The outflow from the Siberian anticyclone, which is a vigorous current over southeast Asia, however spares the Indian subcontinent because the Himalayas act as an effective barrier. The surface circulation in north India during winter months is in fact constituted by a weak northerly flow of subsident air from the tropical anticyclone and the southern branch of the westerly jet stream which overlies India south of the Himalayas. The surface winds thus have the character of a continental trade. The surface circulation during this period points up to the two principal convergence zones. One of them lies to the south and west of Japan, along which the tropical easterlies of the north Pacific establish contact with the continental air from Siberia. The other fragment of this polar front lies in the northwest of the Indian subcontinent making it possible for the northwesterly continental air to contact the Indian trades. There is, however, no stability in the position of this front, and often it may extend up to the middle Ganga valley with the land trajectory of the westerlies following its southeastward displacement.

Higher up, at an elevation of three kilometres and above, an entirely different circulation pattern is observed. As the Siberian anticyclone is shallow at this altitude the zonal westerlies prevail over and across the continent and move southwards with the shift of the sun to the south. In their southward movement the westerly planetary jet is, however, obstructed by the Tibetan highlands which force it to split itself into two branches.[3] The main westerly stream and its jet continue to flow eastwards to the north of the Tibetan barrier. A southern branch of the stream and its jet, on the other hand, asserts itself to the south of the Himalayas, flowing in an eastward direction and coalescing with the northern branch east of the Tibetan highlands to form what is often termed as Tibetan Lee Convergence Zone. The southern branch of the westerly jet has its mean position at latitude 25°N in February, appearing in daily weather charts at 200-300 mb level.[4] It is important to note that this stream plays a critical role in weather-forming processes during the winter months. Another significant feature of the Asiatic circulation during this part of the year at the tropospheric level is the persistence of two discontinuities—one separating the southern branch of the zonal westerlies from the north Pacific trades, and the other separating the latter from the equatorial westerlies fluctuating widely over the equatorial latitudes.[5] Both of them exercise a controlling effect on the circulatory system of the subcontinent.

With the northward shift of the sun the circulatory system of the subcontinent undergoes a complete reversal both at the low-level and aloft. It has been noticed that it has an intrinsic relationship with the poleward displacement of the equatorial trough, also known as the intertropical convergence zone (ITC). This is a deep and fairly extensive surface trough, partly thermal in origin; it prevails over northern India and Pakistan, roughly parallel to the axis of the Himalayas. By mid-July the mean position of the trough is in latitude 25°N, which is believed to be the maximum poleward displacement of the intertropical convergence zone for any part of the earth.[6] By the time it establishes itself in this area, both the zonal westerlies and the southern branch of the jet stream withdraw from over the plains of India, south of the Himalayas. The summer position of the trough induces a number of convergences in the region—to its south converges the southwesterly mT air, popularly known as the southwest summer monsoon, although "actually,

only the northward displaced equatorial westerlies"; to its north an easterly current of the mT air is drawn, while on the northwestern flank of the trough, dry continental air (CT) converges with the southwesterly monsoon current.

The trough is overlain by an easterly stream whose jet is quite pronounced at 150mb level. The two phenomena are perhaps mutually correlated since the mechanism responsible for the drift of the southwest monsoon to India and southeast Asia and the high-level easterly jet is one and the same.[7] The easterly jet plays an important role in steering the tropical depressions over India which are the main weather mechanisms and determine the pattern of summer weather, particularly rainfall distribution in the subcontinent.[8] Recent studies show that the mean jet maximum is located at about latitude 15°N between the northward march of the equatorial trough (ITC) over India and the final withdrawal of the southern branch of the westerly jet on the one hand, and the inflow of the easterly jet stream in the high troposphere over India on the other. Both Flohn[9] and Koteswaram[10] have suggested that the easterly jet is an outcome of the thermal effects of the Tibetan highlands on the upper air circulation in summer months.

The Tibetan plateau and the surrounding mountain ranges together constitute a landmass of great areal extent covering about 4.5 million square kilometres, with an average altitude of over four kilometres. With the northward shift of the sun these highlands are heated enormously as a result of excessive absorption of solar energy. The "re-radiation" from this elevated landmass goes directly to form a "solenoidal field" in the upper troposphere, thus initiating a clockwise circulation at that level. The upper anticyclone, which is thus thermally generated, helps in setting up two main divergent streams of air flowing out of the system. One of them is an equatorward branch with an easterly angular momentum while the other one is a poleward branch and gains a westerly angular momentum. The Koteswaram model thus explains the upper air circulation over the Indian subcontinent and trans-Tibetan Asia during the summer months. The equatorward outflow from the Tibetan anticyclone prevails over India as the easterly jet while the poleward outflow comprises the westerly jet stream over east-Central Asia.[11] The model falls in line with the views of Flohn who attached importance to the summer warming of air over Tibetan highlands at 500mb level and considered it as a key factor in weakening the southern branch of the westerly jet and the eventual appearance of the easterly jet over India.[12]

These developments are of a fundamental nature and exert a direct control on Kashmir weather. Their specific role will, however, be discussed in the following pages.

THE RHYTHM OF SEASONS

Kashmir weather has a marked seasonality. The Valley has rather a longish spring, fairly cold and showery, extending from March through April into half of May. Summers are much less rainy than spring and quite warm. In Srinagar, the mean daily maximum temperature in July may be as high as 30.8°C with a diurnal range of 12.5°C. The total rainfall received during the southwest monsoon period is only three-fifths of the spring rains. As usual the behaviour of the summer rainfall is highly erratic, and an unequal distribution within different parts of the Valley is a norm rather than an exception.[13] Both the daily maximum and the minimum temperatures start falling by August and are quite low by October. Although radiation from the earth is rapid in the later months, September and October have the highest diurnal ranges. Although the Valley normally receives the first snowfall only in December, the surrounding mountains may get it any time after the middle of October. By the end of December snow is almost universal and for two months, up to the middle of February, the Valley remains under the grip of a "cold dampness" with snow covering the ground almost completely and a perennial fog hanging over it. Kashmir winter is, however, only a "dreary monotony" and not exceptionally rigorous as the minimum temperature in January rarely goes below minus 3°C. The snow generally disappears from the Valley by the end of February but not the dampness with rains replacing the snow almost everywhere in the following spring.

On the basis of the general characteristics of weather summarized above, the year can be divided into the following four seasons:

i) Winter—November to February;
ii) Spring—March to mid-May;
iii) Summer—mid-May to mid-September; and
iv) Autumn—mid-September to October.

The Kashmiris, however, recognize the following six seasons of a duration of two months each: *Sorth* (spring) mid-March to mid-May; *Grishim* (summer) mid-May to mid-July; *Wahrat* (rains) mid-July to mid-September; *Harud* (autumn) mid-September to mid-November; *Wand* (winter) mid-November to mid-January; and *Sheshur* (severe cold) mid-January to mid-March.[14] The Kashmiri nomenclature is more expressive of the typical weather conditions that prevail in different parts of the year, although the periodization of the year into seasons is of notional value only. There is, for example, no specific *Wahrat* (rainy season) in Kashmir and the *Wand* (winter) certainly subsumes the *Sheshur* (ice-cold weather).

Winter. The winter in Kashmir is dominated by atmospheric disturbances called the western depressions. The general weather conditions are determined, among other things by the (i) position of the surface polar front which enables the convergence of the northwesterly continental air and the Indian trades along a line of discontinuity in northwestern India; and (ii) the southern branch of the westerly jet stream overlying India, south of the Himalayas. The subsident air from the north-northwest and west remains in circulation, though Srinagar is mostly calm in the winter months and weather processes are extremely feeble. The synoptic situation prevailing during the winter months, as shown on the daily weather maps, is depicted on Figs. 4.1 and 4.2. As noted earlier, the major perturbations are created by the western depressions which frequent the Valley during winter months. The distribution pattern of heat and moisture in this period is essentially controlled by these eastward moving troughs associated with the extra-tropical westerlies. They enter the Valley from the west or northwest from across the Iranian plateau. Some of them are known to originate along the surface polar front which has no fixed position and may fluctuate between Afghanistan and the middle of the Ganga valley. The southern branch of the westerly jet flowing across northern India plays an important role in steering these depressions into the Indian region.[15] The genesis of these depressions is only partly known. Recent studies based on hemispherical analyses charts have indicated a direct and generic relationship between the development of a surface subtropical high cell over the Ukrainian region and the development of frontogenesis over Iran. The southward outbreak of cold air from Ukrainian high creates favourable conditions for the formation of these depressions over Iran. The prevailing synoptic situation favourable to frontogenesis is illustrated in Fig. 4.3. It shows a well developed wane cyclone over northwestern India, Pakistan and southern Iran. Once generated, the systems move in a direction chiefly determined by the pattern of winds prevailing at 300mb level. It has been observed that these depressions approach India

DAILY WEATHER IN OCTOBER, NOVEMBER AND DECEMBER.
(Synoptic View)

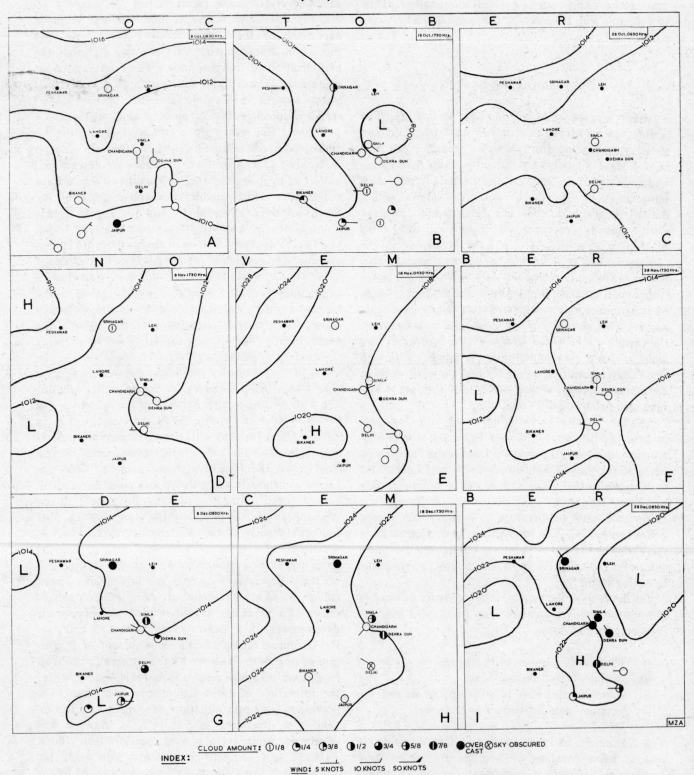

INDEX:

CLOUD AMOUNT: ◖ 1/8 ◔ 1/4 ◕ 3/8 ◑ 1/2 ● 3/4 ◕ 5/8 ◕ 7/8 ● OVER CAST ⊗ SKY OBSCURED

WIND: 5 KNOTS   10 KNOTS   50 KNOTS

FIG. 4·1

DAILY WEATHER IN JANUARY, FEBRUARY AND MARCH.
(Synoptic View)

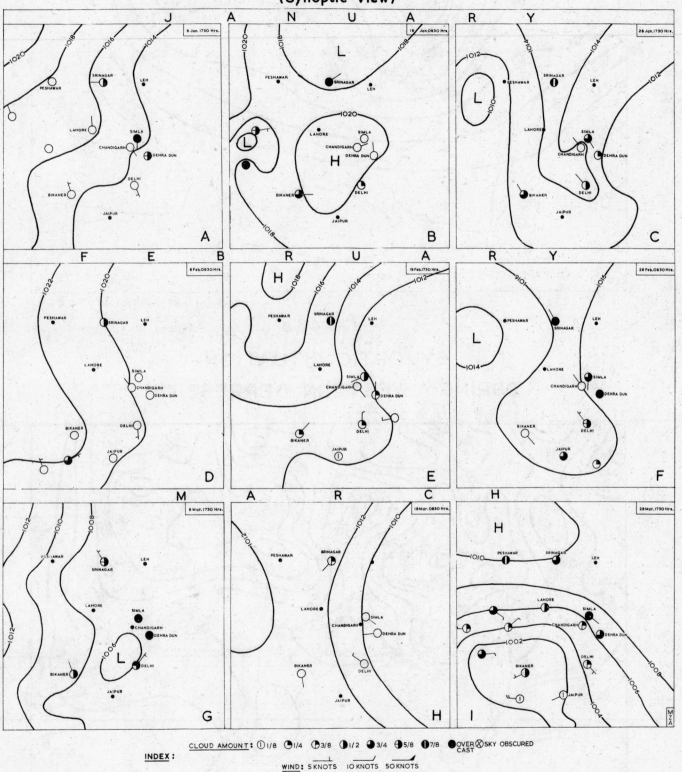

INDEX:

CLOUD AMOUNT: ◔ 1/8 ◑ 1/4 ◕ 3/8 ◐ 1/2 ● 3/4 ● 5/8 ● 7/8 ● OVER CAST ⊗ SKY OBSCURED

WIND: 5 KNOTS 10 KNOTS 50 KNOTS

FIG. 4·2

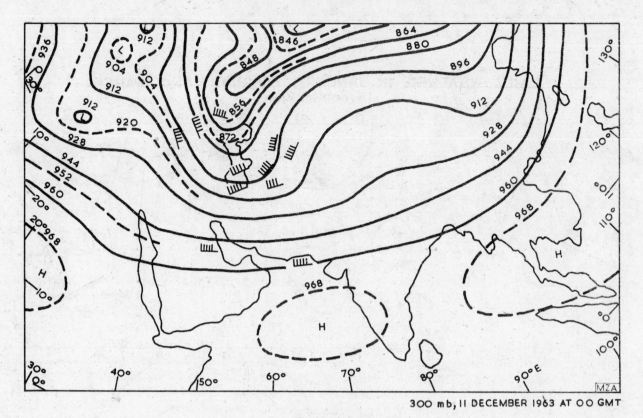

300 mb, 11 DECEMBER 1963 AT 00 GMT

FIG. 4·3 a

SYNOPTIC SITUATION
DURING A WESTERN DEPRESSION

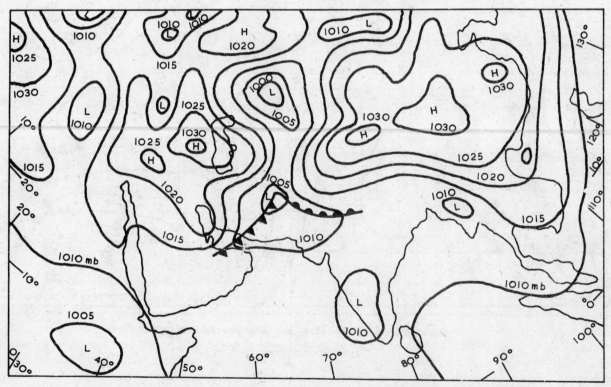

SEA LEVEL, 11 DECEMBER 1963 AT 12 GMT

FIG 4.3 b

only "if flow at 300 mb prevailing radially above them is westerly.[16]

These depressions move very fast, often covering 8° to 10° longitude per day. Although their periodicity and incidence are highly variable phenomena, their impact on local weather is tremendous. They usually come at intervals of seven to ten days and their normal life is short, only three to four days. They however cause widespread changes in the sequence of weather, including the distribution of moisture, both in the form of rain and snow, as well as in temperature and hygrometric conditions. Normally the daily maximum temperatures in winters vary from 15.5°C in November to 4.4°C in January and the daily minimum from-0.1 to −2.3°C (Appendix I). An analysis of the minimum temperature of Srinagar in January for the period 1953-72 shows wide-ranging fluctuations mostly under the impact of the western disturbances (Figs. 4.4; 4.5). In fact, these abrupt falls in the night temperature are a peculiar phenomenon of the winter months. A study of the temperature records for the period 1911-50 reveals that the frequency of the severe cold waves[17] was highest in January (62 occasions) followed by February (45), December (32) and March (29). The night temperature commonly deviates by 10° to 12°C from normal. But such occasions are also not rare when these departures are more spectacular, say 20°C or even more. It has been observed that November, January and March have the highest frequency of such occasions.[18] The incidence of the cold waves is, of course, one of the strong indicators of the passage of a westerly depression.

These depressions are also the chief bearers of winter snow and rains to Kashmir. The data for the period 1957-66 for Srinagar show that the city has on an average seven days with snow in January, six in February, two in March and two to three in December. But there are large variations from year to year and the days with snow may vary within a range of zero to sixteen in January alone (Appendix II). The pattern of snowfall is almost identical at the Srinagar aerodrome also (Figs. 4.6; 4.7). Bhan published an analysis of the snowfall data for Srinagar for the period 1939-1953[19] (Appendix III). It shows that January has the highest frequency of days with snow (44.8 per cent) followed by February (29 per cent) and December (17.3 per cent). The frequency in March is much higher than in November (Fig.4.8). Snowfall is often accompanied with rain and sleet. On as many as 121 out of 431 occasions in the 15-year period snow was accompanied with rain and sleet. Rains are, however, more commonly associated with snow in January and February than in March, October or December. At Srinagar and in the low-lying areas of the Valley, snowfall usually commences by the middle of December and continues up to the end of March (Fig. 4.9). The highest number of occurrences is observed during 25 December to 25 February. Another significant feature of snowfall is its concentration during morning hours, usually between 0430 and 1230 hours. This eight-hourly period alone accounts for almost 40 per cent of the total occurrence in the period under observation (Fig. 4.10).

January holds a leading position in terms of daily average snowfall also. The three months of December, January and February receive on an average 120.25 centimetres of snow, January's share being as high as 49.25 centimetres. The corresponding figure for the months of March, October and November is only 18 centimetres. The average daily intensity of snowfall is highly variable even in the month of January—the range being 2.5 to 15.7 centimetres. It is highest in February (2mm to 22.5 cm) and fairly high in March (2 to 26.25 cm).

Like snowfall, the rainfall generated by these western disturbances is also fairly widespread, although no specific explanation can be given for the areal disparities in its distribution. The lowest rainfall is received at Srinagar and surrounding areas, such as Pulwama, Badgam and Ganderbal—the total for the four winter months nowhere exceeding 200 millimetres. Srinagar, Pulwama and Badgam receive about three-tenths of their annual rainfall in the winter months; the winter months account for only one-fourth of the annual total for Gandarbal. Winter rainfall is much higher on either extremity of the Valley—Doru and Kulgam in the southeast and Sopore, Handwara and Baramulla in the northwest being representative cases. At each of these places winter rain contributes as much as 35 to 40 per cent of the annual total (Appendix IV). The highest amount is recorded at Doru (471.50mm) and the next highest at Handwara (345.75mm) [20]

The Valley has a highly dreary and monotonous winter with very little bright sunshine (Appendix V) and high humidity—between 95 and 90 per cent (Appendix VI).

Spring. By March the weather shows visible signs of improvement, the temperatures start moving up steadily and snow disappears. March is the rainiest month of the year and the major climatic phenomena in spring are not fundamentally different from those of winter. The frequency of the western depressions remains equally high in early spring and declines substantially as summer advances and the southern branch of the

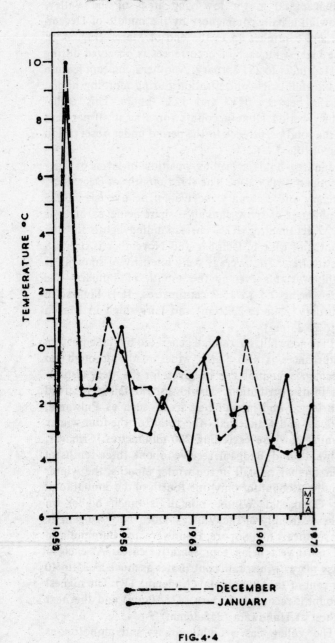

MEAN MINIMUM TEMPERATURE
IN DECEMBER & JANUARY 1953–72
(SRINAGAR)

DECEMBER

JANUARY

FIG. 4·4

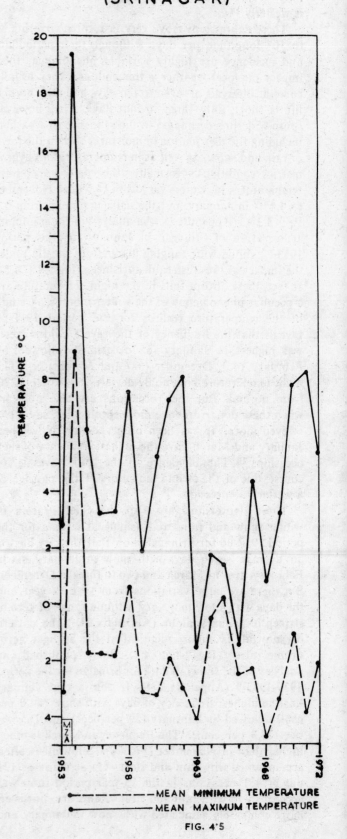

MEAN MINIMUM & MAXIMUM TEMPERATURE
JANUARY (1953–72)
(SRINAGAR)

MEAN MINIMUM TEMPERATURE

MEAN MAXIMUM TEMPERATURE

FIG. 4·5

westerly jet finally withdraws from the Indian area. The synoptic situation prevailing during spring is depicted in Figs. 4.2 and 4.11.

The spring weather in Kashmir is characterized by sunnier and brighter days and cool nights. The day temperature swings between 12°C and 15°C. Wide variations are however commonly observed from year to year and from place to place. Occasions are not rare when the day temperature in March or April may abruptly shoot up, deviating from the normal by 10° to 15°C. The night temperature registers a steady increase from 3.5°C in March to 11.2°C in May.

A remarkable feature of spring weather is its raininess, although snowfall is not unusual. This fact is borne out by the amounts of rain and snow received in different parts of the Valley as well as the number of rainy days. Almost all places in Kashmir receive from one-third to two-fifths of their total rainfall in spring. The share of spring rainfall in some places, such as Langet, is as high as 45 per cent. The total spring rainfall varies from 197 millimetres in Pulwama to 410 millimetres in Handwara. The number of rainy days has a similar increasing trend: from Pulwama's fourteen days and Anantnag's seventeen to the northwest as well as southeast. Srinagar has nineteen rainy days, Kulgam eighteen, Doru twenty, Sopore and Langet twenty-two each and Handwara and Baramulla twenty-four each. It has already been emphasized in the above pages that snow is also a common phenomenon in early spring. Spring rain is often associated with violent thundersqualls. Their frequency is very high both in April and May, and the spring months together may account for 40 to 50 per cent of the total annual frequency (Table XXX).

Table XXX
Average number of thundersqualls per month in Srinagar

March	April	May	June	July
3	7	10	7	7
August	September		October	Annual
6	4		2	47

Summer. Summer weather in the Indian subcontinent is an outcome of the remarkable reversal that takes place in the circulatory system by the northward movement of the intertropical convergence zone (ITC). It is however interesting to note that while the subcontinent receives the bulk of its life-giving moisture through these processes, Kashmir is only a marginal beneficiary. The southwest monsoon hardly supplies one-sixth to one-fourth of the total annual rainfall received by Kashmir Valley. The obstructive role of the Pir Panjal range is borne out by this single fact. A recent study of the tracks of the tropical storms reaching India during the southwest monsoon period has conclusively proved that none of them is ever able to reach the Pir Panjal. This, coupled with the shadow effect of the Pir Panjal on the incoming moisture-laden winds, explains the operation of "distance-decay" function as observable in the areal distribution of summer rainfall in the Kashmir Valley. Unlike the rest of the subcontinent, Kashmir has no specific rainy season. Seen in terms of amount of rainfall alone one can hardly differentiate between the pre-monsoon and monsoon periods. In fact, at most places in the Valley, May is at least as rainy as July or August. At many other places it is more rainy.

The general pattern of the prevailing summer weather is depicted in Figs. 4.11 and 4.12. The popular notion of a cool Kashmir summer is hardly borne out by the day temperature of Srinagar. The daily maximum temperature of Srinagar in July and August—the respective values being 30.8°C and 29.9°C—compares well with New Delhi, Aligarh and Jammu rather than with any of the hill resorts in the Himalayas (Figs. 4.13; 4.14). The day temperature remains remarkably high and constant between June and September, a feature which, coupled with high humidity (70-80 per cent), makes the weather very oppressive. It is in the surrounding hills that the Kashmir summers are really pleasant—the day temperature in Gulmarg during July and August remains at 21.4°C and 20.3°C respectively. The corresponding values for Simla are 21.0°C and 20.1°C. In fact, Simla is far more rainy in August than Gulmarg.

The summer rainfall of the Valley displays an interesting areal distribution. The main trend which is discernible is its progressive decrease with increasing distance from the Banihal crossing (Appendix IV), with Gulmarg, of course, offering a notable exception. This transition is, however, most illustrative between Doru (summer rainfall, 232mm) and Langet (136mm). Like spring, summer is also characterized by a high incidence of thundersquaлls, their average frequency in the summer months being as high as in spring.

Autumn. Autumn is perhaps the best weather in Kashmir. It marks a transition from the warm subtropical summers to temperate winters. Autumn is characterized by least disturbed weather, highest amount of sunshine, high diurnal ranges of temperature and little rain or snow (Fig.4.1; 4.12). This is the part of the year when the determinants of the summer

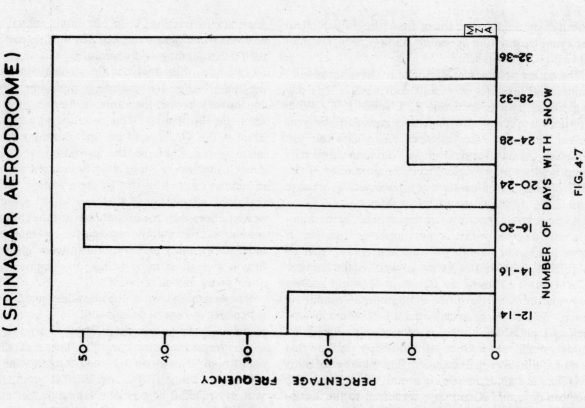

HISTOGRAM OF NUMBER OF DAYS
WITH SNOWFALL(1954–66)
(SRINAGAR AERODROME)

FIG. 4·7

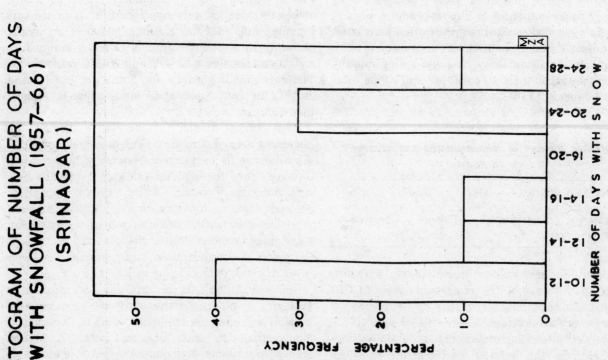

HISTOGRAM OF NUMBER OF DAYS
WITH SNOWFALL (1957–66)
(SRINAGAR)

FIG. 4·6

weather are the feeblest while those of the winter are yet to gain power. The days in September are marked by fairly high temperatures which start declining sharply by the middle of October. Nights, on the other hand, are very cool, even chilly.

Although dryness is a distinctive feature of autumn weather, rain or snow are not entirely unknown. In fact, an early influx of western disturbances may occasionally cause widespread snow or rain in the last week of October, thus heralding the establishment of the winter regime.

CLIMATIC REGIME

The weather elements exercise a cumulative effect on man and determine the levels of comfort of places under different climatic regimes. It is difficult to classify the Valley of Kashmir in a specific climatic regime as sharp variations are observed from year to year and the climate swings between temperate sub-Mediterranean in all its variants from single (unixeric), double (bixeric), triple (trixeric) to quadruple (quadrixeric) dry periods in a year. At best it can be classified as an "irregular" type with no specific affinity with the standard climatic regimes of the world. In a study of the precipitation of Baramulla, Anantnag and Srinagar and of the temperature of Srinagar for the period 1892-1963, Meher-Homji has established that the Valley has a "sub-Mediterranean type of climate in so far as the distribution pattern of rainfall is concerned."[21] The study shows that about 65 per cent of the total annual rainfall is received during winter and spring months. The share of winter and spring rainfall is as high as 75 per cent or above in the northwestern part of the Valley (e.g., Handwara, Baramulla, Langet and Sopore; see Appendix IV). Using the technique of ombrothermic diagrams, Meher-Homji attempted to prove that Srinagar has a bixeric regime with two dry periods in the year, one occurring in June and the other in the September-November period. He identified typical years in which variations from this standard type were found to be very strong (Table XXXI; also see Figs. 4.18-4.24). It was noted that the typical Mediterranean regime, with one dry period during the summer, prevailed over twelve years. The bixeric regime, on the other hand, prevailed over thirty-two years; six of them were, however, characterized by a strong Mediterranean tendency. There were nineteen trixeric years and six quadrixeric. The remaining three did not at all lend themselves to such a classification.

Srinagar has only two months, July and August,

TABLE XXXI
Classification of years according to climatic regimes 1892-1963

Types of Regimes					
Bixeric	Bixeric with Mediterranean tendency	Mediterranean	Trixeric	Quadrixeric	Unclassified
1892	1910	1896	1895	1898	1907
1893	1912	1899	1901	1904	1948
1894	1932	1902	1908	1921	1951
1897	1939	1914	1909	1938	
1902	1949	1915	1911	1955	
1903	1963	1918	1923	1962	
1905		1920	1929		
1906		1934	1930		
1913		1936	1931		
1916		1945	1933		
1917		1946	1937		
1919		1961	1941		
1922			1944		
1924			1947		
1925			1952		
1926			1954		
1927			1956		
1928			1958		
1935			1960		
1940					
1942					
1943					
1950					
1953					
1957					
1959					

Courtesy: Meher-Homji, *Geographical Review of India*, Vol. XXXIII, 1, 1971.

TABLE XXXII
Monthly and annual water need (PE) at Srinagar (cm)

January	February	March	April	May	June	July
0.0	0.8	2.1	5.0	8.9	11.8	14.2
August	September	October	November	December	Annual	
13.1	8.7	4.5	1.7	0.4	71.2	

Courtesy: V.P. Subrahmanyam, *Ind. Jour. Met. Geophys*, VII, 4, 1956.

TABLE XXXIII
Annual water need and moisture index of Srinagar

Water need (PE) (cm)	Water surplus (cm)	Water deficiency	Moisture index (Ix)
71.2	18.5	23.5	+ 6.3

Courtesy: V.P. Subrahmanyam. *Ind. Jour. Met. Geophys*, VII, 4, 1956.

FREQUENCY OF DAYS
WITH SNOW (1939-53)
(SRINAGAR)

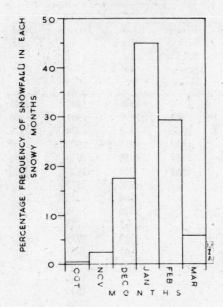

FIG. 4·8

FREQUENCY OF DAYS WITH SNOW
(1939-53)
(SRINAGAR)

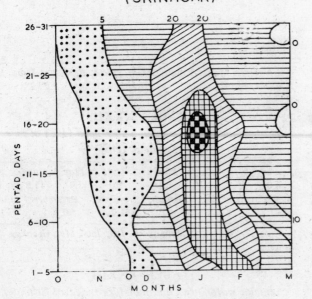

NUMBER OF OCCURENCES IN EACH PENTAD

FIG. 4·9

FREQUENCY OF SNOWFALL
DURING 4-HOURLY PERIODS
(1939-53)
(SRINAGAR)

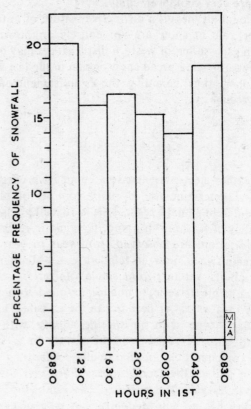

FIG. 4·10

DAILY WEATHER IN APRIL, MAY AND JUNE.
(Synoptic View)

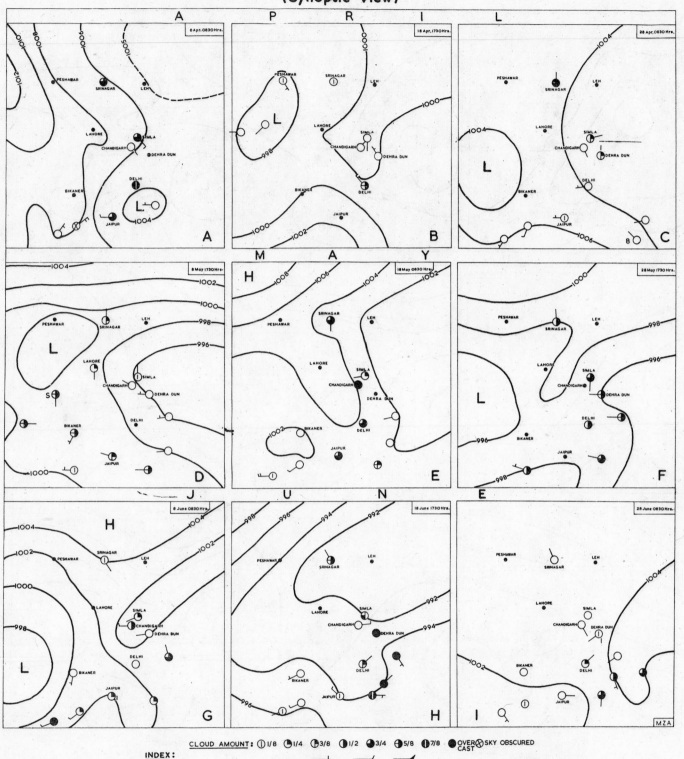

INDEX:

CLOUD AMOUNT: ◐1/8 ◐1/4 ◐3/8 ◐1/2 ◐3/4 ◐5/8 ◐7/8 ●OVER ⊗SKY OBSCURED
CAST

WIND: 5 KNOTS   10 KNOTS   50 KNOTS

FIG. 4·11

DAILY WEATHER IN JULY, AUGUST AND SEPTEMBER.
(Synoptic View)

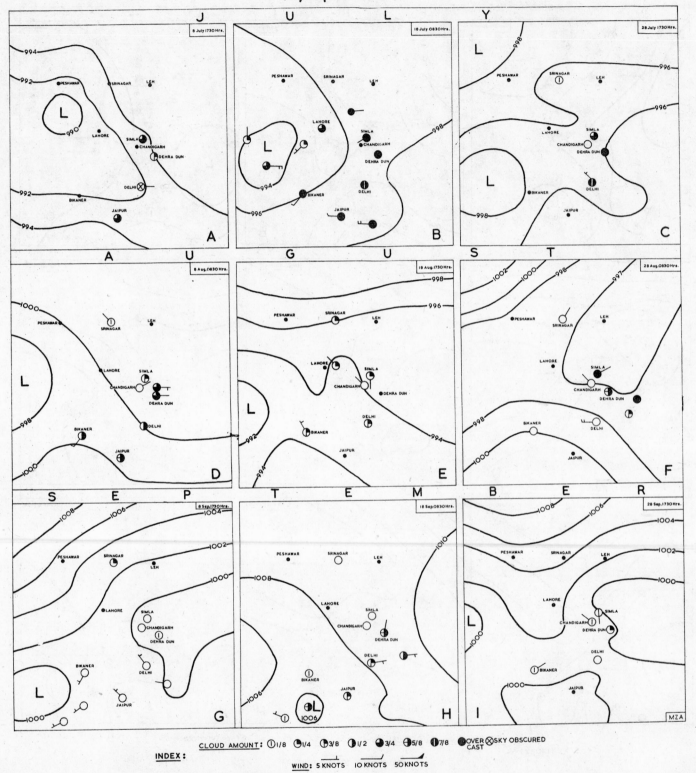

FIG. 4·12

MEAN MAXIMUM TEMPERATURE IN JUNE & JULY (1953-72) (SRINAGAR)

MEAN MINIMUM & MAXIMUM TEMPERATURE JUNE (1953-72) (SRINAGAR)

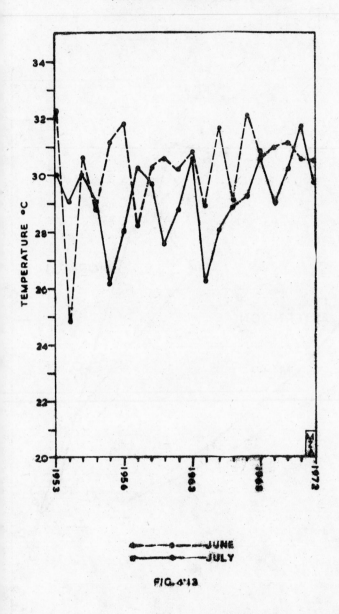

FIG. 4·13

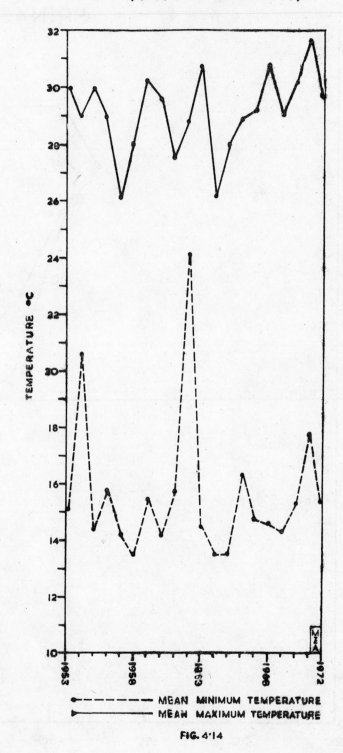

MEAN MINIMUM TEMPERATURE
MEAN MAXIMUM TEMPERATURE

FIG. 4·14

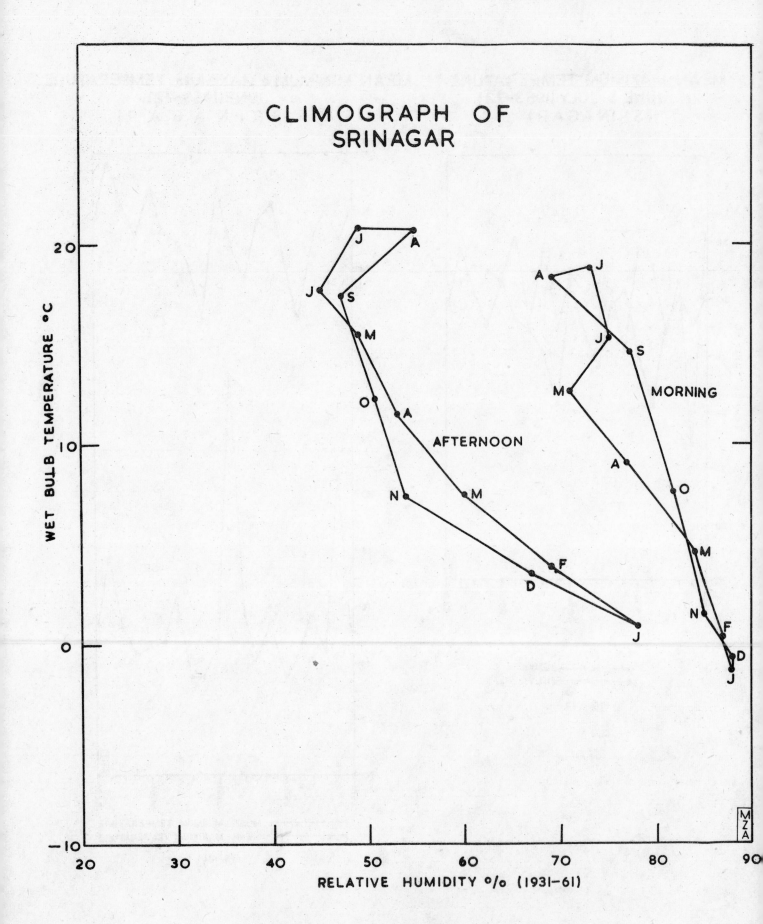

FIG. 4·15

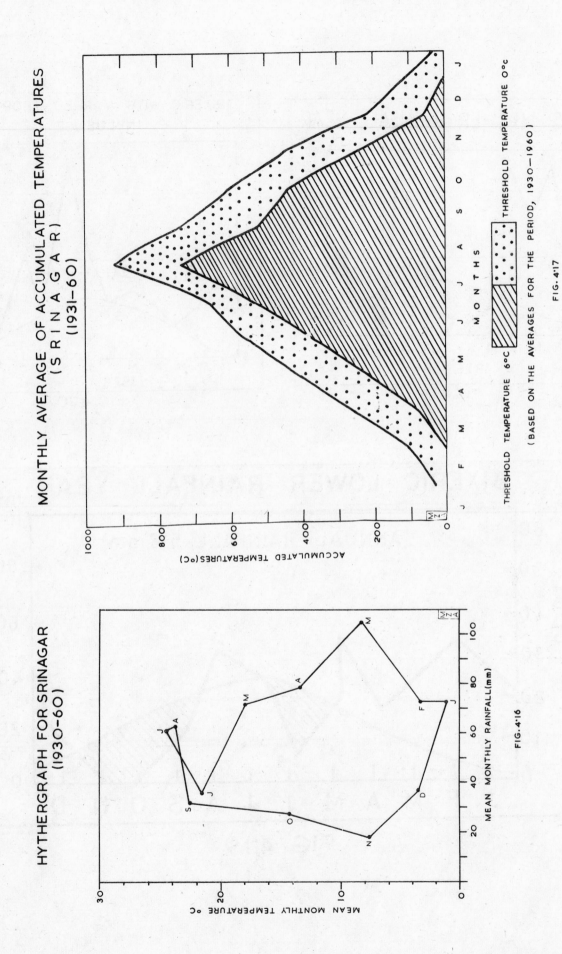

MONTHLY AVERAGE OF ACCUMULATED TEMPERATURES
(S R I N A G A R)
(1931—60)

ACCUMULATED TEMPERATURES (°C)

MONTHS

THRESHOLD TEMPERATURE 6°C   THRESHOLD TEMPERATURE 0°C

(BASED ON THE AVERAGES FOR THE PERIOD, 1930—1960)

FIG. 4·17

HYTHERGRAPH FOR SRINAGAR
(1930—60)

MEAN MONTHLY TEMPERATURE °C

MEAN MONTHLY RAINFALL (mm)

FIG. 4·16

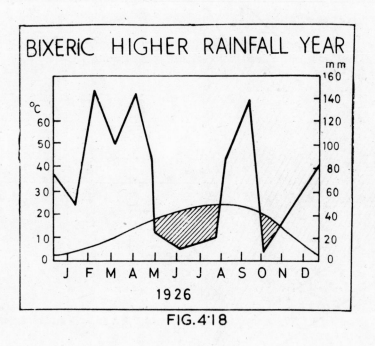

BIXERIC HIGHER RAINFALL YEAR

1926

FIG. 4·18

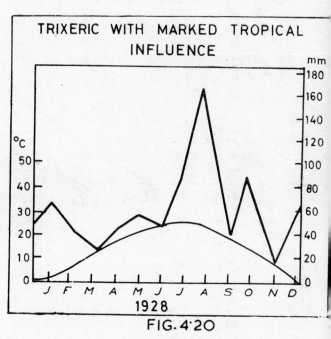

TRIXERIC WITH MARKED TROPICAL INFLUENCE

1928

FIG. 4·20

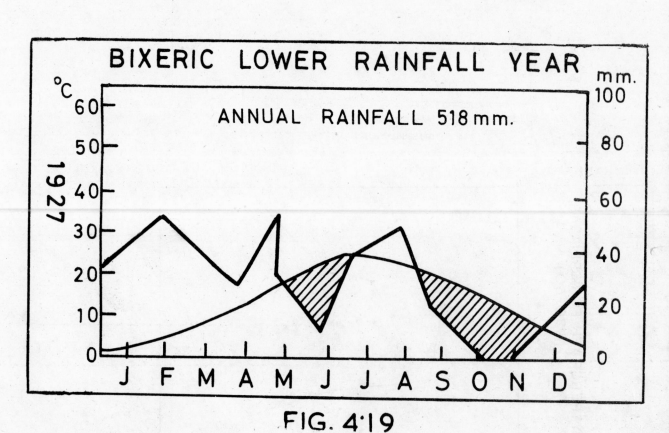

BIXERIC LOWER RAINFALL YEAR

ANNUAL RAINFALL 518 mm.

1927

FIG. 4·19

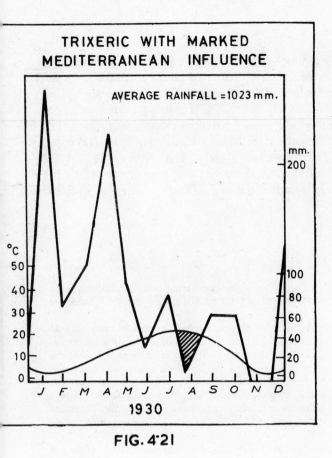

TRIXERIC WITH MARKED
MEDITERRANEAN INFLUENCE

AVERAGE RAINFALL = 1023 mm.

1930

FIG. 4·21

MEDITERRANEAN HIGHER RAINFALL YEAR

AVERAGE RAINFALL 689 mm.

1936

FIG. 4·22

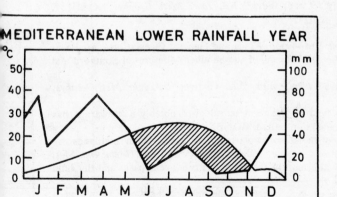

MEDITERRANEAN LOWER RAINFALL YEAR

1938

FIG. 4·23

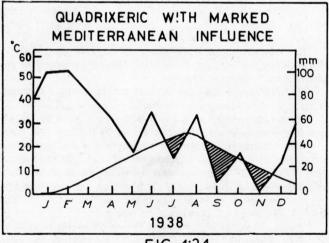

QUADRIXERIC WITH MARKED
MEDITERRANEAN INFLUENCE

1938

FIG. 4·24

with a high index of comfort, although June and September are also characterized by a low index of discomfort. As evident from the above study of winter weather, maximum discomfort is experienced in winter. Sivaramakrishnaiah has depicted the pattern of monthly comfort by plotting the dry and wet bulb temperature and vapour pressure data for Srinagar on a "thermal strain chart."[22] The monthly march of wet bulb temperature and humidity also provides an index of the weather type of Srinagar (Fig.4.15; also 4.16).

Elaborate climatological data are, however, not available for any number of places to make a formal exercise in the climatic classification of Kashmir Valley. Tables XXXII and XXXIII give computed values of monthly and annual potential evapotranspiration (PE) and annual water surplus and moisture index (Ix) based on Thornthwaite's system. The Valley has a C2W moisture regime and a climatic type designated as B'1 with a summer thermal efficiency index of 55.3 per cent.[23]

NOTES AND REFERENCES

[1]Arthur Neve found as large a variety in temperature, humidity and other variables in different parts of Kashmir as in the whole of Europe from the shores of the Mediterranean to the North Cape. (Major Arthur Neve, *The Tourist's Guide to Kashmir, Ladakh, Skardo, etc.*, Lahore, 1933.)

[2]Climatological data on Kashmir is something of a rarity. Srinagar has the only observatory which remains open all year round. In its *Climatological Tables for Observatories in India—1931-60*, the IMD, however, did not publish any data on snowfall even for Srinagar, although snow is an important weather phenomenon in the Valley. It is interesting to note that the observatory at Gulmarg functions only during the four summer months (June-September). Thus, while one can know the mean daily minimum temperature of Verkhoyansk in January, it would be impossible to get a corresponding figure for Gulmarg or Sonamarg, not to say of Bandipur, Sopore or Pahalgam. The Kashmir Valley has only twelve raingauge stations over an area of 12,362 square kilometres, the density of raingauges being one for every 1,000 square kilometres. There are only six stations which have snow gauges, but the records are highly inconsistent. The IMD seems to be inimical to recording any form of precipitation other than rain!

[3]H. Flohn, "Recent Investigations on the Mechanisms of the Summer Monsoon of Southern and Eastern Asia," *Monsoons of the World*, IMD, New Delhi, 1958, p. 81.

[4]There have been occasions when one of the cores of the jet stream has been found in as southerly a position as Aden-Vishakhapatnam, e.g., 24 December 1963, OOGMT (P.V. Joseph, "A Case of Very Low Latitude Occurrence of the Subtropical Jet Stream over the Indian Region," *Ind. Jour. Met. Geophys.*, XVIII, 1, 1967, pp. 217-226).

[5]G.T. Trewartha, *The Earth's Problem Climates*, Madison, 1961, p. 152.

[6]*Ibid.*, p. 153.

[7]P. Koteswaram, "The Asian Summer Monsoon and the General Circulation over the Tropics," *Monsoons of the World, op. cit.* p. 108; also, P.V. Joseph, "Maximum Wind Surface in Easterly Jet over India," *Ind. Jour. Met. Geophys*, XVIII, 1, 1967, pp. 213-216.

[8]Koteswaram, *op. cit.*, p. 108.

[9]H. Flohn, *Ber. dtsch. Wetterdienstes*, XXII, 1955, pp. 134-139; *idem* "Monsoon Winds and General Circulation," *Monsoons of the World, op. cit.*, pp. 65-74; *idem*, "Recent Investigations on the Mechanisms of the Summer Monsoon of Southern and Eastern Asia," *ibid*, pp. 75 88.

[10]P. Koteswaram, *Res. Rep. Met. Dept.*, University of Chicago, 1956; *idem*, with C.A. George, *Ind. Jour. Met. Geophys*, IX, 1, p. 9; *idem*, *Monsoons of the World, op. cit.*, pp. 105-110.

[11]Koteswaram, *Monsoons of the World, op. cit.*, 109-110. This view held by Indian meteorologists, notably Koteswaram, has been further corroborated by data collected by the Soviets in their expedition called MONEX.

[12]Flohn attempted to establish his hypothesis of the "active role" of the seasonal warming of the Tibetan highlands by correlating the temperature conditions of Leh with the burst of monsoon over India. Pramanik and Rao (*Mem. Ind. Met. Dept.* XXIX, pt. 6, 1953) observed a correlation between the burst of monsoon in the Damodar catchment basin and the June temperature in Leh. (*Monsoons of the World, op. cit.*, pp. 85-86.)

[13]"I have known constant rains in the southern end of the Valley, while Srinagar and the northern part of Kashmir were parched with drought." (Lawrence, *op. cit.*, p. 24.)

[14]Raina, *Geography of Jammu and Kashmir*, New Delhi, 1971, p. 39.

[15]P.R. Pisharoty, and B.N. Desai, "Western Disturbances and Indian Weather," *Ind. Jour. Met. Geophys*, VII, 4, 1956, pp. 333-338; also Dutta, R.K., and M.G. Gupta, "Synoptic Study of the Formation and Movements of Western Depressions," *Ind. Jour. Met. Geophys.*, XVIII, 1, 1967, pp. 45-50.

[16]Dutta and Gupta, *op. cit.*, p. 46.

[17]Technically a "cold wave" is described as a severe one if the night temperature deviates from the normal by at least 8°C. (See K. Raghavan, "A Climatological Study of Severe Cold Waves in India," *Ind. Jour. Met. Geophys*, XVIII, 1, 1967, pp. 91-96.)

[18]*Ibid.*

[19]S.N. Bhan, "Snowfall at Srinagar," *Ind. Jour. Met. Geophys*, VII, 1956, pp. 295-300.

[20]Figures are based on averages for the period 1901-50.

[21]V.M. Meher-Homji, "The Climate of Srinagar and its Variability," *Geog. Rev. Ind.*, XXXIII, 1, 1971, pp. 1-14.

[22]K. Sivaramakrishnaiah, "A Study in Human Comfort of Some Places in India," *Ind. Jour. Met. Geophys*, XVII, 1, 1966, pp. 89-94.

[23]V.P. Subrahmanyam, "Climatic Types of India According to the Rational Classification of Thornthwaite," *Ind. Jour. Met. Geophys*, VII, 4, 1956, pp. 253-264.

BIBLIOGRAPHICAL NOTE

Most of the important works on climate having relevance to Kashmir have already been referred to in the notes. The reader may however be interested in a classified list of these contributions.

Data Base. Reference has already been made to the serious gaps that exist in meteorological information on Kashmir. Nevertheless, the following sources of data are of basic importance: India Meteorological Department, *Climatological Tables of Observatories in India*, 1931-60, New Delhi, n.d.; and *Monthly and Annual Rainfall and Number of Rainy Days*, 1901-50, part II, New Delhi, 1965. Both of them are sources of basic data, although the former contains records for Srinagar only. IMD's other volumes such as *Normal Monthly Rainfall and Number of Rainy Days* and *Monthly Weather Reports* are equally useful.

Rainfall data for a number of new raingauge stations, such as Babapora, Kokarnag, Pahalgam, Charari Sharif, Prang, Shopiyan, Tanmarg, Bandipora, Sogam and Arizal are now available, particularly since 1965.

Analyzed snowfall data for Srinagar for the period 1939-53 are given in S.N. Bhan, "Snowfall at Srinagar," *Indian Jour. Met. Geophys.*, VII, 3, 1956, pp. 295-300.

Weather Mechanisms. Besides the studies already acknowledged, a number of useful papers are available on mechanisms of Indian weather. Notable among these are:

J.H. Chang, "The Indian Summer Monsoon," *Geographical Review*, Vol. LVIII, 1969, pp. 373-396.

H. Flohn, "Contribution to the Meteorology of the Tibetan Highlands," Atmospheric Science Paper, No. 130, Colorado State University, Fort Collins, 1968, p. 120.

P. Koteswaram, "The Easterly Jet Stream in the Tropics," *Tellus*, Vol. X, 1958, pp. 43-57.

C. Ramaswamy, "Breaks in the Indian Summer Monsoon as a Phenomenon of Interaction Between the Easterly and the Sub-tropical Westerly Jet Streams," *Tellus*, XIV, 1962, pp. 337-349.

M.S. Singh, "Study of the Jet Stream over India and to its North in Winter," *Ind. Jour. Met. Geophys*, XXII, 1, 1971, pp. 1-14.

C. Ramaswamy, "The Problem of Fronts in the Indian Atmosphere," *Ind. Jour. Met. Geophys*, XVII, 1, 1966, pp. 151-170. Other studies of direct relevance are:

B.W. Thompson, "An Essay on General Circulation of the Atmosphere over Southeast Asia and the West Pacific," *Quart. Jour. Roy. Met. Soc.*, LXXVII, 1951, pp. 569-597.

Staff members of the section of Synoptic and Dynamic Meteorology, Institute of Geophysics and Meteorology, Academia Sinica, "On the General Circulation on East Asia," *Tellus*, IX, 1957, pp. 432-46; also *Tellus*, X, 1958, pp. 58-75 and 299-312.

Western Disturbances. The early contributions on this subject such as that of J. Elliot "An Account of the more important cold weather storms of India etc.," IMD *Memoirs*, IV, pt. 8, 1893, pp. 820-873, are only of historical significance. The subject has received new, much more elaborate treatment, largely based on new methods of meteorological investigation. The following references are of basic importance:

D.A. Mooley, "The Role of Western Disturbances in the Production of Weather over India during Different Seasons," *Ind. Jour. Met. Geophys.*, VIII, 1957, pp. 253-260.

S.L. Malurkar, "Notes on Analysis of Weather of India and Neighbourhood," IMD *Memoirs*, XXVIII, pt. 4, 1950, pp. 202-211;

————"A Brief Report of a Discussion on Western Disturbances Held at New Delhi," *Ind. Jour. Met. Geophys.* VII, 1, 1956, pp. 1-6.

P.R. Pisharoty, and B.N. Desai, "Western Disturbances and Indian Weather," *Ind. Jour. Met. Geophys.*, VII, 4, 1956, pp. 333-338.

R.K. Dutta, and M.G. Gupta, "Synoptic Study of the Formation and Movements of Western Depressions," *Ind. Jour. Met. Geophys.*, XVIII, 1, 1967, pp. 45-50.

Chapter Five

Water—Scarcity in Plenty

I do not know much about gods; but
I think that the river
Is a strong brown god.—T.S. Eliot, *Four Quartets*

Water in the Kashmir Valley is an extraordinary para-dox. Considering the total run-off, area of water bodies and length of water courses, the Valley has no match in the Himalayas. In fact, its water features are the principal components in its scenic beauty. The geomor-phic character of the Valley is, however, such that the distribution of water resources is extremely uneven—a situation which renders vast stretches of land totally or partially out of use either due to the excess of water or its deficiency. Water is most plentiful in the low-lying parts of the Valley, which remain literally deluged, while the adjoining Karewa uplands suffer from aridity imposed by its chronic deficiency. In both these res-pects the situation seriously constrains the optimal use of the Valley's land potential. The consequence is that the Valley presents the anomalous case of scarcity in the midst of plenty. The rivers carry large volumes of water which they cannot possibly contain as their chan-nels get increasingly choked with silt, making floods a recurrent phenomenon with disastrous consequences on agriculture. Naturally, in the absence of any systematic scheme for water management, the spillover from the ever-rising channels spreads all over the low-lying tracts, which have been converted into extensive swamps, called the Nambal. The rest of the water flows out practically unharnessed, without being put to any substantial use before it escapes out of the Baramulla gorge. Recent data show that only a tiny fraction of this vast potential is being utilized for hydroelectric genera-tion, the aggregate annual production from all power houses being about 20,000kws. The only other use of this enormous resource is in gradient irrigation, through the distribution system of *kuhls*, in the making of which modern technology has hardly any contribution.

The above remarks are, however, relevant only in the context of the present understanding of the Valley's water potential, which is by no means complete. It is interesting to note that no serious attempt has yet been made to assess this potential, its mode of occurrence,

spatial distribution and temporal variations in its availability. Evidently, no comprehensive planning is possible in the absence of such primary data, whether aimed at draining the swamps, augmenting water supply in agriculture or generating hydroelectricity. In fact, the present state of knowledge inhibits even the estima-tion of the gap between the water potential and the actual amount that is being used productively.

An attempt will be made here to make an analytical study of the water resources of the Valley, both surface and subterranean, temporal variations in its supply as perceived in the incidence of floods or droughts and the current level of its utilization. The Jhelum and its nume-rous tributaries, a large number of lakes, depressions and springs are the main water bodies of the Valley. Their geomorphic characteristics have been brought out in an earlier chapter, the present study will, therefore, deal with the problems of hydrology.

HYDROLOGICAL NETWORK AND DATA

There is a general dearth of consistent hydrological data for Kashmir for any reasonable period of time. This makes a meaningful temporal study of local hydro-logical phenomena impossible. The meteorological obser-vatory at Srinagar was opened in 1891 and at Gulmarg in 1897. The position has not substantially changed since then. Regular meteorological data are, however, available only for Srinagar, as the Gulmarg observatory functions only during the four summer months—June to September—for reasons best known to the IMD only. The rainfall is measured at a number of places, though in many cases the records are far from consis-tent.[1] Other than Srinagar, there are only four places —Wantipore (Pulwama), Anantnag, Uttarmachipura (Handwara), and Sri Partap Singhpura (Badgam)— which have rainfall records for at least seventy-four years. Kulgam and Baramulla have a record for

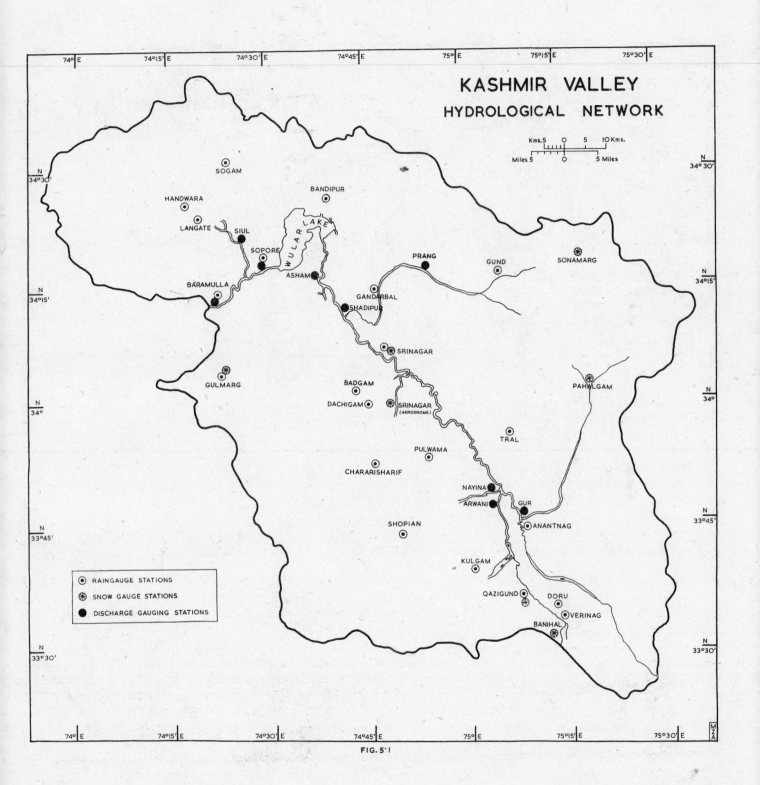

KASHMIR VALLEY
HYDROLOGICAL NETWORK

RAINGAUGE STATIONS
SNOW GAUGE STATIONS
DISCHARGE GAUGING STATIONS

SOGAM
BANDIPUR
HANDWARA
LANGATE
SIUL
SOPORE
WULAR LAKE
ASHAM
BARAMULLA
PRANG
GUND
SONAMARG
GANDARBAL
SHADIPUR
SRINAGAR
GULMARG
BADGAM
PAHALGAM
DACHIGAM
SRINAGAR (AERODROME)
TRAL
PULWAMA
CHARARISHARIF
NAYINA
ARWANI
GUR
ANANTNAG
SHOPIAN
KULGAM
QAZIGUND
DORU
VERINAG
BANIHAL

FIG. 5·1

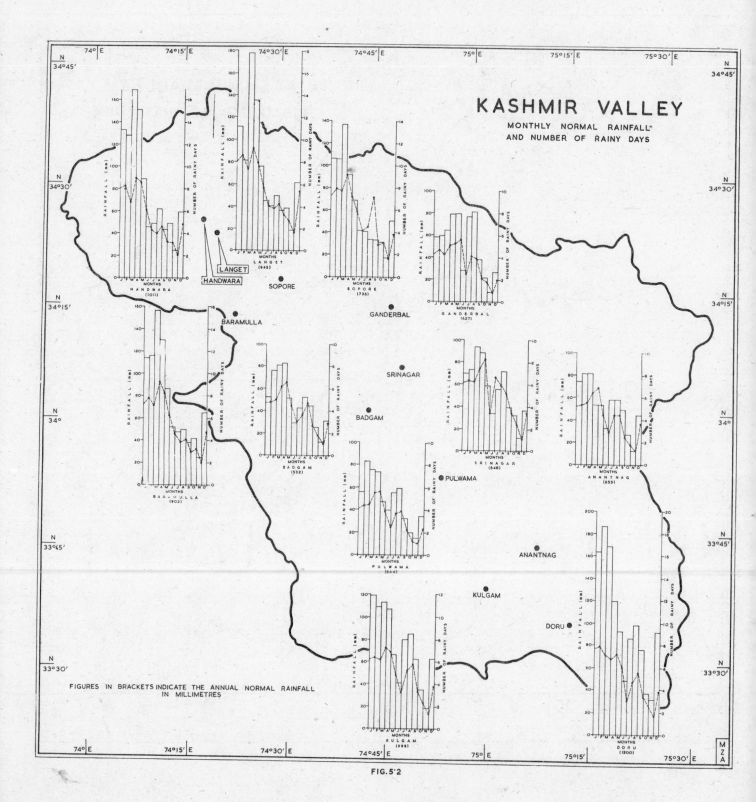

KASHMIR VALLEY

MONTHLY NORMAL RAINFALL
AND NUMBER OF RAINY DAYS

FIGURES IN BRACKETS INDICATE THE ANNUAL NORMAL RAINFALL
IN MILLIMETRES

FIG. 5·2

seventy-two years; Langet fifty-eight years; Duru and Sopore fifty-eight years each. Mala Shahibag (Ganderbal) has a record for forty-four years only, beginning with 1924 and with a gap between 1933 and 1940.

Despite its heavy contribution to the Valley's moisture supply, snowfall is only casually measured. There are snowgauges at the observatories of Srinagar city and aerodrome, and at Sonamarg, Gulmarg, Pahalgam, Qazigund and Banihal. Of these, the observations at the last five places are highly occasional (Fig. 5.1).

The story of river discharge data is also not much different. A study of the surface run-off is, however, handicapped both by inadequate measurement and inaccessibility to data. The Uppal report used data mainly for the following discharge-gauging stations on the Jhelum—Islamabad, (Khanabal) Sangam, Avantipura, Padshahibagh, Munshibagh, Gagarzoo, Mujgund, Asham, Banyari, Sopore, Seer and Baramulla. Although hourly and daily gauge readings were available to him, Uppal gives the impression that the data were irregular as well as badly maintained.[2] The present study is based on the average daily data contained in the departmental files of the Central Water and Power Commission for selected years and gauges only (Table XXXIV).

TABLE XXXIV
Particulars of river discharge data

River	Gauge	Period of data
Jhelum	Sopore	1965, 1973
	Baramulla	1965, 1973
	Baramulla	1964-73
Sind	Prang	1952-56
Liddar	Gur	1956
Pohru	Siul	1956
Vishav	Arwani	1954-56
Rembiara	Nayina	1952-54

Source: Central Water and Power Commission, New Delhi.

The inconsistency in the data maintained by the Central Water and Power Commission is also no less impressive.[3]

The data on groundwater resources of the Kashmir Valley are not inconsistent, they are simply nonexistent. The available estimates of the occurrence of groundwater and the recharge of aquifers are no better than intelligent guesses as a rigorous hydrological survey is yet to be undertaken.[4]

FACTORS IN WATER AVAILABILITY

The availability of water in a region is a function of the whole set of variables which determine the quantum of water *inflow*, *outflow*, and storage changes at a given point of time. While meteorological factors play a fundamental role in these processes, geological strata and topographical setting are decisive in determining the complexion of storage changes. The inflow of water, whether in the form of rainfall, snow or run-off over or through the surface, is of critical importance as later changes in its state or place are only consequential in nature.

Rainfall. The Kashmir Valley receives precipitation both in the form of rain and snow. It has been noted that the rainfall has a peculiar distribution pattern through the year (Fig. 5.2). It is overwhelmingly concentrated in the winter and spring months in all parts of the Valley. The share of the winter and spring rainfall is, however, more than three-fourths of the annual total in the northwest (e.g., Handwara, Baramulla, Langet and Sopore), while it is only about one-third in the central and the southeastern parts of the Valley (e.g. Srinagar, Pulwama, Anantnag, Kulgam and Ganderbal). The annual rainfall shows a regular increasing trend from Badgam and Srinagar in all directions. It is the lowest at Badgam (579mm) and increases towards the northwest from Srinagar (663) through Sopore (756) Langet (873) to Handwara (1,005); and towards the southeast from Pulwama (592) through Kulgam (898) to Doru (1,195).

Intensity of Rainfall. Another interesting feature of the rainfall of Kashmir Valley is its low average intensity per rainy day. An analysis of the fifty-year data (1901-50) has indicated that the average intensity varies from 5.08mm to 26.27mm (Appendix VIII). Doru has a consistent record of highest intensity throughout the Valley which remains well above the other recording gauges in as many as nine months in a year. The rains are usually heavy in the southwest monsoon period in the central parts and in winter or spring in the rest of the Valley. There is a high expectancy of heavy rainfall in August or September which is often caused by a sudden cloudburst and is invariably followed by widespread floods in the Jhelum. Bhan[5] has computed frequency of occasions with different twenty-four hour intensities of rainfall for Srinagar to show that there has been the highest frequency of occasions with an intensity of less than 12.7 millimetres of rain per day. There have been only three occasions in a fifty-year cycle when the intensity of rain exceeded seventy-five millimetres (Appendix IX).

Rainfall Dispersion. The rainfall dispersion diagram is often employed as a tool to study the characteristics of temporal variation in rainfall. It gives a synoptic

RAINFALL DISPERSION DIAGRAMS

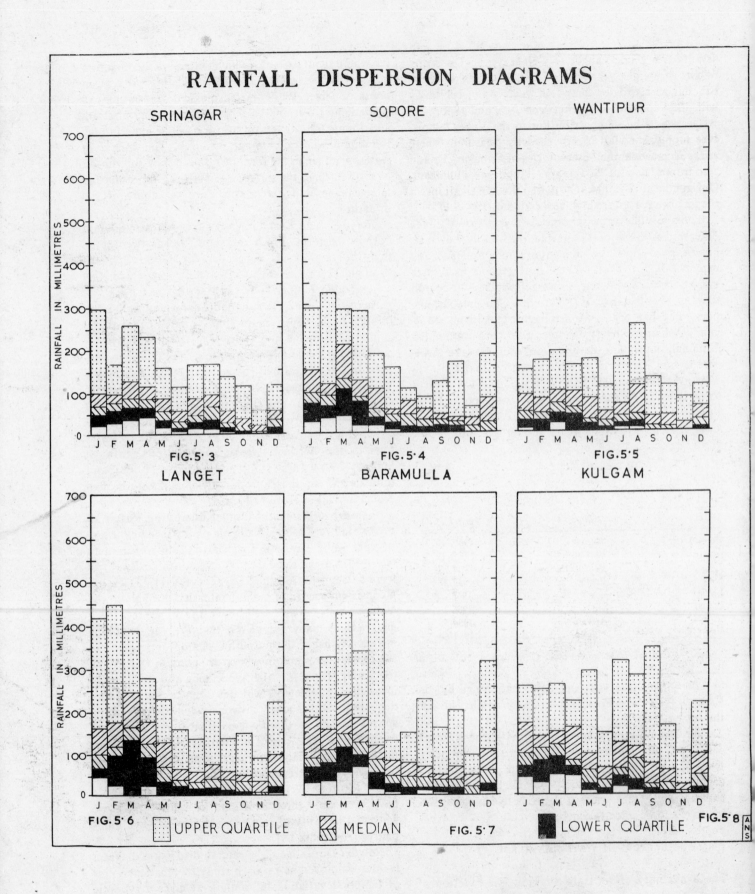

SRINAGAR

SOPORE

WANTIPUR

FIG. 5·3

FIG. 5·4

FIG. 5·5

LANGET

BARAMULLA

KULGAM

FIG. 5·6

FIG. 5·7

FIG. 5·8

UPPER QUARTILE   MEDIAN   LOWER QUARTILE

view of the sequence which the rainfall of a place follows through one year over a long period of time. Although rainfall is measured at a number of places in the Valley, continuous records for a reasonable period are available only for a few places. This has led to restricting this study to ten places only. The study covers a period of thirty-seven years (1914-50).[6]

It has been noted that the Valley of Kashmir gets rainfall almost all the year round. The rainfall is, however, marked by disparate characteristics in different parts of the Valley. The winter and spring rainfall is of a higher magnitude everywhere than the summer. The rainfall is characterized by a double "maxima"[7] at places lying in the central part of the Valley and by a single maximum in the northwest. Srinagar, Anantnag and Pulwama have double maxima in spring as well as in summer (March, August); Sopore, Baramulla, Badgam, Langet and Handwara have a single maximum either in February or March. Doru and Kulgam in the extreme southeast have no clear maximum in any month (Figs. 5.3-5.11).

While variations in the amount of rainfall from month to month are often of a substantial nature, there is no place in the Valley which has a rainfall discontinuity of the first order in any month of the year.[8] A discontinuity of the second degree is, however, observable at all places in September at Badgam, Pulwama, Doru and Kulgam; in June at Handwara, May and June at Baramulla, May and November at Langet and April and June in Srinagar. Sopore and Anantnag have no marked discontinuity even of the second order in any month of the year. Although interesting regional variations are observed both in the timing and intensity of rainfall in different parts of the Valley, marked contrasts are found only between the places in the central and the northwestern regions.

Rainfall Variability. Rainfall data for the three rain-gauge stations—Srinagar, Anantnag and Baramulla—have been used to analyze the pattern of rainfall variability. The study reveals that the coefficient of variation of annual rainfall is more or less the same for the three places—the respective values being 22, 24 and 21 per cent. The frequency distribution in different categories of rainfall is given in Table XXXV.

A striking feature of the rainfall of Kashmir is a high coefficient of variability in the months with low average rainfall.[9] The highest variability has been observed in the months of November, October, December, September and June in a descending order at almost all places in the Valley. The rainfall, on the other hand, is least variable in the winter and spring months (see also Figs. 5.12; 5.13).

TABLE XXXV
Frequency of rainfall in different classes
(1901-66)

Amount (mm)	Srinagar	Anantnag	Baramulla
398-400	1	0	0
400-500	5	2	0
500-600	15	7	1
600-700	15	14	7
700-800	14	15	12
800-900	9	12	18
900-1000	4	4	14
1000-1100	3	4	5
1100-1200	0	3	4
1200-1300	0	3	3
1300-1400	0	2	2

Modified from V.M. Meher-Homji, *Geographical Review of India*, Vol. XXXIII, 1, 1971.

Incidence of Drought. The fact that the Valley receives rain throughout the year should not overshadow the incidence of unusually prolonged droughts. In fact, the summer monsoon is known for its erratic behaviour all over India, and Kashmir is no exception. The failure of monsoon rainfall and late arrival of the western depressions may often combine to cause long spells of dry weather. In a cycle of seventy-two years, Srinagar experienced nineteen droughts extending over four to six consecutive months. The mean expectancy of a dry spell of at least a three-month duration has been as high as one in one and a half years (Appendix X).

SURFACE WATER RESOURCES

The surface water resources of Kashmir Valley are by any definition very large. The total run-off that escapes down the rivers or accumulates in a large number of lakes and marshes is a powerful indicator of this plentiful supply.

The river systems of the Valley are fed both by rain and snow. Naturally, the flow is poor during winter months as most of the precipitation comes in the form of snow. The quantum of surface run-off increases with the onset of summer when the snow melts, and, with the rain, generates a higher run-off. Normally, not less than three-fourths of the total annual discharge of the Jhelum flows during the summer months—April to August. In winter the discharge falls down substantially—only ten per cent of the annual discharge passes down during November-February, and not more than fifteen per cent during October-February.

As noted earlier, the major streams of the Jhelum

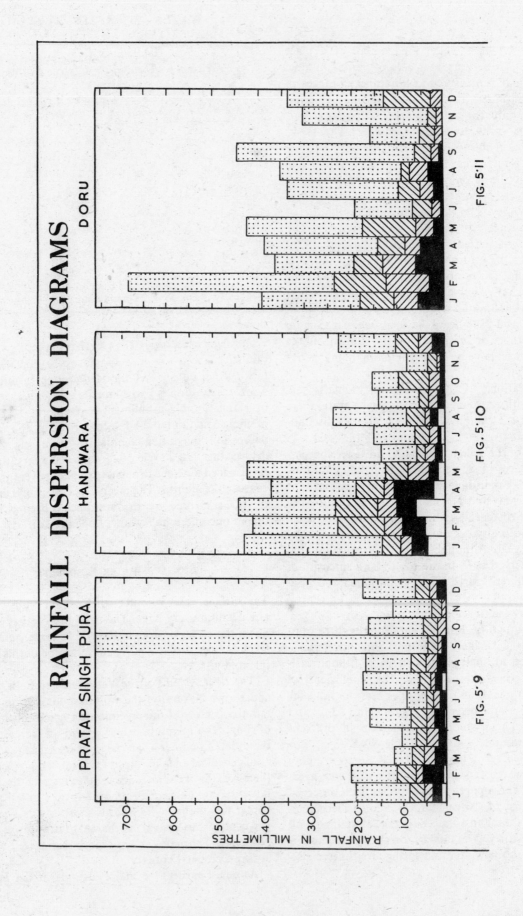

RAINFALL DISPERSION DIAGRAMS

PRATAP SINGH PURA

HANDWARA

DORU

FIG. 5·9

FIG. 5·10

FIG. 5·11

RAINFALL IN MILLIMETRES

system have their sources in the snow fields of the surrounding mountains which feed them during summer. The streams rising in the Pir Panjal have a lesser share of the snowmelt and their supplies are augmented by summer rains. The streams of the Great Himalayan range, on the other hand, are dependent more on snow than on rain. This produces interesting contrasts between the flow pattern of the Pir Panjal and the Himalayan rivers. The discharge of the Pir Panjal rivers is not only low, it is highly variable as the quantity of rainfall is the major component.

While the intensity of snowfall depends on the frequency and intensity of western disturbances which hit the Valley during winter, the quantum of summer snowmelt depends on the amount and duration of sunshine and the total intake of solar energy. Summer discharge also depends on monsoon rains, which have a high variability and may be very heavy in the period of high discharge from snowmelt. As a consequence, the run-off in the summer is very high as compared to the discharge during the rest of the year. Thus the discharge in May is ten to twelve times that of December. Discharge data from all the gauging stations show a marked maximum in May and an equally marked minimum in November, December and January. The discharge rises with the rise in temperature from March onwards when low altitude snow starts melting. The area of the snow fields, however, lessens as the initial phase is over, with the consequence that the run-off sharply falls in July and August unless otherwise augmented by occasional heavy rains. Unlike May and June the months of July and August are characterized by sharp diurnal variations in discharge caused by vicissitudes of rainfall which by now becomes a significant component in river flow. Occasional heavy rain may increase the amount of discharge out of all proportion and to the extent that it is beyond the capacity of the river to carry this volume. Naturally, the spillover causes disastrous floods affecting agrarian economy severely. The volume of water supply in July and August is also dependent on rainfall and not on snow alone; the contribution of snow to river discharge gradually declines as autumn advances.

A study of the decennial averages (1964-73) of the monthly discharge of Jhelum at Baramulla (Table XXXVI) shows that only 11.65 per cent of the total annual run-off flows during the four winter months (November-February). This is as much as the total discharge for the months of September and October and a little more than the discharge for the month of March alone. The five summer months (April-August) account for 68.65 per cent of the aggregate discharge.

The maximum comes in June although May also does not lag far behind (Fig. 5.14).

There are sharp variations in run-off from year to year and from day to day even in the peak period. In a lean year, say 1965 (Table XXXVII), the discharge in April deviated from the decennial average by 8.5 per cent; it deviated by minus 2.0 per cent in May and by minus 28 per cent in June (Fig. 5.15).

TABLE XXXVI[10]
Average monthly discharge of Jhelum at Baramulla (1964-73)

(*Data in cusecs*)

Month	Discharge	% of the total discharge	% of the discharge in June
January	148,985	3.48	22.16
February	214 583	5.10	31.91
March	368,565	8.60	54.81
April	587,480	13.70	87 37
May	665,498	15.52	98.98
June	672,382	15.68	100.00
July	514,356	12.00	76.50
August	503,680	11.75	74.91
September	286,413	6.68	42.60
October	189,565	4.32	28 19
November	73,685	1.72	10.96
December	62,340	1 45	9.27
Total	4,287,532	100.00	—

TABLE XXXVII
Average monthly discharge of Jhelum at Baramulla (1965)

(*Data in cusecs*)

Month	Discharge	% of the total discharge	% of the discharge in May
January	181,227	4.34	27.88
February	208,878	5.00	32.13
March	402,991	9 65	61.99
April	636,694	15.25	97.95
May	650,009	15.57	100.00
June	525 114	12.58	80.78
July	413,527	9.90	63.61
August	619,517	14.84	95.30
September	307,028	7.35	47.27
October	118,797	2.85	18.27
November	58,722	1.41	9.03
December	52,486	1.26	8.07
Total	4,174,990	100.00	—

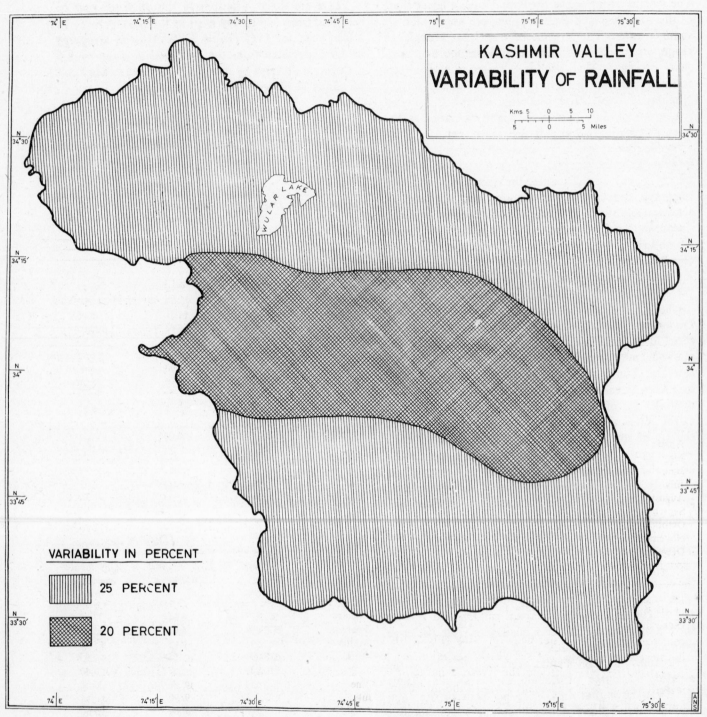

KASHMIR VALLEY
VARIABILITY OF RAINFALL

VARIABILITY IN PERCENT

25 PERCENT

20 PERCENT

FIG. 5·12

TABLE XXXVIII
Average monthly discharge of Jhelum at Baramulla
(1973)

(Data in cusecs)

Month	Discharge	% of the total discharge	% in the discharge in June
January	99,783	2.33	12 14
February	208,555	4.85	25.38
March	294,074	6.83	35.78
April	568,463	13.22	69.18
May	687,905	15.98	83.71
June	821,712	19.10	100.00
July	661,741	15.37	80.53
August	428,207	9.95	52.11
September	264,735	6.15	32.21
October	109,888	2.55	13.37
November	87,759	2.04	10.68
December	69,993	1.63	8.51
Total	4,302,815	100.00	—

TABLE XL
Average monthly discharge of Jhelum at Sopore
(1973)

(Data in cusecs)

Month	Discharge	% of the total discharge	% of the discharge in May
January	158,596	4.26	26.63
February	170,825	4.58	28.68
March	343,103	9.19	57.61
April	545,349	14.63	91.57
May	595,498	15.96	100.00
June	485,324	13.02	81.49
July	381,689	10.23	64.09
August	549,860	14.74	92.33
September	287,439	7.71	48.26
October	108,541	2.91	18.22
November	54,587	1.46	9.16
December	48,935	1.31	8.21
Total	3,729,746	100 00	—

TABLE XXXIX
Average monthly discharge of Jhelum at Sopore
(1965)

(Data in cusecs)

Month	Discharge	% of the total discharge	% of the discharge in June
January	81,919	2.48	12.82
February	159,753	4.82	25.00
March	169,414	5.12	26.51
April	266,853	8.04	41.76
May	567,196	17.10	88.76
June	638,970	19.26	100.00
July	591,913	17.84	92.63
August	409,471	12.34	64.08
September	178,394	5.38	27.91
October	106,601	3.22	16.68
November	81,167	2.46	12.70
December	64,395	1 94	10.07
Total	3,316,046	100.00	—

TABLE XLI
Average monthly discharge of Vishav river at Arwani
(1954-56)

(Data in cusecs)

Month	Discharge	% of the total discharge	% of the discharge in May
January	10,468	5.07	32 67
February	11,894	5.76	37.12
March	19,693	9.54	61.47
April	29,884	14.47	93.28
May	32,034	15.52	100.00
June	30,434	15.82	97.39
July	28,580	14.00	93.50
August	18,483	9.09	56.53
September	11,334	5.11	35.98
October	5,334	2.58	16.65
November	34,300	1.66	10.70
December	2,840	1.38	8.86
Total	206,408	100.00	—

In a year of high precipitation (Table XXXVIII), these deviations from the decennial average are 22 per cent for June and 3.6 per cent for May (Fig.5.16). It is interesting to note that the yearly variation in precipitation is not reflected in the river discharge in the initial phase. It is significant only in the midsummer months when it would deviate positively or negatively from the normal values in direct proportion to the intensity of precipitation, particularly snow. Seasonal vagaries of rainfall may, however, change the complexion of river flow entirely. Interesting patterns are observed in the Jhelum discharge as recorded at the gauging stations of Sopore and Baramulla. While the aggregate discharge is understandably higher at Baramulla than Sopore, in years of both lean and good rainfall, the peak discharge may come in May at Baramulla and in June at Sopore (Tables XXXIX and XL). Interestingly, there was a difference of about 180,000 cusecs between the discharge recorded at Sopore and Baramulla in July 1965, Sopore recording a higher flow. In 1973, on the other hand, January and March discharges were higher at Sopore than at Baramulla. They were roughly comparable in April, September and October. The discharge was significantly

PERCENTAGE DEVIATION OF PRECIPITATION AT SRINAGAR

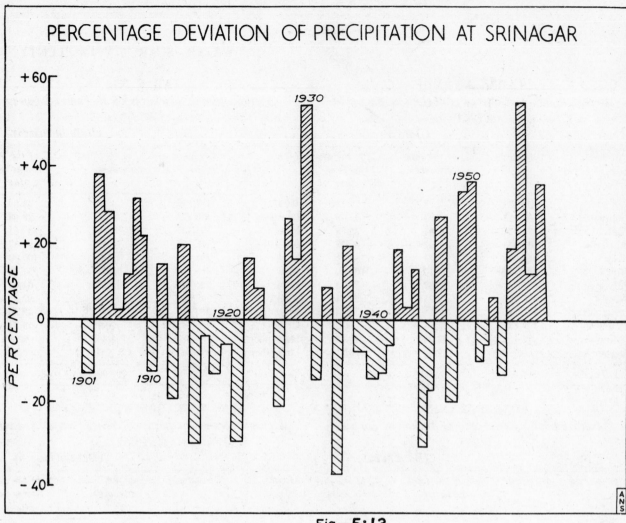

Fig.—5·13

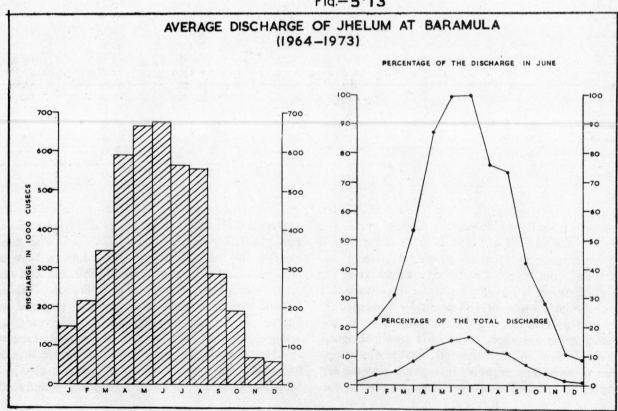

FIG. 5·14

low at Sopore in June and July, the difference being 337,000 cusecs in June and 281,000 cusecs in July. It was significantly high in August (122,000 cusecs). Baramulla had its peak discharge in June; Sopore, on the other hand, had two maxima, May and August. These differences are largely attributed to the seasonal differences in the meteorological conditions prevailing in the catchment areas of the different rivers and the spillover from the Jhelum before the discharge actually passes down the Baramulla gorge (Fig.5.17; 5.18).

The maximum discharge in Vishav (Table XLI) is usually recorded in May, although April, June and July also have a high run-off, respectively accounting for 93.3, 97.4 and 93.5 per cent of the peak discharge (Fig.5.19). In the case of Rembiara (Table XLII) the peak discharge may be only half that of the Vishav (Fig.5.20).

The discharge pattern in the three main right bank

TABLE XLII
Average monthly discharge of Rembiara river at Nayina (1952-54)
(Data in cusecs)

Month	Discharge	% of the total discharge	% of the discharge in May
January	5,381	5.61	32.74
February	6,480	6.20	39.43
March	9,540	9.14	58.06
April	14,803	14.20	90.09
May	16,431	15.71	100.00
June	13,702	13.12	83.39
July	9,234	8.80	56.19
August	14,240	13.70	86.66
September	8,151	7.82	49.60
October	2,704	2.60	16.45
November	1,802	1.70	10.96
December	1,452	1.40	8.83
Total	103,920	100.00	—

TABLE XLIV
Average monthly discharge of Sind river at Prang (1952-56)
(Data in cusecs)

Month	Discharge	% of the total discharge	% of the discharge in May
January	33,895	2.89	21.10
February	40,352	3.44	25.12
March	120,734	10.30	75.18
April	160,532	13.84	99.84
May	160,580	13.74	100.00
June	141,893	12.11	88.36
July	135,532	11.51	84.17
August	125,342	10.71	78.62
September	101,482	8.66	63.19
October	80,341	6.75	43.91
November	50,523	4.31	31.46
December	20,425	1.74	12.71
Total	1,171,631	100.00	—

TABLE XLIII
Average monthly discharge of Liddar river at Gur (1956)
(Data in cusecs)

Month	Discharge	% of the total discharge	% of the discharge in May
January	32,452	3.90	25.26
February	41,321	5.00	32.17
March	81,490	9.81	63.44
April	120,346	14.50	93.70
May	128,437	15.40	100.00
June	117,549	14.12	91.52
July	104,588	12.75	81.85
August	100,739	12.05	79.44
September	60,340	7.43	47.32
October	19,341	2.02	15.05
November	14,352	1.74	11.17
December	10,890	1.28	8.47
Total	831,845	100.00	—

TABLE XLV
Average monthly discharge of Pohru river at Siul (1956)
(Data in cusecs)

Month	Discharge	% of the total discharge	% of the discharge in May
January	44,356	4.32	26.99
February	56,325	5.59	34.27
March	115,241	9.36	70.03
April	161,050	15.80	97.99
May	164,342	16.12	100.00
June	156,430	15.39	95.93
July	105,340	10.37	64.09
August	101,423	9.89	60.44
September	70,524	6.98	42.91
October	25,430	2.58	15.47
November	13,420	1.39	8.16
December	12,434	1.21	7.46
Total	1,025,315	100.00	—

MONTHLY AVERAGE DISCHARGE OF JHELUM AT BARAMULA

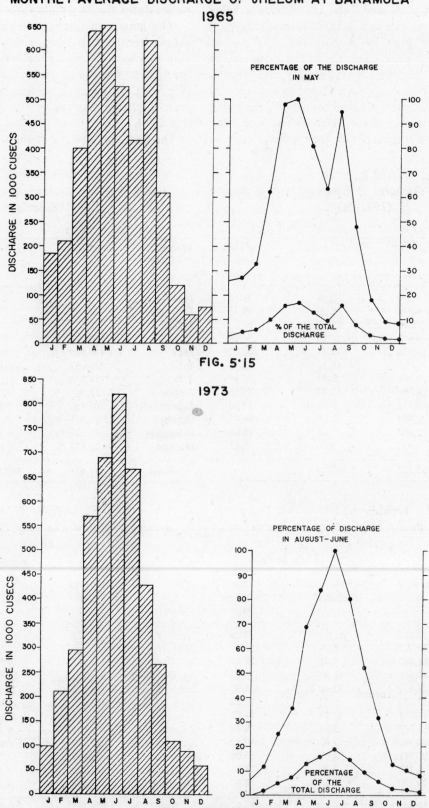

1965

PERCENTAGE OF THE DISCHARGE IN MAY

% OF THE TOTAL DISCHARGE

FIG. 5·15

1973

PERCENTAGE OF DISCHARGE IN AUGUST—JUNE

PERCENTAGE OF THE TOTAL DISCHARGE

FIG. 5·16

K

tributaries of the Jhelum—the Liddar, the Sind and the Pohru, is roughly identical (Tables XLIII-XLV) although time series data are not available for any reasonable period of time. All the three have their maximum discharge in May with April and June closely following in the same order (Figs.5.21; 5.22; and 5.23).

FLOODS

Floods have been a recurrent phenomenon in the Kashmir Valley. Their frequency and the devastation caused by them are fairly understandable in the bowl that the Valley is. For one thing, the Jhelum is faced with the predicament of carrying the cumulative discharge of all its streams through a narrow passage down the Valley, where silting goes on choking the channels infinitely, incapacitating the river from performing its primary function. The past behaviour of Jhelum shows that it has a maximum capacity of "safely" carrying only half of a high flood discharge. The other half has but to spill over the banks breaching the embankments that have been constructed to contain floods. Thus, in the topographic situation in which the Jhelum is, the floods are but a natural phenomenon (Fig.5.24).

The hydrographic features and the drainage characteristics of the Jhelum river system have been described in an earlier chapter. The magnitude of the flood problem can well be appreciated in that perspective. Even a casual look at history shows that the frequency of floods has been very high ever since the Valley assumed its present form. In the 20th century alone, of which we have a continuous record, there had been fifteen major floods up to 1965, the mean expectancy being 1 in 4.3 years. Among the major floods, those of 1959 and 1965 have no parallel in living history. The sequence of events in flood is always the same (See Figs. 5.25; 5.26). A heavy precipitation, usually coming during the end month of the summer monsoon and caused by a sudden cloudburst, leads to a severe flood. By now the catchment area of the river is already saturated and the high run-off swells the rivers beyond their capacity, with the result that the river *bunds* are breached and the whole Valley is converted into a big Nambal. The spillover from the rivers, particularly the Jhelum but also the Sind and the Pohru, flows to the depressions lying on the fringe of the rivers and inundates the agricultural lands with incalculable losses to the crops, livestock and human settlements.

Not all the havoc is created by nature; man has also added to his predicament in a big way. With every increase in population, human settlements have grown and expanded, swallowing up new lands for agriculture and habitation. As cities have grown on the banks of the Jhelum, its course has been narrowed and new embankments have been raised to contain its fury. The silting problem being what it is the bed of the river goes on rising to the extent that no embankment can really arrest the floods. The bund itself acts as a causal factor to floods since it inhibits all the drainage from being debouched into the mainstream. One consequence has been the emergence of extensive swamps on either bank of the river, particularly on the left bank.

The Jhelum in the Valley, especially above Awantipura, is bordered by a chain of these low-lying swamps, called Nambals and lakes which often act as natural absorption basins during floods. Significant among these are the Wular, Dal, Nagin and the Anchar lakes and the Batmalu, Hokarsar, Naugam and a host of other Nambals. They contain in them a good deal of the high flood discharge. It has been estimated that no less than 120,000 cusecs of flood spillover is accumulated in these depressions every year The actual run-off that can possibly pass down the Baramulla gorge is not more than 28,000 cusecs, which is perhaps the maximum volume the river can safely carry.[11]

It seems that the present precarious situation owes its origin to a number of factors which may be briefly listed. In the first instance, the general layout of the Valley is such that it is highly conducive to flooding. With the spread of settlement and growth of human population such measures as gradual encroachment on the water courses, reclamation of low-lying areas for agriculture, channellizing of rivers, creation of bunds along river banks and construction of transport lines in the floodplain have further worsened the situation.

Flood control measures have been given top priority since the early stages of history. But effective steps to mitigate the damage caused by floods have all been taken in the 20th century. By 1930 a flood-spill channel had been provided to divert a part of the flood discharge from a point a little above Srinagar to the adjoining depressions below the city. The spill channel however rejoins the Jhelum a few kilometres below the city. Other measures that have been adopted from time to time include construction of embankments along the river banks and of diversion channels, along with clearing silt from the river bed.[12] The Irrigation Commission has recommended that the solution to this menace perhaps lies in

i) Strengthening and realigning the bunds without

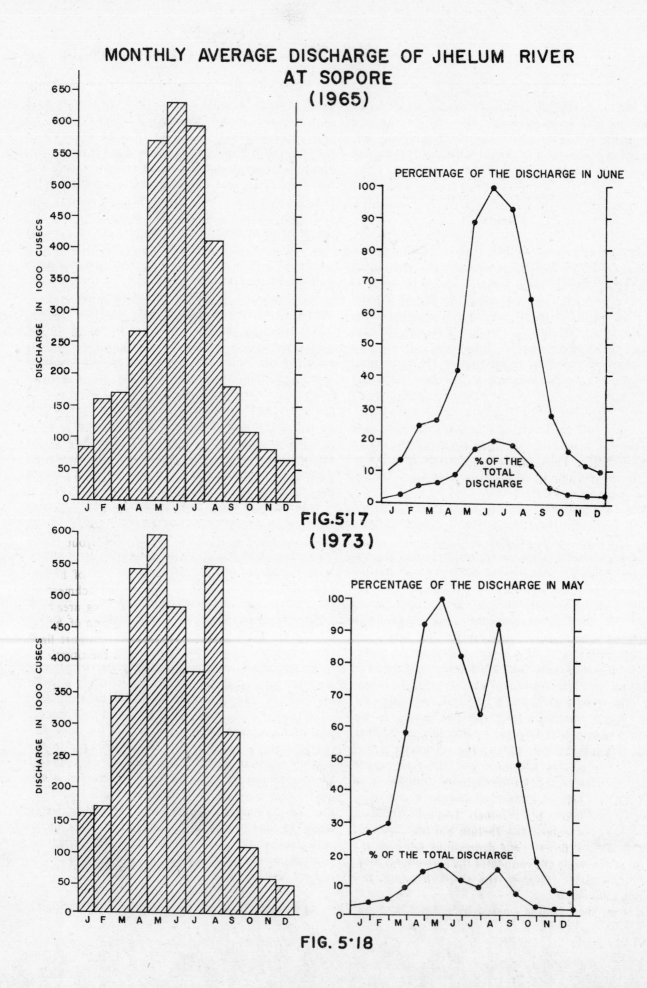

MONTHLY AVERAGE DISCHARGE OF JHELUM RIVER
AT SOPORE
(1965)

PERCENTAGE OF THE DISCHARGE IN JUNE

% OF THE TOTAL DISCHARGE

FIG. 5·17

(1973)

PERCENTAGE OF THE DISCHARGE IN MAY

% OF THE TOTAL DISCHARGE

FIG. 5·18

raising them;

ii) improving the river channel by making cut-offs;

iii) providing a supplementary channel or floodway from Dogripura to Wular, and improving the outfall channel[13] by diverting the Ningle (Ningal) and the Pohru rivers into the Wular lake; and

iv) stabilizing the torrents below Baramulla and clearing debris from the bed of the outfall channel.[14]

The Commission hoped that if these measures were properly implemented the Wular lake would be completely silted up and would be "available for cultivation." The Commission's recommendation to silt up the Wular is, however, unrealistic. In the Wular lake the Jhelum has a vast reservoir which plays a positive role in minimizing the load on the outfall channel during floods. The rise and fall of level in the Wular lake has a cause-effect relationship with the discharge at the point of outfall. Uppal estimated that during the floods the lake may receive about 60,000 cusecs, although it has the capacity to discharge 30-35,000 cusecs only. Understandably, the reclamation of low-lying tracts around the lake is likely to affect adversely the capacity of the lake to act as a moderator of flood in the outfall channel (Appendix XI).

GROUNDWATER RESOURCES

The groundwater resources of Kashmir Valley are only marginally known. No systematic surveys have been conducted to assess the groundwater potential of the Valley. There seem to be two main reasons for this lack of concern. First, an abundant supply of moisture from the surface sources, particularly in the floodplain of the Jhelum and other low-lying areas, ruled out the need to depend on underground water. Secondly, the political situation before and after the accession of the state of Jammu and Kashmir never aroused the rulers to care for an integrated development of the Valley through optimally managing the land and water resources of the region. For most of the recent history, mounting pressure on land and a subsistence agriculture have been taken for granted, leaving the problem of dry Karewas as something lying out of the ambit of human effort. But it is on the Karewa uplands that the water problem is most acute and where agricultural development is contingent on the feasibility of successfully tapping groundwater reserves.[15]

Lately, the government of Jammu and Kashmir seems to have become conscious of this problem as the Central Water and Power Commission has been asked to launch a programme to assess the groundwater potential of the Valley.[16]

In the absence of elaborate hydrological surveys, it is not possible to make a comprehensive study of the groundwater problem. The present study will therefore confine itself to casual observations regarding the availability and utilization of groundwater in certain parts of the Valley. Geologically, the strata that compose the low-lying areas of Kashmir Valley are favourable for the occurrence of groundwater. Indirect evidence is provided by the natural springs which seem to draw their supply from the affluent seepage of groundwater to the fringe of the alluvial tract. These springs are known to have sufficient discharge of water which is often put to miscellaneous local uses, though the bulk of it remains unharnessed and unused. A number of borings in the neighbourhood of Srinagar have yielded water within a depth of 150 metres, the discharge being as high as 91,000 litres per hour.[17] While these findings are encouraging, a vigorous exploratory effort is needed before the extent of groundwater reserves can be finally established.

As noted earlier, systematic work has yet to be done. Rough estimates about the groundwater potential are, however, available. The scientists of the Central Groundwater Board have some data pertaining to the processes of recharging of aquifers for the state of Jammu and Kashmir as a whole. The estimates have little relevance to Kashmir Valley.

UTILIZATION OF WATER RESOURCES

Water plays a limited though vital role in the economy of Kashmir. Its use is mainly in agriculture and to an average Kashmiri its plentiful supply means prosperity. The main uses are still traditional ones—gradient irrigation, navigation and primitive fishing—reminiscent of Neolithic times. The generation of hydro-electricity is only marginal, and, if compared with the available potential, infinitesimal.

Irrigation. The main use of surface water resources of the Valley is in gravity irrigation with the help of primitive technology. There are, however, both political and environmental constraints on the optimal utilization of water potential. The Jhelum is one of the rivers covered by the Indus Waters Treaty which regulates the use of Indus rivers between India and Pakistan. According to this treaty, while Pakistan is entitled to have a major claim on the waters of the

MONTHLY AVERAGE DISCHARGE OF VISHAV RIVER AT ARWANI

(AVERAGE FOR 2 YEARS 1954-56)

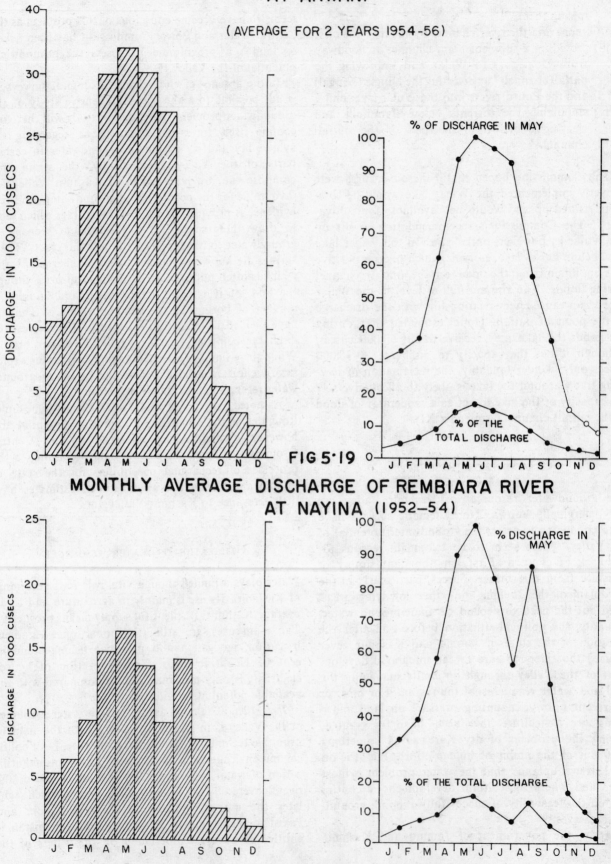

FIG 5·19

MONTHLY AVERAGE DISCHARGE OF REMBIARA RIVER AT NAYINA (1952-54)

FIG. 5·20

Indus, the Jhelum and the Chenab and their tributaries, India can utilize their waters only to a limited extent. In its use of these waters, notably in the case of the Indus, India is further incapacitated by the difficult nature of terrain and communication problems. This is however not true in the case of Jhelum in Kashmir where an extensive alluvial plain enhances prospects of more varied and intensive uses of water. But prospects apart, there is no indicator to show that there is a need for an intensive use of the Valley's water resources as engendered by either an expansion of the sown area or diversification of economy. Nothing can be conceived of at the present level of technology.

It has already been stated that the most noted use of Jhelum waters is for irrigation. The Kashmiri system of irrigation consists of *kuhls*[18] which take off from water courses at convenient points. The *kuhls* far surpass the government canals in terms of area covered as well as length of channels. At the beginning of the first five-year plan the area irrigated by *kuhls* was as much as sixteen times that of government canals.[19] Although government canals have been consistently expanding their command area since 1950, there is no comparison between them and the *kuhls*. The Kashmiri *kuhl* irrigation system emerged under the feudal lords who were concerned with the construction and maintenance of these channels. With the abolition of the zamindari system the *kuhls* fell into negligence and proved to be a menace to the adjoining agricultural land as the spillover from these channels caused recurrent floods. The government has become conscious of this problem only recently and a comprehensive scheme has been chalked out to expedite their restoration and renovation.[20] Initially the scheme was designed to cover 2,046 *kuhls* only, though it envisaged an eventual takeover of all the remaining *kuhls* with a command area of 1,012 hectares. The government has however displayed little interest in the extension of irrigation to drier parts of the Valley, particularly the chronically dry Karewas. Nor will it be possible to extend irrigation to these uplands unless more complex technology is employed which ensures lifting of water to areas tens of metres higher from the river valley floors.

Domestic Uses of Water. One of the commonest uses of water is for drinking. Despite a plentiful supply of water in the Valley, there is no systematic distribution except in large urban centres. Among the districts of the Valley, Anantnag seems to be best served. A number of reservoirs have been constructed at different places in the district and tap water is supplied to the public. The towns of Pampore, Shupiyan, Awantipura and Sedov Tsotopora have water supply schemes. Of the nine urban centres in Baramulla district only four—Baramulla, Sopore, Bandipore and Gulmarg (Tanmarg)—have a regular water supply. So far as rural areas are concerned, only large villages of Wanigam and Bunagam in Baramulla tahsil; Nadihal, Tiyar, Seer and Ajar Aithmulla in Sopore; and Sogam in Handwara tahsil have been provided with a water supply system [21]

Navigation. Watercourses also act as navigation channels. The Jhelum river and most of its tributaries in the floodplain as well as the Dal and the Wular lakes are navigable. Their role as arteries of transport can hardly be overemphasized.

Generation of Hydroelectricity. Although the Valley has a considerable potential for the generation of hydroelectricity, no major attempt has so far been made to exploit it substantively for either industrial or domestic use. There are very few urban areas and fewer villages which are served with electricity.

The Valley has two hydroelectric stations at Gandarbal and Moharra with an installed generating capacity of 15,000 and 6,000kws respectively. They cater to the needs of all urban centres besides important tourist resorts and a few villages. The villages so far electrified are few—2 per cent of all villages in Anantnag, 1.4 per cent in Baramulla and 8 per cent in Srinagar. Besides these two hydroelectric stations, work on the three projects—Chenani, Upper Sind and Lower Jhelum—is in progress. Of the three, Chenani was ready to be commissioned in 1972. A 220kv transmission line will take the supply to Srinagar and will be linked to an inter-regional grid augmenting the Gandarbal supply. It is further proposed that a 33kv line will connect Pattan to Tanmarg, Sopore to Bandipore and Anantnag to Shupiyan.[22]

One may expect that in the foreseeable future water will be put to more and more varied uses as the economy diversifies and new schemes of resource conservation and utilization receive increased attention. It is therefore necessary to fix priorities at the very outset and chalk out a comprehensive strategy for the optimal utilization of the Valley's water resources.

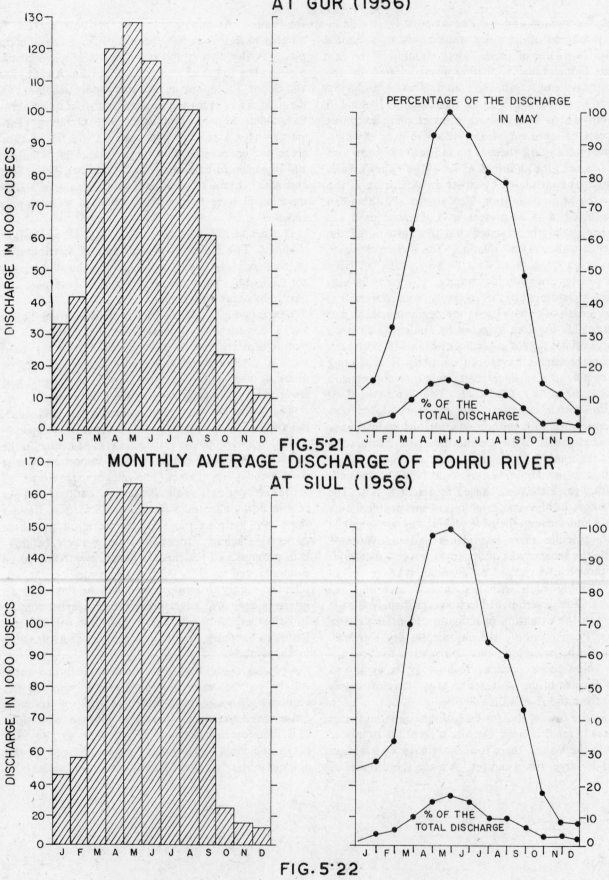

MONTHLY AVERAGE DISCHARGE OF LIDDAR RIVER
AT GUR (1956)

PERCENTAGE OF THE DISCHARGE
IN MAY

% OF THE
TOTAL DISCHARGE

FIG. 5·21

MONTHLY AVERAGE DISCHARGE OF POHRU RIVER
AT SIUL (1956)

% OF THE
TOTAL DISCHARGE

FIG. 5·22

MONTHLY AVERAGE DISCHARGE OF SIND RIVER
AT PRANG
(AVERAGE OF 4 YEARS -1952-56)

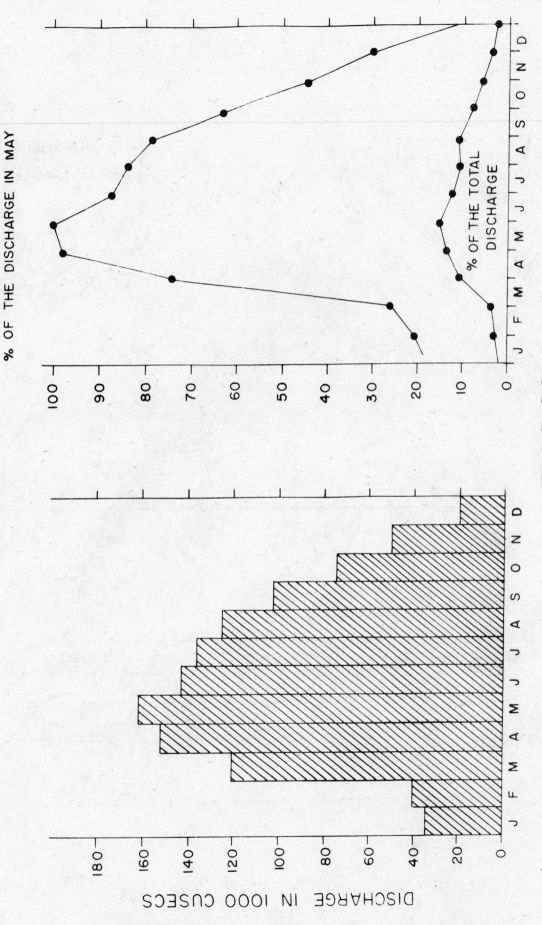

FIG.5·23

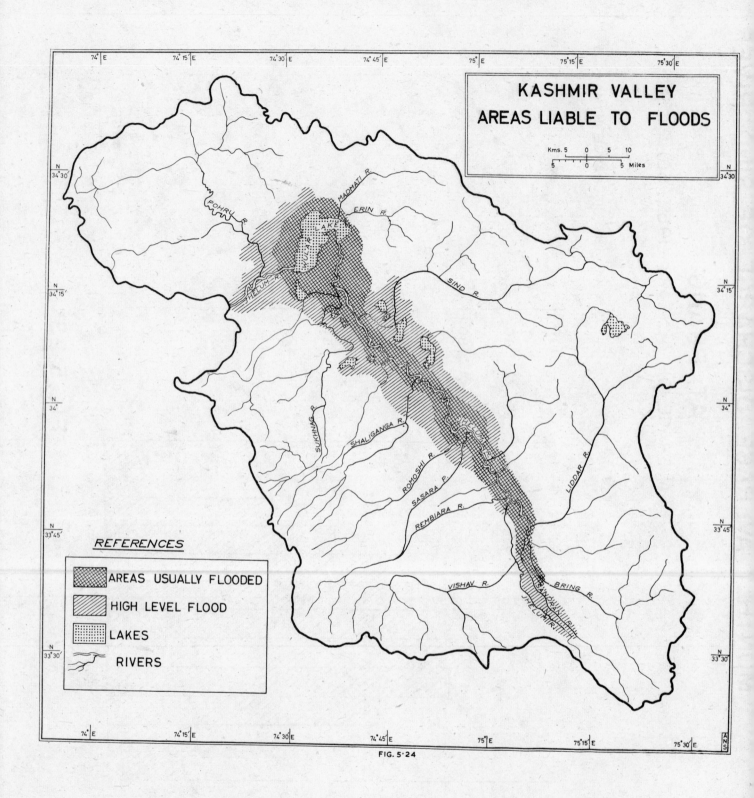

KASHMIR VALLEY
AREAS LIABLE TO FLOODS

Kms. 5   0   5   10
5   0   5   Miles

REFERENCES

AREAS USUALLY FLOODED

HIGH LEVEL FLOOD

LAKES

RIVERS

FIG. 5·24

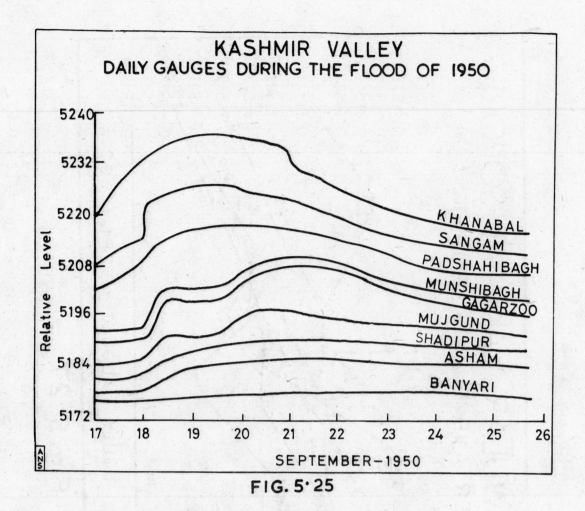

KASHMIR VALLEY
DAILY GAUGES DURING THE FLOOD OF 1950

FIG. 5·25

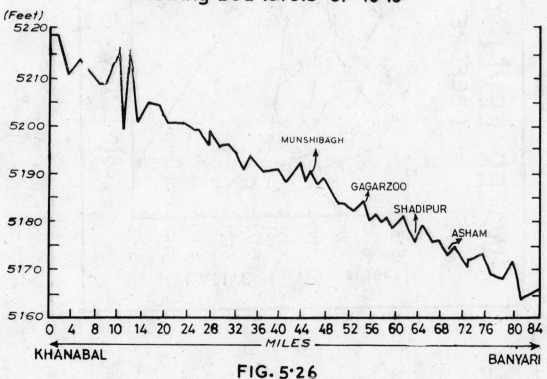

Long Section of the Jhelum River
showing bed levels of 1949

FIG. 5·26

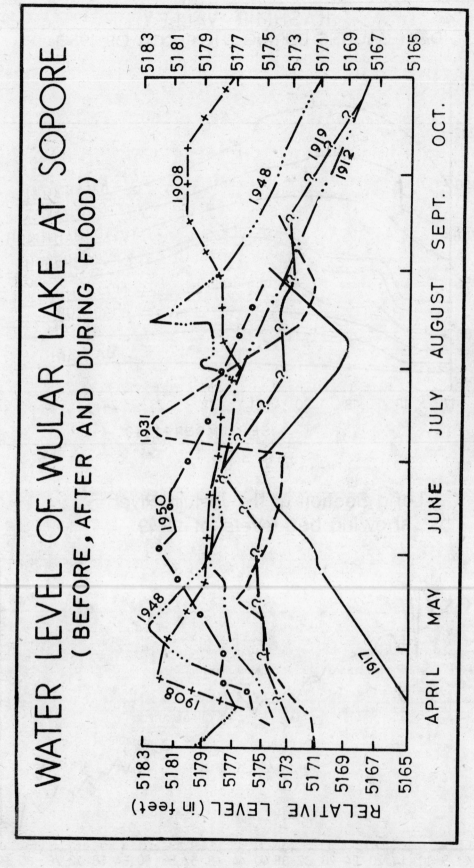

WATER LEVEL OF WULAR LAKE AT SOPORE
(BEFORE, AFTER AND DURING FLOOD)

Fig. 5·27

NOTES AND REFERENCES

[1]Rainfall and other meteorological data are available in the following IMD publications: *Climatological Tables of Observatories in India*, n.d.; and *Monthly and Annual Rainfall and the Number of Rainy Days, 1901-1950*, pt II, New Delhi, 1965.

The IMD did not, however, bring out a similar volume on snowfall—a meteorological variable of great significance for the Himalayan region. The monthly weather reports of the IMD contain such data for the Srinagar city and aerodrome observatories. S.N. Bhan of the Srinagar observatory published a useful analysis of snowfall data for Srinagar for the period 1939-53 which has been profitably used in this study.

[2]For his study of the floods in the Kashmir Valley, Uppal acquired the following data;

i) Daily gauge registers for permanent, gauges for the stations mentioned above;

ii) daily gauge register for temporary gauges;

iii) hourly gauge reading for 1950 for permanent discharge sites;

iv) hourly gauge reading for Munshibagh discharge site for the year 1931;

v) daily gauge register for the years 1908, 1910, 1912, 1917 and 1919 of Sopore gauge. (H.L. Uppal. *Flood Control Drainage and Reclamation in Kashmir Valley*, Central Water and Power Commission, New Delhi, 1956. p. 102.)

[3]For particulars of CWPC data, see Appendix VII.

[4]The Irrigation Commission report refers to a suggestion made by the state government in this respect. "It was suggested to us by the State Government that the Central Groundwater Board be requested to carry out investigations on the Karewas for groundwater." Report of the Irrigation Commission, Vol. II, New Delhi, 1972, p. 168.

[5]S.N. Bhan, "A Study of Fifty Years Rainfall of Srinagar (1901-50) and Jammu (1893-1942)," *Mem. Ind. Met. Dept.*, XXXI, pt. 4, 1965.

[6]The present study is based on a method developed by P.R. Crowe. See his paper "The Analysis of Rainfall Probability—A Geographical Method and Its Application to European Data," *The Scottish Geographical Magazine*, XLIX, 1933, pp. 73-91.

[7]The word "maximum" has been used by Crowe to denote the highest point in a dispersion diagram where the rainfall stops to increase and shows a clear tendency to decrease.

[8]A decrease is of the third or the highest degree if Q1 of one month is less than Q3 of the other; it is of the second degree if Q1 of one month is less than M of the other, and M of the former is less than the Q3 of the latter. All other changes where all the three values show a decrease are, however, indicative of a decrease of the first degree.

[9]Median values of rainfall have been used to measure variability. The formula used is given below:

$$CV = \frac{\text{(Inter-quartile Range)}}{\text{Median}} \times 100$$

[10]Tables XXXVI to XLV are based on daily gauge data contained in the departmental files of the Central Water and Power Commission.

[11]H.L. Uppal, *Flood Control, Drainage and Reclamation in the Kashmir Valley*, Central Water and Power Commission, New Delhi, 1956, p. 61.

[12]Silting, particularly in the lower course of the Jhelum after it emerges from the Wular lake is a serious problem. The Irrigation Commission noted that "during the last 20 years, the bed of the river . . . has risen appreciably. Below Srinagar also, in certain reaches, the bed has risen by two metres." Report of the Irrigation Commission, II, *op.cit.*, p. 157.

[13]The reach of the Jhelum below Sopore is often termed as the "outfall channel" by hydraulic engineers (cf. Uppal, *op. cit.*, p. 9).

[14]Report of the Irrigation Commission, *op. cit.*, pp. 157-158.

[15]Irrigation Commission Report, II, *op. cit.*, p. 159.

[16]*Ibid*, p. 168.

[17]*Ibid.*, p. 159.

[18]*Kuhls* are irrigation channels in which river water is diverted by erecting weirs or "projecting snags." "The main channels pass into a network of small ducts and eventually empty themselves, into the Jhelum or into the large swamps." (Lawrence, *The Valley of Kashmir*, *op.cit.*, p. 323.)

[19]Irrigation Commission report.

[20]*Annual Plan* of the Jammu and Kashmir State, 1970-71, p. 5.

[21]For more details, see Census of India, 1961, District Census Handbooks of Srinagar, Anantnag and Baramulla.

[22]*Annual Plan*, 1970-71.

BIBLIOGRAPHICAL NOTE

On river discharges, floods, flood control and reclamation of the Nambals and depressions, Uppal's work is of great value. Equally useful is G H. Khan's *Irrigation, Flood and Flood Problems of the Jammu and Kashmir State*, Srinagar, 1961. The report of the Irrigation Commission, 1972, furnishes a useful survey of the existing position in water availability and use in the states of the Indian Union. The report is, however, highly sketchy on Jammu and Kashmir.

Chapter Six

Magnificence Called Woods

> . . . the trees of the Valley form one of its greatest
> charms. The delightful plane trees, the magnificent
> walnuts; the endless wiliows, the poplars and the elms,
> the countless orchards of apples, pears and apricots
> give the Valley the appearance of a well-wooded park.
> —Lawrence, *The Valley of Kashmir*, p. 24

The character of natural vegetation in a region is the outcome of the environmental complex which exercises its influence, among other things, through soil and climate, particularly moisture supply. A critical role is also played by structure, relief, altitude and aspect. In the highland areas, such as Kashmir Valley, variations in altitude and aspect are of great significance and may even be deterministic in the distribution of such phenomena as moisture and sunshine, thus affecting the character of natural vegetation. Undoubtedly, the spatial distribution of natural vegetation in Kashmir can be well appreciated only in the context of the environmental frame.

The Kashmir Valley presents a highly varied picture in respect of physical configuration, altitude, soil and the climatic variables, such as temperature, moisture, intensity and duration of sunshine and atmospheric humidity. All these exercise a definite influence on the form, size and type of characteristic vegetation found in varied assemblages and association patterns in different parts of the Valley both horizontally and vertically. Thus two different aspects at the same altitude may have entirely different, even contrasted, plant communities subject to their exposure to the sun and moisture-bearing winds.

A study of the rainfall characteristics made earlier has indicated that its distribution is far from homogeneous in the Valley. This factor, in close conjunction with altitude and exposure to sun, has an impact on the distribution pattern of forest types. Besides moisture and sunshine a host of other meteorological factors, such as number of days with snowfall, seasonal variations in humidity and exposure to hot, dry or cold winds play a significant role in the distribution of tree types.

In direct response to these varied factors of environment the natural vegetation of Kashmir is highly variegated. It is luxuriant and well developed or stunted in tracts when edaphic and climatic factors thwart its growth. The primordial vegetation has however, been substantially modified by climatic chan ge and millinnia of human interference, as evident from intensive exploitation, clearance of forest cover for agriculture and indiscriminate felling and overgrazing.

There is some palaeontological evidence to show that the vegetal cover of Kashmir Valley underwent a stupendous change from tropical and subtropical to temperate types during the glacial phase of the Pleistocene. While recurrent glaciation destroyed the original vegetation completely, the uplift of the Pir Panjal also played a key role in this climatic and floral transformation by preventing the southwest monsoon from penetrating the Valley. This expedited the disappearance of the broad-leaved species which were once predominant in the low-lying areas in the Valley, and their replacement by coniferous types, such as deodar (*Cedrus deodara*), became a smooth affair.[1] Studies conducted on the Liddarmarg and Lavedura flora of the Valley during the Pleistocene have yielded useful evidence in this respect. It has been noted that at least three species of oaks and many subtropical forms, such as *Mellotus*, *Woodfortia*, *Myrsine*, *Engelthardtia*, *Olea*, etc., now unrepresented in the existing vegetation of Kashmir, once dominated the landscape in the Valley. They are believed to have been developed under tropical conditions which, however, no more exist. The mesophytic flora of the northern slopes of the Pir Panjal range is attributed to the uplift of the range which brought about a climatic change from subtropical to temperate.[2]

VEGETATION TYPES

The vegetation of Kashmir Valley may be systemati-

ALTITUDINAL ZONATION OF FORESTS
IN THE KASHMIR HIMALAYAS

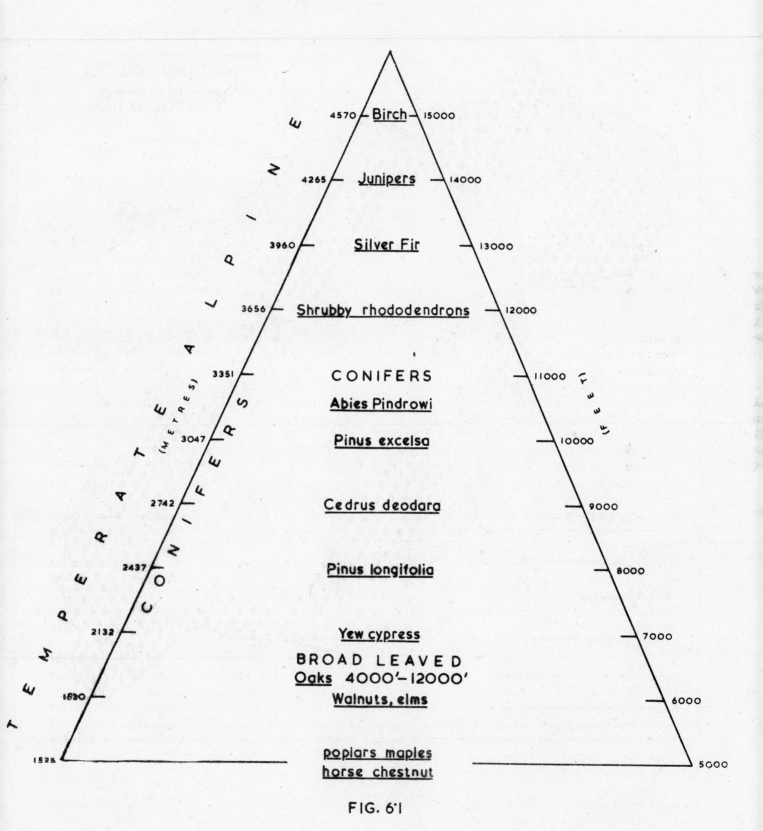

FIG. 6·1

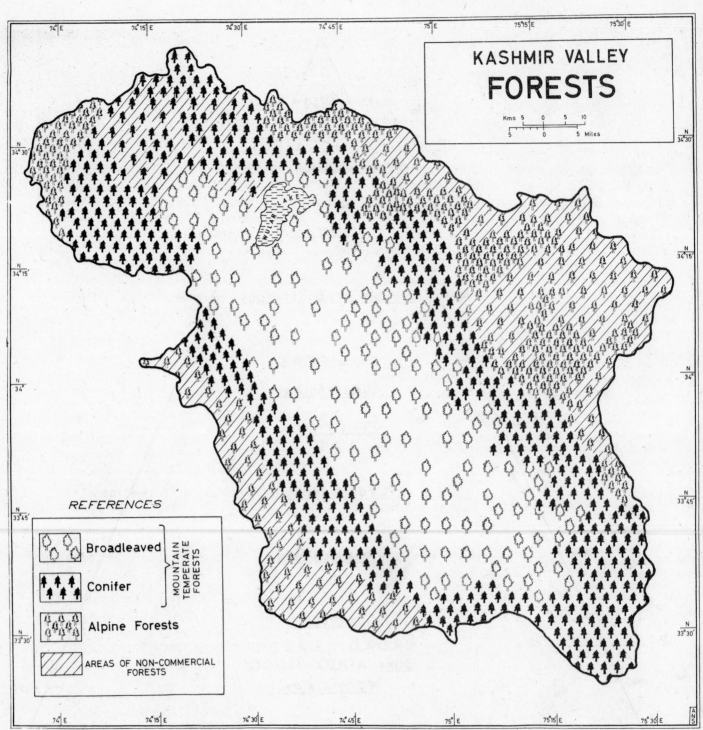

KASHMIR VALLEY
FORESTS

Kms 5   0   5   10

5   0   5 Miles

WULAR LAKE

REFERENCES

Broadleaved ⎫
           ⎬ MOUNTAIN TEMPERATE FORESTS
Conifer ⎭

Alpine Forests

AREAS OF NON-COMMERCIAL FORESTS

FIG. 6·2

cally studied in broad typological divisions of (i) forests, and (ii) grasslands. But there are many other types belonging to the intermediary varieties which appear as undergrowth in the forests or extensively cover the hill slopes, uncultivated tracts along the river banks, lakes and even lagoons. In fact, a classification of the natural vegetation is quite possible according to their habitat and based on compositional variations which are caused by locational factors.[3] While the ecological and locational factors generate variations in the character and composition of plant communities at any level, far more interesting is the zoning of vegetation in the vertical plane as observed in the Kashmir Himalayas. There are three main sets of factors which seem to explain this altitudinal zoning of vegetation: (i) locational factors, such as terrain slope and soils; (ii) altitude; and (iii) aspect. Although altitude and aspect play an important role in determining the availability of heat, moisture and humidity, structure and soils exercise a far greater influence than altitude or climate (Fig. 6.1). The following belts may be identified as a generalized expression of the altitudinal zoning of vegetation.[4]

i) A low-altitude temperate forest occurs in the Kashmir basin between 1,525 metres (5,000 ft) and 2,286 metres (7,500 ft) consisting of mixed vegetation of broad-leaved varieties such as poplars (*Populus citiata*, *P. nigra Var*, *P. alba*), walnuts (*Juglans regia*) and elms (*Ulmus Wallichiana*) and conifers, mainly blue pine (*Pinus excelsa*) and deodar (*Cedrus deodara*). It has however been noted that the deodar has its zone of potential growth at an altitude of 1,676-2,438 metres.[5]

ii) Above 2,135 metres, the broad-leaved varieties are outnumbered by conifers. This is the zone of the coniferous forest *par excellence*. The elm is, however, known to occur up to an elevation of 2,745 metres. The chief coniferous varieties which occur between 2,100 and 3,200 metres include blue pine, fir (*Abbies pindrow*) and the low-level silver fir (*Abbies webbiana*). The blue pine is often associated with *Picea smithiana* and *Taxus baccata*. The broad-leaved varieties which occur in the coniferous forest zone include *Prunus cornuta*, *Aesculus indica*, *Acer caesium*, *Juglans regia* and *Rosa macrophylla*.

iii) The next zone consists of the alpine forest usually above 3,200 metres. Initially, at altitudes of 3,200-3,660 metres occurs the white birch (*Betula utilis*), the most common species. Above it, between 3,660 and 4,110 metres, the commonest tree is the stunted juniper (*Juniperus communis*; *J. squamata*). *Rhodendron companulatum*, *Salix denticulata*, *Syringa*

emodi, and *Lonicera spp.* are among the other species known to occur in this zone.

iv) The alpine forest is often associated with alpine meadows in which temperate species such as *Poa*, *Glyceria* and *Festuca* are predominant (Fig. 6.2).

FORESTS

In response to the peculiarities of habitat, particularly climatic and edaphic factors, the biotic types of the Kashmir Valley sharply differ from those of the southern face of the Pir Panjal. The following are the salient features of the flora of the Kashmir Valley: (i) absence of oaks as a climax species and of laurels and low-level rhododendrons; (ii) a preponderance of fir; and (iii) negligible occurrence of spruce.

The forests are generally composed of a large number of species, although tracts with stands of pure communities are also not uncommon (Fig.6.3).

The more common trees found in the forests of the Kashmir Valley are given in Table XLVI.

TABLE XLVI
Common tree species of Kashmir

English name	Kashmiri name	Botanical name
Deodar	*Deodar*	*Cedrus deodara*
Himalayan Blue pine	*Kairu (Kail)*	*Pinus excelsa*
Himalayan silver fir	*Budal*	*Abies webbiana*
Yew	*Posthal*	*Taxus baccata*
Elm	*Brenn*	*Ulmus wallichiana*
Walnut	*Dun*	*Juglans regia*
Italian poplar	*Phrast*	*Populus nigra*
White poplar	*Dudh phrast*	*Populus alba*
Maple	*Kanar*	*Acer spp.*
Willow	*Vir*	*Salix tetrasperma*
White Birch	*Burza*	*Betula utilis*
Plane	*Boin (Chenar)*	*Platanus orientalis*

Classification. Botanists employ a number of criteria in classifying the forests of the Kashmir Valley. The different classification systems commonly recognized are based on the following criteria: (i) genetic characteristics; (ii) composition; (iii) management; and (iv) economic exploitability.

On the basis of their genetic characteristics the forests may be classified into montane, temperate and alpine. The montane and temperate forests are usually found between 1,500 and 3,200 metres. They have a lower zone in which the broad-leaved varieties are preponderant and a higher zone (2100-3200m) in which the conifers predominate. The alpine forests occur at an average elevation of 3,200 metres and above. As noted earlier, the birch is the most common tree type, although stunted junipers and rhododendrons are also found.[6]

tion of area under forests for the tahsils of the Valley is given in Table XLVII.

The proportion of area under forests is the lowest in Srinagar and the highest in Baramulla. There are as

TABLE XLVII
Area under forests by tahsils[7]

Tahsils	Geographical area square kilometres	Forest area square kilometres	Percentage of forest area
Ganderbal	1453.25	397.98	27.3
Badgam	1241.90	217.69	17.5
Srinagar	469.05	302.97	71.2
Total (Srinagar)	3121.20	918.64	29.4
Anantnag	2688.42	1889.59	70.1
Kulgam	1570.83	592.07	37.7
Pulwama	1171.72	781.43	66.7
Total (Anantnag)	5430.97	3263.09	60.1
Sopore	2652.42	946.07	88.8
Karnah	406.63	107.28	26.4
Handwara	1588.45	1309.55	82.4
Uri	697.23	306.91	44.0
Baramulla	829.32	355.56	42.6
Sonawari	394.20	222.74	56.5
Total (Baramulla)	6568.25	3248.11	71.0

The Kashmir forests may be classified into coniferous and broad-leaved varieties on the basis of their specific *composition*. As noted above, the broad-leaved species are generally found below 2,100 metres. For systematic management and better exploitation of forests they are often grouped into reserved, protected, and unclassified types. This distinction is made between first class forest estates meant for better production (these are either reserved or protected) and the inferior stands of forests which are left unprotected and unclassified. The development and exploitation of forests are both dependent on their economic importance and accessibility. A distinction is often made between commercial and uncommercial forests. Forests which are accessible and are capable of yielding good quality timber are considered to be exploitable and classified as commercial. A forest may be considered uncommercial if it is inaccessible, or its yield is of such inferior quality that its exploitation would be largely uneconomic (Appendix XII).

Forest Management and Conservation. Forests contribute significantly to the economy of Kashmir. Recent statistics show that they account for about one-fifth of the state income which is slightly more than half the share of agriculture. The importance of forests to the economy of Kashmir may also be judged from the fact that they occupy about sixty per cent of the total geographical area of the state. The distribu-

many as five tahsils in the Valley in which forests occupy more than three-fifths of the total area.

Forests as ecosystems have a much greater significance for man than is revealed by mere statistics. In the first place, they play a crucial role in the maintenance, preservation and regeneration of the gamut of land resources. They enrich the soil by providing much needed organic matter and enhance its water holding capacity. Equally important is their role in checking soil erosion and excessive run-off from hill slopes and other areas susceptible to erosion. In fact, they are a vitally important component in man's environment and are inextricably linked with all other ecosystems. The mutual dependence of air, land and water is so crucial that interference in one component may entail a whole series of changes in the rest of the system. It is therefore obvious that the problems of exploitation, management and conservation of forest resources cannot be considered in isolation since a policy regarding these would have a direct impact on the entire environment expressing itself in soil and water regimes and all living organisms, including man, dependent on them.[8] Forest conservation can only be a component of a larger conservation policy encompassing all of them.

Happily, a further exploitation of the forest wealth of Kashmir Valley is constrained by the occurrence of forests on difficult terrain in areas which are highly

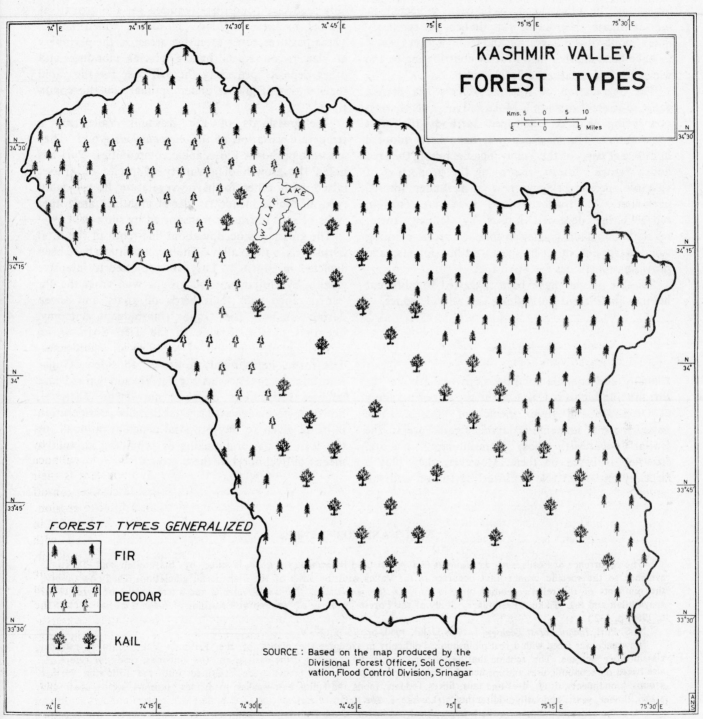

KASHMIR VALLEY
FOREST TYPES

Kms. 5   0   5   10
5   0   5 Miles

WULAR LAKE

FOREST TYPES GENERALIZED

FIR

DEODAR

KAIL

SOURCE : Based on the map produced by the
Divisional Forest Officer, Soil Conservation, Flood Control Division, Srinagar

FIG. 6·3

inacessible. The forest cover in such areas is still wholly or partly untouched. The accessible tracts of forest, on the other hand, have been subjected to indiscriminate destruction for timber. A carelessly liberal policy towards grazing and felling of trees seems to have been another major factor contributing to the widespread devastation of floral wealth.

The degradation of Kashmir forests has been a cause of general concern.[9] More and more emphasis is now being laid on improved methods of forest conservation. The measures that have been adopted in different parts of the Valley include: raising the area under "stock" forests; improving the proportion of valuable species; bringing new areas under forests, particularly in tracts exposed to severe erosion; rehabilitating degraded forests by fencing them; regulating nomadic grazing in forested areas; planting suitable species in open spaces within forests; and providing substitutes for wood fuel.

Suitable species have been suggested for different habitats in different soil regimes and altitude zones.

GRASSLANDS

Climatic and edaphic conditions, particularly in the surrounding highlands, favour the growth of a variety of temperate and alpine species of grasses. These pastures are of immense economic significance to the Gujjar *bakarwals* whose transhumant, pastoral economy is based on them. However, they play a far more important role in thwarting run-off and soil erosion from the steep slopes with a thin soil cover. An abundant supply of sunshine and moisture are the only necessary conditions required for the growth of grasses in these highland meadows, called *margs*. These pastures cover extensive areas on the periphery of glaciers on tracts having glacial moraines and other deposits providing the soil base for the rapid regeneration of grasses under optimal climatic conditions.

The grasslands of the Kashmir Valley are a temperate variation of the *mesophiclons* group. They are recognized as bio-edaphic communities. Puri has noted the growth of a variety of species of grasses mixed with other forms of vegetation in two main types of alpine meadows: glacial moraines and other types of soils *in situ* or transported by snow-melt.[10]

The grasslands occupy about one-tenth of the total tahsil area in the Valley. The main pastures have been depicted in Fig. 6.4. They are subjected to intensive grazing by Gujjar pastoral groups who cross the Pir Panjal range with their herds of goats and sheep during summer. The Gujjar transhumant economy, like that of the Kirghiz in the Tien Shan, is an interesting phenomenon of great social significance. The forest department, however, considers Gujjar transhumant practices as a great erosion hazard and imposes restrictions on their movement. There is, however, no evidence to suggest that due consideration is being given to any proposal aimed at rationalizing this form of pastoral grazing or providing alternative means of livelihood to these groups.

NOTES AND REFERENCES

[1]The occurrence of fossils, such as *Mallotus Phillippensis* and *Woodfortia fruticosa*, is cited by Inayatullah and Tikku as evidence to the specific change that occurred in the Valley with the onset of the Pleistocene glaciation. They now observe the remnants of this relict vegetation only in *Parrotia Jacquemontiana*, *Skimunica leureolia* and a few species of pyrus. (Mir Inayatullah and B.L Tikku, "Preliminary Study of the Forest Typology of Jammu and Kashmir," *Indian Forester* Vol. XC, 6, 1966, p. 332.)

[2]G.S. Puri, *Indian Forest Ecology*, I, New Delhi, 1960, pp. 75-76, 79.

[3]Lawrence was faced with a real philosophical difficulty in grouping the plants of the Kashmir Valley into a rational classificatory scheme. The scheme that he followed was, as he admitted, "the easiest, and the one most ready for reference, was based on economic uses and medicinal properties of the plants. The plants were classified into the following further groups: 'condiments, drugs, dyes and tans, fibres, fodders, foods and fruits, hair-washes, medicines, poisons, scents, soap and alkali, timber, yeast, and lastly adulterants." (Lawrence, *The Valley of Kashmir, op. cit.*, p. 66.)

[4]". . .the vegetation mosaic in the topographical conditions of the Himalayas is naturally often very complex; it is impossible . . . to do justice to its permutations." (Spate, *India and Pakistan, op. cit.* p. 90.)

[5]In a study of the deodar communities of Kutihar and Buniyar belts, Muthoo and Wali have noted the occurrence of this species mostly on the northern aspects. (M.K. Muthoo and M.K. Wali, "Deodar Belt of Kashmir. Its Occurrence and Ecology," *Indian Forester*, XCI, 1965, pp. 443-453.)

[6]G.S. Puri, *Indian Forest Ecology*, I, New Delhi, 1960.

[7]Data based on official *Digest of Forest Statistics, Jammu and Kashmir Forest Record*, 1, 1969, p. 10

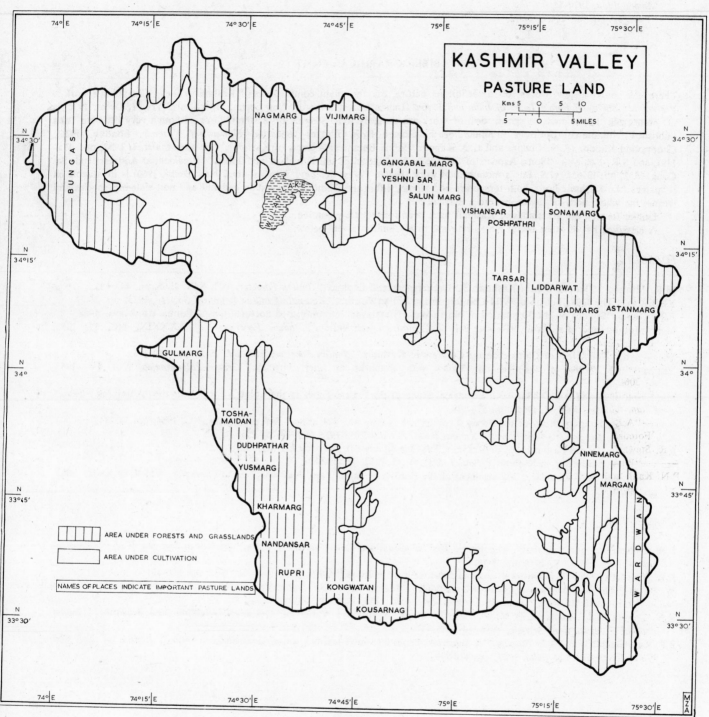

KASHMIR VALLEY
PASTURE LAND

Kms 5   0   5   10
5   0   5 MILES

BUNGAS

NAGMARG   VIJIMARG

LAKE

GANGABAL MARG
YESHNU SAR
SALUN MARG
VISHANSAR   SONAMARG
POSHPATHRI

TARSAR   LIDDARWAT
BADMARG   ASTANMARG

GULMARG

TOSHA-
MAIDAN

DUDHPATHAR
YUSMARG

KHARMARG

NANDANSAR

RUPRI

KONGWATAN

KOUSARNAG

NINEMARG

MARGAN

WARDWAN

||||| AREA UNDER FORESTS AND GRASSLANDS

AREA UNDER CULTIVATION

NAMES OF PLACES INDICATE IMPORTANT PASTURE LANDS

FIG. 6·4

It may be noted that the Valley of Kashmir as delineated for the purpose of this study includes parts of Handwara, Sopore and Karnah tahsils, while the entire tahsil of Uri is excluded.

[8]M.K. Muthoo, "The Concept of Renewable Resources," *The Geographer*, XVII, 1970, pp.4-20.

[9]*Annual Plan*, 1970-71.

[10]Puri, *op. cit.* pp. 114, 271-272.

BIBLIOGRAPHICAL NOTE

There are only a few works of a definitive nature on the plant communities of Kashmir Valley. Champion's work *A Preliminary Survey of Forest Types of India and Burma* (Indian Forest Records, New Series, Silviculture, Vol. I, Delhi, 1936) is of pioneering importance. A good deal of work was done by R R. Stewart on Kashmir flora, although very little has been published. Notable contributions on alpine flora have come from Blatter (*Beautiful Flowers of Kashmir*, London, 1926), Chopra and Kapoor (R.N. Chopra and L.D. Kapoor "Some Botanical Aspects of Kashmir," *Palaeobotanist*, I, 1952, pp. 115-119), and S.R. Kashyap ("Some Aspects of the Alpine Vegetation of the Himalaya and Tibet," Presidential Address, Ind. Sc. Cong. 1932, pp. 13-65). G.S. Puri's monumental work (*Indian Forest Ecology*, two volumes, New Delhi, 1960) is invaluable as it places the Kashmir flora, both temperate and alpine, within the frame of the Indian endemic and non-endemic species and weaves the whole body of literature into a system.

Unlike forests, the grasslands of Kashmir have been inadequately studied.

A classified list of other useful works relevant to Kashmir is given below:

FORESTS

M.K. Muthoo, "Deodar Belt of Kashmir, Its Occurrences and Ecology," *Indian Forester*, Vol. XCI, 1965, pp. 443-453.

K. Biswas, "The Distribution of Wild Conifers in the Indian Empire," *Journal of Indian Botanical Society*, 1933, pp. 24-27.

R.K. Gupta "Studies on the Vegetation of North-West Himalayas," unpublished doctoral thesis, Poona University, 1968.

M.K. Muthoo, and M.K. Wali, "Deodar Belt of Kashmir, Lolab Valley," *Indian Forester*, Vol. LXXXIX, No. 11, 1963, pp. 716-726.

Sher Singh, "The Effect of Climate on the Conifers of Kashmir," *Indian Forester*, Vol. LV, 1929, pp. 189-203.

Vishnu-Mittre, "Oaks in the Kashmir Valley with Remarks on their History," *Grana Palynotogica*, Vol. IV, 1963, pp. 306-312.

Mir Enayatullah and B.L. Tikku, "An Ecological Study of the Forest Types in the Lolab Valley and the Adjoining Areas," *Indian Forester*, XCI, 8, 1965, pp. 538-547.

————"A Preliminary Study of the Forest Typology of Jammu and Kashmir," *Indian Forester*, XC, 1964, pp. 332-347.

A.N. Fotedar, *Revised Working Plan for Kamrai Forest Division 1955-1956 to 1974-75*, 1956.

R.R. Stewart, "Notes on the Flora of Kashmir," *Punjab (Pakistan). For. Rec.*, 1 (2), 1951.

————"Plant Collecting in Kashmir," *Pak. J. Sci.*, IV, 3, 1952, pp. 89-95.

P.N. Kaul, and A.N. Fotedar, "Management of the Forests of Jammu and Kashmir," *Indian Forester*, Vol. LXXXVII, 1961, pp. 667-677.

GRASSLANDS

P.M. Dabadghao, and B.D. Patil, "Ecological Basis of Grassland Conservation in India," *Journal of Soil and Water Conservation in India*, Vol. V, 1956, pp. 7-10.

F.R. Bharucha, "The Problems of Grassland Improvement in India," *Curr. Sci.*, Vol. VI, 1938, pp. 600-601.

W. Burns, "The Improvement of Natural Grasslands in India," *Agr. Jour. India*, Vol. X, 1915, pp. 288-293.

————"Grassland Ecology," *Pusa Agric. Res. Inst. Bull.*, 150, 1923, pp. 18-21.

R.N. Chopra, K.L. Handa, L.D. Kapoor and Tej Singh, "Nutritive Value of Grasses of Jammu and Kashmir," *Indian Journal of Agricultural Science*, 1956, pp. 415-457.

S.P. Raychaudhuri, and T.D. Biswas, "A Suggested Procedure for Classification of Grasslands in India," *Journal of Soil and Water Conservation of India*, 1957, pp. 118-119.

Chapter Seven

The Source

The earth and the sun are the sources of life and if we keep away from them for long life begins to ebb away. Modern industrialized communities have lost touch with the soil and do not experience that joy which nature gives and the rich glow of health which comes from contact with mother earth.—Jawaharlal Nehru in *Discovery of India*

Little work of a scientific nature has been published on the soils of Kashmir Valley. This may not be interpreted to mean that no work has been attempted on this vital resource. The data on soils, however, lie buried in unpublished dissertations, departmental reports of the soil testing laboratory of the state agriculture ministry and official documents of the soil science division of the Indian Agricultural Institute, New Delhi, and the Indian Photo Interpretation Institute, Dehra Dun.[1] There is also a good deal of material on Kashmir soils available in gazetteers and early settlement reports.[2] There is, however, no comprehensive, up to date study based on a synthesis of this stray material.

The soils of the Kashmir Valley vary in origin from alluvial to lacustrine and glacial. Their present day variations have been caused mainly by climatic processes and have little relation to the parent or the bedrock. They have evolved through a long geomorphic history punctuated by alternations of fluvial and glacial phases. The soil cover has enormous thickness in the bowl of Kashmir and in the adjoining terraces where massive deposition has taken place since Pleistocene times. It is richest in the low-lying areas along the Jhelum, where it is periodically renewed and enriched by floods which are a recurrent phenomenon in the Valley. The thickness of the soil cover and its fertility status however deteriorate with altitude. In the highlands the rock bed is often devoid of soil cover as the slope is too steep and low temperatures and strong winds keep soil-forming processes in suspension.

The soils have been deposited in their present sites by the two main agents—rivers and glaciers—and are continually subjected to tremendous transformation both by natural and human agencies. It is proposed here to study the soils of Kashmir with reference to road physiographic divisions as given below:

i) The Valley basin and the side valleys of the Jhelum, up to 1,850 metres;
ii) the highlands, mainly between 1,850 and 3,350 metres; and
iii) the Karewa uplands.

VALLEY SOILS

The soils of the Valley basin and the low altitude terraces abound in nitrogen content, organic matter and other plant nutrients which raise their fertility status. They are estimated to have a high content of P_2O_5 and K_2O and are fairly rich in calcium and magnesium. Texturally they vary from clayey loams to loams with a variable nitrogen content ranging between 0.4 and 0.08 per cent. It has been observed that there is an accumulation of F_e and A_1 in B horizon, particularly in low-lying areas. The pH value varies from 6.5 to 7.2.

HIGHLAND SOILS

The soil of the highlands is deficient in bases and becomes more and more acidic. In a study of the soil profiles under deodar, silver fir and blue pine forests of Kashmir, Hoon observed a striking resemblance between these and the podzol group of soils found in the coniferous belt of the Kulu Valley.[3] A generalized classification of the highland soils appears in a soil map contained in the *Techno-Economic Survey* of Jammu and Kashmir (Fig. 7.1). There is, however, little technical data to bring out typological differentiation between such groups as forest and hill soils and mountain and meadow soils. Within the highlands, important differences are observed in soil types mainly depending, among other things, on the site, nature of slope and altitude. The valleys and patches of flat land, even at higher elevations, may have a deep soil layer with high humus content.

The young and immature soils usually found on the steep mountain slopes owe their origin to a set of environmental factors including climate, particularly decreasing temperature with altitude and sluggish weathering processes. The vertical change in temperature expresses itself more emphatically in a shorter growing season and lesser vegetative growth. One impact of these factors on soils is seen in a high tendency to leach. The mountain slopes are mostly forested interspersed with extensive patches of grasslands. A considerable amount of organic matter which is available to the soil from forests and other vegetation types contributes significantly to the soil properties.[4]

A recent IPII study of the soils of the Pohru river catchment basin shows that the soils are richer on aspects less exposed to sun and having a luxuriant forest. These soils are however not very deep and are mixed with pebbles. The main soil types identified on the cultivated terraces of the Pohru basin include Hapludolls, Hapludalfs and Udorthents. The Hapludolls are fairly deep and rich in organic matter. They are occasionally stony and are found on partially exposed forested slopes. A fourth variety of soil found in this area has been identified as Eulrochrepts. Udorthents and Eulrochrepts have little organic matter and a high content of stones and pebbles and are generally shallow. Hapludalfs, however, occur only in isolated pockets.[5]

Kaul collected and analyzed fifteen soil samples from different altitudinal belts in the Kashmir Valley. The study revealed that those soils have textural and morphological characteristics favourable to plant growth (Appendix XIV).

Mechanical Analysis. Texturally, these soils are mostly silty, clay loams and the relative proportions of the textural separates is generally favourable to ideal growth. These soils have a good water-holding capacity which has been mainly contributed by the clay, silt and humus content. The proportion of total soluble salts in these soils is low since their location in hilly tracts in areas of high rainfall and low evaporation inhibits waterlogging and concentration of salts (Appendix XV).

Chemical Analysis. These soils have a high nutrient status as revealed in the available nitrogen, potash and phosphates. With the exception of the Khilanmarg sample which shows a low pH value, the reaction of all these soils varies from acidic to neutral. The available nitrogen content is medium to low and the proportion

of organic matter is positively correlated with altitude. They are generally characterized by a low content of calcium carbonate. Their degree of weathering suggests that they are mostly skeletal and juvenile and may perhaps be classified as degraded Podzols[6] (Appendices XVI-XVII).

Karewa Soils. Karewa soils are poorer. They are mostly composed of silts, although considerable differences exist between the Karewa gurti varieties and the rich gurti soils of the Valley basin. The Karewa gurti types are distinguished on the basis of colour differences.[7] The colour of the soil varies from light (e.g. Ompara Karewa) to red-hued soil resembling gurti (e.g. Badgam Karewa), to the dark blackish soil known as surhzamin. In fertility, surhzamin is rated as the best, followed by the red gurti, while the yellow-hued soil is regarded as the worst.[8]

The Karewas are often composed of horizontal beds of coarse sand mixed with small pebbles. A typical section near Anantnag which was studied by Drew[9] consisted of an uppermost layer of pebble-studded coarse sand having a thickness of about 60 metres. This is replaced by another layer of fine sand about 1.0 metre in thickness, followed by a bed of highly compacted fine-grained sand. It has a thickness of about 4.5 metres and gives way to a thin layer of blue sandy clay with a thickness of 1.5 metres only.

Stray chemical studies conducted on the Kerewa soils reveal that the nitrogen content varies from 0.644 to 0 00132 and K_o from 0.06 to 0.08. It may be noted that the Karewas are by and large devoid of a vegetal cover, and the soil lacks in organic matter. The moisture-retaining capacity of the soil is poor as the upper layer has a high sand content.

A study of the two soil profiles in the Pampur Karewas[10] has indicated that the surface layer of the soil in the saffron-producing tracts has been leached of $CaCO_3$ which has accumulated in the fourth layer about one metre below. The concentration of $CaCO_3$ is just the reverse in the adjoining tracts not given to saffron cultivation. Interesting differences have been observed in the morphological characteristics and the chemical properties of the soils in the two profiles (Appendix XVIII). The A horizon (0-230mm) in the saffron-growing soil has a dark brown colour with a loose structure, sand, silt and clay proportions being 33.94, 43.12 and 20.28 per cent respectively. It is poor in nitrogen content (0.086) and in CaO (0.395). The pH value is 7.55. The B horizon (230-380 mm) shows more compactness, with a slight increase in the clay content. The contents of nitrogen and organic carbon suffer a loss, while the pH value slightly improves. The A horizon in the soils

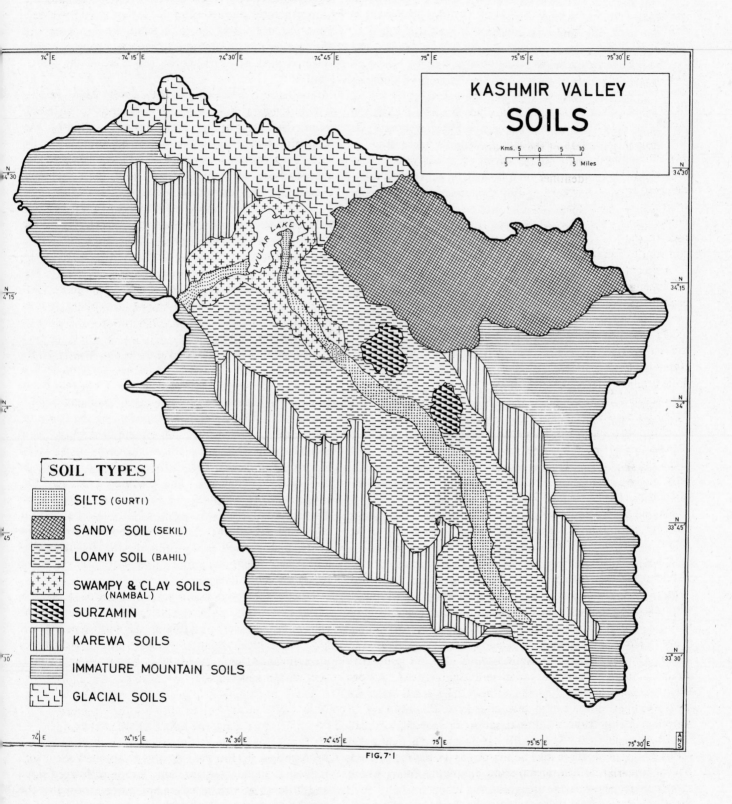

KASHMIR VALLEY
SOILS

Kms. 5   0   5   10
5   0   5   Miles

WULAR LAKE

SOIL TYPES

SILTS (GURTI)

SANDY SOIL (SEKIL)

LOAMY SOIL (BAHIL)

SWAMPY & CLAY SOILS (NAMBAL)

SURZAMIN

KAREWA SOILS

IMMATURE MOUNTAIN SOILS

GLACIAL SOILS

FIG. 7·1

not growing saffron is structureless with a light brown colour. It has a high content of $CaCO_3$ (14.07) while the sand, silt and clay contents are relatively low as compared to the A horizon of the earlier profile, the respective values being 24.44, 34.20 and 22.55. No significant difference is observed in the contents of nitrogen and organic carbon, although the pH value (8.15) as well as C_aO (6.56) are high. The B horizon (230-500 mm) registers a further increase in pH as well as C_aO. The clay content of the soil also slightly increases.

The IPII study of the sloping Karewa soils of the Pohru basin identifies the following types: Ochraqualfs, Hapludolls, Udiflurents and Haplaquents. The Ochraqualfs and Hapludolls are characterized by a high silt content. They are poorly drained. The soils assume a different character in areas where the soil rests on boulders and stones and the sand content increases because of proximity to the river course. Such soils are designated as Udiflurents and Haplaquents[11] (Appendix XIII).

LOCAL CLASSIFICATION

The Kashmiri peasant has his own perception of the soil types of his locality (Fig. 7.2). He usually recognizes the following four main types of soil: gurti, bahil, sekil, and dazanlad.[12] Gurti (or grutu)[13] literally means silt. It is a rich soil with a high percentage of both clay and silt. It has a high water-retaining capacity and can support good crops even in years of scanty rainfall. The fertility status of the gurti is high which is further improved by recurrent floods. The gurti soil zone is roughly conterminous with the Jhelum floodplain which is regularly subjected to fresh deposition of silt by Jhelum floods. This zone may be demarcated by an imaginary line joining the towns of Vernag, Doru, Achhabal, Anantnag, Awantipura, Pampur, Bandipur and Sopore on the right bank and Kulgam, Shopyan, Bijbahera, Pulwama, Badgam, Magam, Sumsal and southern Baramulla on the left bank. The gurti suffers from serious setback in years of heavy rainfall as the soil compresses under waterlogging, with the result that its productive capacity is seriously reduced. Recent studies conducted by Uppal show that the silt materials brought down by the Jhelum and its affluents vary in diameter from 1.027 millimetres at Sangam to 0.078 millimetres in the bed of the Sukhnag.[14] This variation in grade is attributed to the disparate nature of rock materials in the surrounding mountains from where these materials are brought down.

Bahil. Next in importance are the bahil soils which are excellent loams, although the proportion of silt, clay and sand may vary from region to region. In fact, the proportionate share of silt and clay progressively declines with increasing distance from the floodplains of the Jhelum and its tributaries. The main zone of occurrence of bahil soils lies above the level of the floodplain.

The bahil is a prized soil with a very high fertility status. It has a darkish colour and tends to be black when dry. Despite its high natural strength, the Kashmiri peasant is always tempted to manure it heavily with consequential adverse effects on crops.[15] An excessive use of manure often leads to a common disease in paddy called *rai*.

Sekil. With increasing sand content in the soil the bahil changes into sekil. It has a coarse texture and vast differences in the sand content have been observed. The sekil is mainly found in the Sind valley both in the lower reaches and in the terraces higher up. Most of the sekil area is, however, under forests, although its suitability for cultivation is well known. It is rich in humus content and may yield good crops under conditions of assured water supply.

Dazanlad. The low-lying tracts in the Valley, particularly those on the left bank of the Jhelum, have a chronic problem of waterlogging. Here the two main types of soil known to occur are called the dazanlad and the nambal. The dazanlad is found along the fringe of the swamps. The nambal soil, on the other hand, is a peculiarity of the swampy lands. The dazanlad is highly compact and heavy and is considered to be exceptionally good for paddy. The low-lying tracts near the banks of the Jhelum which remain waterlogged seasonally have the rich, peaty soil, the nambal, with a high fertility status. Cultivation on the reclaimed swamps has proved successful and with increasing silting of the Wular lake more and more land is being reclaimed for cultivation.

Besides the above four types, a number of special soil varieties are known to occur locally. Their nomenclature is, however, puzzling as the main types of soil have many local variants. Notable among these types are surhzamin, lemb, rad, tand, zabalzamin, kharzamin, ront, shath and tats.[16]

SOIL EROSION AND CONSERVATION

In highland basins such as the Kashmir Valley soil, erosion is a menacing problem. Lands with steep slope and little or no vegetal cover are more exposed to the erosion hazard as rainfall and snow-melt both play their notorious role of depleting the soil resources with

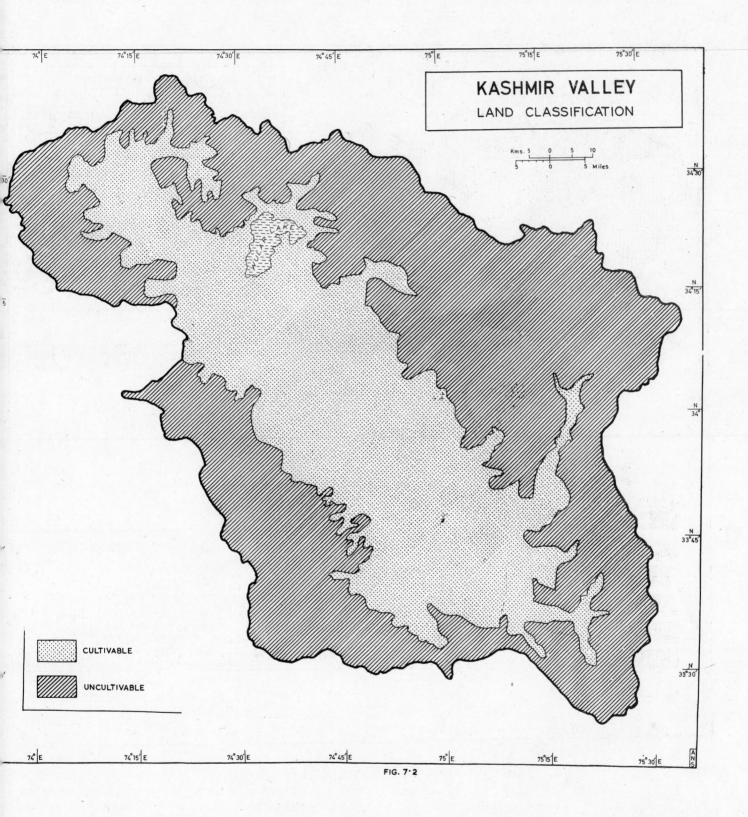

KASHMIR VALLEY

LAND CLASSIFICATION

Kms. 5   0   5   10

5   0   5 Miles

LAKE

CULTIVABLE

UNCULTIVABLE

FIG. 7·2

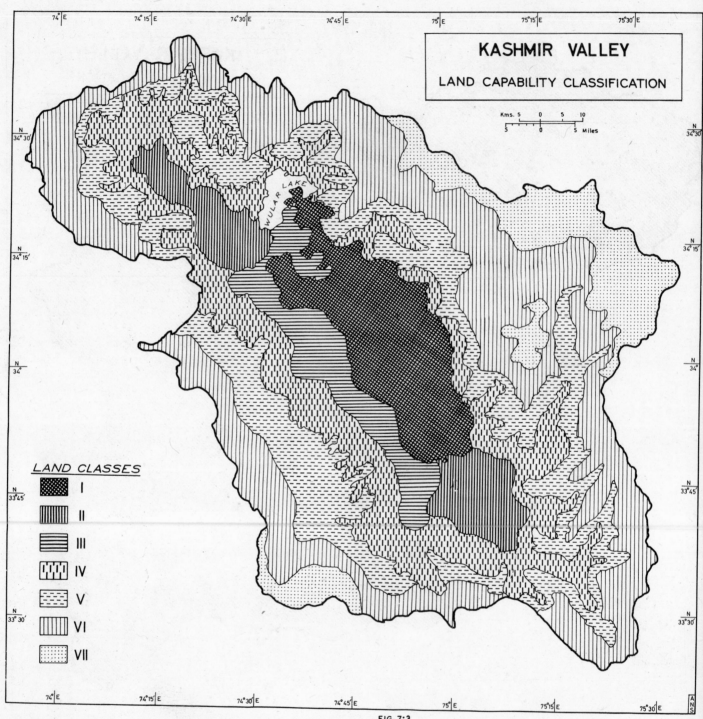

KASHMIR VALLEY

LAND CAPABILITY CLASSIFICATION

Kms. 5   0   5   10
5   0   5   Miles

WULAR LAKE

LAND CLASSES
I
II
III
IV
V
VI
VII

FIG. 7·3

utmost efficiency on such tracts. While natural factors of terrain, slope characteristics and density of natural vegetation act as causative factors, a good deal of erosion is also caused by wasteful agricultural practices, overgrazing and unimaginative destruction of the forest cover perpetrated by man. The intensity of erosion is dependent on a number of factors including the amount, periodicity and intensity of rainfall, volume of snowmelt, type of terrain, nature of vegetal cover and type of soil and land use. There is of course an intimate relationship between rainfall and the intensity of erosion. The impact of heavy rainfall is, however, never uniform as the degree of slope, morphological character of the soil and the type of vegetation create differences in the responsiveness of the surface layer to the erosive power of the running water.

The soils of the Kashmir Valley may be categorized into the following three groups in terms of erodability:

i) largely resistant to erosion;
ii) fairly susceptible to erosion; and
iii) highly susceptible to erosion.

The soil zone which is largely resistant to erosion is characterized by a calcareous content in the soil which acts as a resistance agent. The soil has a fine texture with a high clay content which cannot easily be disintegrated. The soils which are fairly susceptible to erosion are poor in calcareous content and are known to have a hard substratum which discourages the downward flow of water. This leads to oversaturation of the surface layer whose materials dissolve quickly in water for an eventual outward transportation. Studies conducted by the land conservation unit of the forest department of Jammu and Kashmir in the catchment basins of the Pir Panjal affluents of the Jhelum have indicated that the brown forest soils, which are largely non-calcareous, are most susceptible to erosion. Under thick forest growth the soil particles are tightly held by roots and the soil does not easily yield to erosive force. The open patches within the forest or areas with scanty vegetation are, however, exposed to intensive erosion.

Besides soil properties, land use and prevalent farming practices also determine the magnitude of erosion. Maize cultivation, under dry farming conditions, may promote more rapid erosion than, say, paddy cultivation under intensive irrigation. It has been observed that the magnitude of erosion is high in the upper reaches of the valleys, particularly those with scanty vegetal cover. Studies conducted in the Dudhganga and other catchment basins of the Pir Panjal range bring out vividly the relationship between altitude and intensity of erosion (Table XLVIII).[17]

No comprehensive estimates of the extent of land affected by erosion in Kashmir Valley are, however, available as systematic work is yet to start in this respect.

A notable exception is the Pohru catchment basin on which a detailed report has been produced by the IPII. The study area covers 1,846 square kilometres in Baramulla district and extends over almost all terrain types. It has been noted that all south-facing slopes have been intensively exploited and are exposed to severe erosion. A comprehensive plan for arresting soil erosion and for the reclamation of affected areas has been chalked out with reference to the following six regions: southern Himalayan slopes, northern and southern aspects of the Himalayan foothills, Karewa

TABLE XLVIII
Intensity of erosion

Altitude (m)	Topographical zone	Percentage of topsoil depleted	Extent of erosion
1500-2000	Floodplain	—	Practically negligible erosion
	Paddy belt	25	Slight
	Dry farmland	25-75	Moderate
2000-2500	Forested slopes	75-100	Moderately heavy
2500-3500	Alpine pastures and *margs*	25-75 (subsoil)	Severe
Above 3500	Rocky slopes and glacial heights	Parent material exposed	Very severe

Source: Soil Conservation Scheme, Dudhganga Catchment Basin, 1964.

uplands, Karewa slopes, old alluvium of the floodplain and, recent alluvium.[18]

In one of the useful studies conducted by Singh[19] an attempt was made to correlate the degree of erosion with altitudinal zones and prevailing land use. An estimate of the magnitude of erosion is possible within the frame of the following six regions: the Valley bottom, adjoining paddy-growing zone with a gentle slope, Karewa slopes and uplands, the forest zone, the alpine pasture land, and the rocky precipices and glacial zone.

Naturally, the first and the last region have no erosion problem as such. The Valley bottom is almost flat and its major problems arise from excessive silting and deposition of detrital material as a consequence of heavy flooding. The high altitude rocky exposures and the glacial zone, on the other hand, have no soil cover to be eroded either. Likewise, the erodability is of a lower order in the paddy-growing fringe of the Jhelum floodplain where pressure on land is heavy and all slopes have been skilfully terraced. It is in the dry farming lands of the Karewas that erosion is a real hazard. The processes of gullying, ravine formation and sheet erosion, so intensive in the Karewas, offer enough evidence of the rampant affliction. The damage done to the topsoil is illustrated by the fact that in certain areas as much as 75 per cent of the soil cover has been eroded. The bare surface, loose structure of the soil and absence of irrigation agriculture are some of the causal factors in this extensive devastation. Singh's estimates of the depletion of topsoil in the forest and pasture zone are also equally high as precipitous slopes, mismanagement of slopes and overgrazing are causing severe erosion.

It is therefore evident that land conservation in the Kashmir Valley is a colossal task. The problem cannot, however, be tackled on a piecemeal basis, as it is intrinsically linked with the general problem of management of resources, including water, forests and pastures. Evidently, fixing of priority areas would be a necessary first step, before any comprehensive conservation programme is actually put into action. It seems that in a rational strategy to control and minimize the processes of erosion such measures as afforestation and regulated grazing in critical areas will hold a key position. The Irrigation Commission observed that the forest department of the state was already seized with the problem and a comprehensive programme for afforestation in the areas severely threatened by erosion had been drawn up.[20] Closely linked with it are the questions of introducing and popularizing soil conservation methods such as terracing and contour-bunding in areas where even steep slopes are cultivated. The need to educate and persuade the farmers in these methods and to provide a state mechanism which supports the farmers in planning and implementing such action programmes is immediate and overriding.

LAND CAPABILITY CLASSIFICATION

The land in Kashmir is proving inadequate for the burgeoning population that is dependent on it. It is now being realized that all wasteful uses of land should be discouraged and rational land policy should be chalked out to face the challenge. More and more emphasis is now being laid on using land according to its best capability. This is especially significant in view of the growing competition between different uses of land, such as residential, recreational, industrial and agricultural. An overemphasis on one use might have a chain reaction on the other. Besides the different competitive uses, the land in the Valley is continually menaced by severe erosion and waterlogging, both seriously inhibiting its productive uses. A hopeful feature is that a large chunk of this land is, reclaimable provided a rational strategy is chalked out in this respect.

For all this, and for ensuring rational use of land in the future, a regular survey to establish the capability of different types of land for optimal uses is badly needed. An empirical exercise is, however, being attempted here to identify the generalized capability classes based on site, properties of soil, proportion of land under different slope categories, exposure to erosion hazards and dominant land use. Various methods have been developed to categorize lands into capability classes by different authorities.[21] These include some of the most sophisticated techniques, such as the one developed by the US National Resources Planning Board which integrates the whole gamut of physical, economic and institutional factors into a single scheme,[22] as well as most rudimentary ones. The present study is based on a method developed by Bennet which is based on site (altitude, degree of slope and drainage) climate, soil type and major land use. It is suited to such areas as the Kashmir Valley where nonavailability of classified information on specific aspects of land inhibits the application of more rigorous methods.

Factors in Land Capability. According to Bennet,[23] the land capability classification is based on the following criteria:

i) Soil type;
ii) degree of slope;
iii) erodability of surface soil or degree of erosion;
iv) drainage; and
v) predominant land use pattern.

The soils of the Kashmir Valley, already described in a foregoing section, reveal great variation in texture, permeability and fertility status. These typological differences have been used as a variable in the identification of land capability classes. Areas characterized by steep slopes are liable to erosion the intensity of which will depend on the nature of terrain and vegetal cover.

Land Capability Classes. The land of the Kashmir Valley has been classified according to its capability, using Bennet's method based on site peculiarities and physical factors. Primarily, two major categories have been distinguished (Fig.7.2), lands suited to cultivation, and lands not suited to cultivation.

The first category can further be grouped into four capability classes. The lands unsuitable for cultivation, on the other hand, lend themselves to a classification into three groups. The general characteristics of these seven land capability classes are described below (Fig. 7.3).

A. *Lands Suited to Cultivation. Class I:* The soil of class I lands is deep, highly fertile and mostly consists of best quality loams and clayey loams. The texture, however, gets heavier with increasing depth. The soil has a high retention capacity and is rich in humus. Class I lands are found in areas which are either flat or characterized by gentle slope. These lands are by and large free from the hazards of erosion or waterlogging and the physical environment favours their maximal utilization.

The area occupied by Class I lands, although it extends over the entire length of the Valley on either side of the Jhelum, has its main expanse in the central part consisting of parts of Srinagar, Pulwama, Badgam and Sonawari Ganderbal tahsils.

The fertility status of these lands can be further raised if farmers are induced to take to new methods of farming and land management and their capacity to use new inputs enhances.

Class II: The Class II lands are characterized by coarse-textured soil. The subsoil is heavy and gets heavier with increasing depth. The surface soil has low to moderate permeability; low at the subsoil levels and very low at the substratum. These lands are not liable to waterlogging or erosion, although lands in sloping areas suffer from moderate erosion. Substantial areas

in Kulgam, Sopore and Handwara tahsils are dominated by class II lands. They occur in two compact blocks—the southern one lies in the Kulgam tahsil while the northern extends over parts of Sopore and Handwara tahsils. Terrace cultivation is a common phenomenon on the periphery of the northern block.

Class III: The class III lands form a narrow belt along the Karewa uplands. The land is dominated by soils with a coarse texture and there is a marked increase in the degree of slope. The permeability decreases with depth. This class of land is bordered by extensive marshy tracts in the northern part of the Valley. Both erosion and waterlogging impose serious limitations on its use. The utility of these soils can be improved if erosion is controlled and suitable drainage methods are introduced to combat the problem of waterlogging.

The main concentration of class III land is found in Sonawari, Baramulla, Badgam, Pulwama and parts of Kulgam tahsils.

Class IV: The class IV lands are found along the Karewa slopes with their tongues extending higher up in the side valleys of the Jhelum. The slope increases rapidly with the result that cultivation is possible only on terraces using rigorous measures of soil conservation and drainage. The soil is shallow with variable texture and permeability. The depth of the soil decreases as stoniness increases with increasing altitude.

These four classes of land under cultivation differ vastly in their cropping pattern. Rice is the dominant crop on class I lands and is alternated by maize on higher areas. Among other crops grown are barley and wheat mainly on lands irrigated by wells. Rice continues to be important on class II lands as well with maize as close associate on drier tracts. Wheat and barley sharply decline in importance. Maize emerges as a principal crop on class III land with barley and wheat flourishing on lands provided with ensured water supply. A major proportion of the class IV land is also devoted to maize, although rice is also grown extensively on well-watered terraces.

B. *Lands not Suited to Cultivation. Class V:* Lands with predominant uses such as grazing and forestry have been categorized as class V. They are characterized by steep slopes and contain shallow, stone-studded soils. The low-lying slopes on rainy aspects are thickly forested. Above the treeline lie grazing lands which are used as summer pastures by transhumant groups. The soil of these *margs* is fairly fertile with a high moisture-holding capacity.

Class VI: This class consists of lands with steeper slopes and poorer soil which has no capability even to support the growth of vegetation. They consist of rocky wastes mainly in the higher precipices of the Pir Panjal and the Great Himalayan ranges.

Class VII: The higher slopes of the mountain ranges which remain covered with perennial snow have been grouped into this class. These lands have been subjected to rigorous glaciation in the past and are occupied by glaciers even today.

NOTES AND REFERENCES

[1]Notable among these are S.P. Raychaudhuri, *et al, Final Report of All India Soil Survey Scheme*, ICAR Bull., 73, 1957, and *Soils of India*, ICAR, 1963, pp. 105-110. Generalized information on the soils of Kashmir Valley and the surrounding mountains is inserted in a number of soil maps of India such as Z.J. Schokalskya, "The Natural Conditions of Soil Formation in India," in B. Polynov (ed.), *Contributions to the Knowledge of the Soils of Asia*, No. 2, Leningrad, 1932, pp. 53-155; D.N. Wadia, M.S. Krishnan and P.M. Mukherjee, Mem. GSI, 1935, plate XXV; S.P. Raychaudhuri, *NIS Bulletin*, No. 3, 1954; and the soil map of the National Atlas of India.

[2]Stray information on soils is available in Bate's *Gazetteer* as well as in Drew and Lawrence. The work done by Lawrence during his settlement operation in Jammu and Kashmir is exceptionally useful and is available in the fifteen assessment reports. These reports cover, among other things, "rates of assessment, the mode of classifying and valuing soils, and many facts bearing on the past revenue administration of Kashmir." (*The Valley of Kashmir, op. cit.*, p. 1.)

[3]R.C. Hoon, "A Study of the Soils in the Hill Areas of Kashmir: An Investigation of Soil Profile under Deodar, Blue Pine, Silver Fir and Chir," *Indian Forest Record*, Silviculture, V, 3, 1955.

[4]M.L. Kaul, "Study of Soil at Different Altitudes in Kashmir State," unpublished ASSOC thesis, SSAC, Indian Agricultural Research Institute, New Delhi, 1956, p. 1.

[5]Consultancy Report on Soil Conservation Planning for Pohru Catchment, Jammu and Kashmir (mimeographed) Soil Survey Division, Indian Photo Interpretation Institute, Dehra Dun, March 1974, p. 10.

The classification of soils is based on an international scheme worked out in the USA for the interpretation of photographs taken by satellite Gemini VII.

[6]Kaul, *op.cit.*, p. 65.

[7]For gurti and other local nomenclature see *infra*, p. 118.

[8]Lawrence, *op. cit* , pp. 320-321.

[9]Lydekker, *op. cit.*; Lawrence, *op. cit.*, pp. 45-46.

[10]N.R. Dutta-Biswas, S.P. Raychaudhuri and C. Dakshinamurti, "Soil Condition for the Growth of Saffron at Pampore, Kashmir," *Ind. Jour. Agric. Sc.*, XXVII, 1957, pp. 413-419.

[11]Indian Photo Interpretation Institute, Report, *op.cit.*, p. 12.

[12]Lawrence, *op.cit.*, pp. 319-321; A.N. Raina, *Geography of Jammu and Kashmir*, NBT, New Delhi, 1971, pp. 45-51.

[13]Lawrence, *op.cit.*

[14]H.L. Uppal, *Flood Control, Drainage and Reclamation in Kashmir Valley*, Central Water and Power Commission, New Delhi, 1956, pp. 66-70.

[15]Lawrence, *op.cit.*, p. 321; "in recent years chemical fertilizers have done great harm to this kind of soil due to overdose... that makes plants run to leaf." (Raina, *op.cit.*, p. 47).

[16]Surhzamin is an especially cured and highly manured soil for vegetable culture. It is distinguished by its darkish ash colour and a thick layer of manure. Lemb is the tract of land served by a natural spring. Rad is the Kashmiri term for the soils of the floating gardens. Soils reclaimed from the forest and lying on its periphery lose their original fertility in about ten years and are then known as tand. Lands damaged by percolation from neighbouring irrigated tracts are termed as zabalzamin. Kharzamin is the term for the tract of saline soil unfit for cultivation. Stone or pebble-studded soils which absorb radiation rapidly are called tats while those found along the mountain rivers with a high content of sand are known as shath. Some clays are stiff and have a strong tendency to cake. They are described as ront soils.

[17]"Soil Conservation Scheme, Dudhganga Catchment," Government of Jammu and Kashmir, Srinagar, 1964.

[18]Indian Photo Interpretation Institute, Report, *op.cit.*

[19]H. Singh, "Land Erosion in the Kashmir Valley," *Indian Forester*, Vol. LXXXIV, 10, 1958, pp. 617-622.

[20]Report of the Irrigation Commission, New Delhi, 1972, Vol. II, p. 169.

[21]See Bibliographical Note below.

[22]United States National Resources Planning Board, *Report on Land Classification in the United States*, Washington, 1941.

[23]H.H. Bennet, *Elements of Soil Conservation*, New York, 1955, p. 144.

BIBLIOGRAPHICAL NOTE

While a scientific study of the soils of the Kashmir Valley is of great significance in understanding a region's agricultural resource base and for developing a suitable strategy for its optimal use, very little work of a serious nature has so far been attempted in this direction. As noted earlier, the basic data on the soils of Kashmir is scanty; and whatever is available lies scattered in the British *Settlement Reports*, gazetteers and the technical report of the soil survey units of the Kashmir Government. Many of them are inaccessible to the ordinary researcher. These and other works have been acknowledged in the notes.

More relevant studies on land capability analysis and other works of a general nature are classified below:

GENERAL

The following studies or surveys of the work done on the soils of India have relevance to Kashmir also.

S.P. Ray Chaudhuri, *et al*, *Soils of India*, Indian Council of Agricultural Research, 1963, pp 105-110.

Indian Council of Agricultural Research, "Final Report of All India Soil Survey Scheme," *ICAR Bulletin*, No. 73, 1957.

LAND CAPABILITY

U.S. National Resources Planning Board, *Report on Land Classification in the United States*, Washington, 1941.

G.V. Jacks, "Land Classification for Land Use Planning," *Imperial Bureau of Soil Science, Technical Communication*, 1946.

T.E. Storie, "An Index for Rating the Agricultural Value of Soils," *California Experiment Station Bulletin*, No. 556.

G.D. Hudson, "The Unit Area Method of Land Classification," *Annals of the Association of American Geographers*, Vol. XXVI, 1936.

C.E. Kellog, "The Theory of Land Classification," *Missouri Agricultural Bulletin*, No. 421, 1940, pp. 164-173.

H.H. Bennett, *Elements of Soil Conservation*, New York, 1955.

M. Shafi, "Land Use Planning, Land Classification and Land Capability—Methods and Techniques," *The Geographer* Vol. XVI, 1969.

K.B. Cumberland, "The Survey and Classification of Land in New Zealand: A Basis for Planning," *Transactions of Royal Society of New Zealand*, Vol. LXXIV, 1944, pp. 185-195.

K.V. Zvorykin, "Scientific Principles for an Agro-Production Classification of Lands," *Soviet Geography*, Vol. IV, 1963, pp. 3-10.

C.P. Barnes, "Land Resource Inventory in Michigan," *Economic Geography*, Vol. V, 1929, pp. 22-35.

North-Western University, Department of Geography, "The Rural Land Classification Programme of Puerto Rico," *North-Western University Studies in Geography*, No. 1, Evanston, 1952.

Chapter Eight

A Regional Overview

The principal features of Kashmir's regional identity emanate from its location in the northwestern Himalayan complex. The Valley owes its origin to the orogenic processes that carved out the Himalayan ranges and thus described the major lineaments of its physical personality. It is therefore in the context of the natural configuration of the enveloping crest that the geographical complexion and the space relations of the Valley can be best appreciated. The surrounding mountain ramparts highlight its generic relations with the macro region as they lay down the premises of this affinity evident in its geological formation, surface features, river systems, erosional history, pedological attributes, climatic and biogeographic peculiarities and, no less significantly, in the ethno-cultural characteristics of its people. They also determine the range of its exposure to the exogenetic processes and impose constraints on its spatial interactions with the surrounding lands, thus largely rendering it to a partially closed self-sufficient ecosystem surviving on its own viability.

Although the Valley is a structural trough within the anticlinal Himalayan ranges that girdle it, the major parametres of its geographical entity draw their essence from the Jhelum that occupies the trough. The fact that the Jhelum holds a definite position within the drainage hierarchy of the northwestern Himalayan complex defines the specific place of the Valley within the Indus system. It is therefore necessary for definitional purposes to delineate the Kashmir Valley within the frame of the macro basin of the Indus, and the meso basin of the Jhelum, on the one hand, and the Jhelum system within the Kashmir trough and without it on the other.

The stratigraphic and structural plan of Kashmir Valley is unique in more than one respect. Being a sizable depression with an almost flat basin and nestled in the heavily-eroded fold mountain ranges, the Valley has been a repository of the worn down materials from the encompassing crest, besides being a major sharer in their immense moisture supply. The surface features of the Valley bear testimony to the operation of the mutually complementary process of deposition and subareal erosion. The initial land surface has further been metamorphosed by the puzzling complexities of the Pleistocene phase which was punctuated by alternations of glacial and fluvial activity.

The Valley of Kashmir as delineated for the purpose of this study lies divided into the two principal geomorphic units—the surrounding mountain ramparts and the Valley basin. The fundamental differences in their geomorphological character and locational setting not only determine their respective roles but also explain the variety of their ecosystems and the diversities of their resource endowment. While these differences are spectacular in themselves, the flanking mountain ranges have nothing common to them other than the broad-based homogeneity in their topographic and erosional features. Their contrasts are too many and some of these are best expressed in the disparate character of their drainage and the upland valleys carved by these river systems. They are mirrored in the facets of their human geography no less significantly.

The characteristically dendritic drainage of the Great Himalayan and the north Kashmir ranges presents sharp contrasts to the linear drainage of the Pir Panjal range. The northern face of the Pir Panjal range is less extensive in width and, therefore, inhibits the development of the lateral valleys, such as those of the Pohru and the Sind. As a consequence the Pir Panjal streams fall down from the mountain precipices in parallel, often irregular lines and divide themselves into an intricate network of braided channels. On the other hand, the formation of the lateral valleys in the Great Himalayan range is a remarkable phenomenon. It is in these neatly cascaded valleys that one observes the incising alluvial tongues supporting terraced agriculture deep into the interior of the mountains.

The Valley basin in its own turn is constituted by two diverse landforms—an alluvial plain characterized by aggradational features and the bordering lacustrine uplands dominated by erosional topography. In fact, these Karewas have been subjected to intensive erosion and prolonged fluvial activity has reduced them to a highly dissected mass with a confusing network of ravines and intertwined gullies. It is necessary to distinguish between the two main forms of Karewa deposits. There are the sloping Karewas whose beds have been dissected into a multitude of steepsided ravines with a typical "immature" look bordering the Valley floor all along the edge of the hills from Shopiyan to Sopore. They are interspersed with flat-topped Karewa uplands, mostly dreary and parched in appearance and standing as features of imposing relief seventy to a hundred metres above the level of the alluvial plain.

The floor of the Kashmir Valley, along with its bordering Karewa prominences, has a distinct regional entity having a characteristic socio-cultural milieu evolved through millennia of continuous settlement and largely secluded history. Historically, the Valley lies divided into two principal regions—one known as the Maraj (Sanskrit Madavarajya) comprising the land on both sides of the Jhelum above Srinagar and the other called Kamraj (Sanskrit Kramarajya) encompassing the land below Srinagar. Striking evidence is furnished on the areal extent and political complexion of these historical divisions in important chronicles, particularly Kalhana's *Rajatarangini*[1] and Abul Fazal's *Ain-i-Akbari*.[2] Traditionally, the dividing line between the two regions is supposed to be passing through Srinagar with the city itself belonging to the Maraj. The disparate nature of the Valley basin below and above Srinagar and of the course of the Jhelum in the two reaches offer an adequate geomorphologic basis for such a regionalization. The narrow bottleneck through which the river passes by Srinagar, its highly sluggish flow, rapid silting of the bed and flooding of the bordering flats, which have been reduced to extensive Nambals as a result of this spillover, are some of the factors which have contributed to a natural division between the two alluvial basins. Each of them has served as a focus of human settlement since time immemorial.

An extension of the Valley's socio-cultural milieu is seen in the neatly cascaded side valleys of the Jhelum whose alluvial terraces introduce interesting altitudinal zonation in physical and human features. Notable among them are the valleys of the Sind, Liddar and the Pohru and its affluent valley of the Lolab in the Great Himalayan and the north Kashmir ranges and that of the Rembiara in the Pir Panjal range.

The above characterization may provide us with useful guidelines in the identification of the regional structure of Kashmir Valley as emerging from the preceding study. Although general descriptions of the landform types of the Kashmir Valley are not lacking, mainly owing to the work done by such pioneers as Medllicot, Blanford, Oldham, Burrard and Hayden, Wadia, de Terra and Paterson,[3] no comprehensive attempt has yet been made to regionalize the Valley on the basis of physical parameters. The present attempt takes into account the totality of natural environment as mainfesting itself in the surface features, such as the type of landforms, their morphogenetic characteristics, pedological and climatological attributes and biotic associations. The macro level units display distinct differences in these variables both at the meso and the micro levels, thus lending themselves to a further subdivision into lower order units. At the meso level they exhibit general homogeneity in their genesis and physical appearance which, along with climate and vegetal cover, foster an essentially fundamental unity.

It is natural that such a classificatory scheme should involve a thorough consideration of the gamut of physical factors which have gone into the make-up of these regions so inextricably. The criteria used in this exercise are mainly qualitative, although altitude, landform and terrain types and altitudinal zonation of vegetation furnish fairly substantial quantitative bases for regionalization. It is needless to labour the point that the regions thus carved out are useful in more than one way. In fact, they offer a basic frame of reference for any exercise aimed at locating in space targets of development planning, management and optimization of resource use and chalking out a suitable strategy for combating the hazards of soil erosion and the depletion of forest and pastural resources.

The following regions of the first order can be identified:

I. The surrounding mountain ramparts including the high slopes and the foothills of the Pir Panjal, Great Himalayan and the north Kashmir ranges; and

II. the valley basin along with the bordering lacustrine Karewa uplands and slopes.

The surrounding mountain ramparts can further be subdivided into the following regions of the second order:

I. 1 The Pir Panjal flank enclosing the Valley from Baramulla to the extreme southeast where it coalesces with the axial ridge of the Great Himalayan range; and

I. 2 the Himalayan flank (including the Kashmir range) which encloses the Valley in the east, northeast, north and northwest.

The Pir Panjal flank lends itself to a further subdivision into the following third-order regions:

K. 1 (i) The zone of the glaciers and alpine forests and pastures above 3,200 metres;

(ii) the zone of the temperate forest and pastures between 2,100 and 3,200 metres;

(iii) the side valleys, particularly those of the Rembiara and the Vishav, with terraced agriculture often extending up to 2,450 metres.

The following are the third-order regions of the Himalayan flank:

I. 2 (i) The zone of the glaciers and alpine forests and pastures;

(ii) the zone of temperate forests and pastures;

(iii) the side valleys of the (a) Sandran, Anlan, Razparyin and the Nanbug and Kutihar in the southeast; (b) Liddar; (c) Arapal; (d) Sind and the Wangat; (e) Erin and Bodkol (Madhumati); (f) Pohru and the affluent valleys of the Lolab, Kahmil, Talar and the Mawar.

The Valley basin lies divided into the following two regions:

II. 1 The alluvial flats characterized by aggradational features; and

II. 2 the bordering Karewa uplands and slopes dominated by erosional topography.

Locally, little distinction is made between these two principal geomorphic regions of the Valley basin as the entire cultivated zone of the Valley is historically divided into the Maraj and the Kamraj with cultivated Karewas being a constituent part of both of them. Geographical realism would, however, demand a differentiation between them on the basis of their obvious morphogenetic and land use differences.

The alluvial flats of the Jhelum floodplain consisting of extensive waterlogged areas, marshes and lakes and the intensively cultivated tracts can thus be classified into the following third-order regions:

II. 1 (i) The upper Jhelum plain up to Srinagar (Maraj); and

(ii) the lower Jhelum plain below it (Kamraj).

Equally important is the distinction between the two main forms of the Karewa deposits:

II. 2 (i) The sloping Karewas from Shopiyan to Sopore all along the foot of the Pir Panjal and the north Kashmir ranges; and

(ii) the Karewa uplands markedly flat-topped, mostly dreary in appearance and parched. Notable in this category are the Karewa uplands of Pampur, Payech and Anantnag.

The above scheme of classification can be tabulated as below:

I. The surrounding mountain ramparts.

1. The Pir Panjal flank.

(i) The zone of the glaciers, alpine forests and pastures;

(ii) the zone of temperate forests and pastures

(iii) the side valleys of (a) The Rembiara and (b) the Vishav

2. The Himalayan flank.

(i) The zone of the glaciers, alpine forests and pastures;

(ii) the zone of temperate forests and pastures;

(iii) the side valleys of (a) the Sandran, Anlan, Razparyin, Nanbug and Kutihar; (b) Liddar; (c) Arapal; (d) Sind and the Wangat; (e) Erin and Bodkol (Madhumati); (f) Pohru and the affluent valleys of the Lolab, Kahmil, Talar and the Mawar.

II. The Valley basin.

1. The alluvial plain.

(i) The upper Jhelum plain—the Maraj;

(ii) the lower Jhelum plain—the Kamraj.

2. The lacustrine Karewa flats and slopes.

(i) The Karewa slopes;

(ii) the Karewa uplands.

NOTES AND REFERENCES

[1] M.A. Stein, *Kalhana's Rajatarangini*, II, p. 436.

[2] The list of the Mahals (parganahs) contained in the *Ain-i-Akbari* has been tabulated according to the two main political divisions: the Maraj and the Kamraj. It is interesting to note that the city of Srinagar has been treated with Maraj. Whether these two divisions enjoyed separate administrative status throughout history is highly doubtful. Stein has noted that "Abul Fazl's account as well as the usage traceable from his time to the present day show that the terms in their popular geographical significance could maintain themselves quite independently of administrative division" (p. 436).

[3] For the physiographic divisions recognized by de Terra and Paterson, see *supra*, Chapter III, fn. 1.

1

2

3

4

5

6

7

8

9

10

11

12

13

14

15

16

17

18

19

20

21

22

23

24

APPENDICES

APPENDIX I

Srinagar—air temperature degrees centigrade
(1931-60 averages)

Month	Mean of		Mean daily	Diurnal range
	Daily max.	Daily min.		
January	4.4	—2.3	3.3	6.3
February	7.9	—0.8	4.3	8.7
March	13.4	3 5	8.8	10.0
April	19.3	7.4	13.3	11.9
May	24.6	11.2	17.9	13 4
June	29.0	14.4	21.7	14.6
July	30.8	18.4	24.6	12.4
August	29.9	17.9	23.9	12 0
September	28.3	12.7	20.5	15.6
October	22.6	5.7	14.1	16.9
November	15.5	—0.1	7.8	15.6
December	8.8	—1.8	5.3	10.6

Source: India Meteorological Department, *Climatological Tables for Observatories in India,* 1931-60.

APPENDIX II

Average monthly number of days with snowfall

Month	Srinagar (1957-66)	Srinagar aerodrome (1959-66)
November	0.60	1.00
December	2.30	2.20
January	7.00	6.00
February	6.00	5.00
March	1.80	1.40

Source: India Meteorological Department, *Monthly Weather Reports,* 1957-66.

APPENDIX III

Frequency of days of snowfall at Srinagar
(1939-53)

Date	October	November	December	January	February	March
1	...	...	...	5	6	2
2	...	...	...	5	6	1
3	...	...	1	4	6	1
4	...	...	1	4	5	2
5	...	...	...	4	3	...
6	...	...	2	5	2	1
7	...	...	...	8	5	2
8	...	...	1	7	5	2
9	...	...	3	5	4	3
10	...	...	2	3	5	2
11	...	...	...	6	4	1
12	...	...	1	5	2	1
13	...	1	...	6	2	1
14	...	...	...	6	2	...
15	...	...	...	6	1	...
16	...	...	2	3	2	...
17	...	...	...	4	3	...
18	...	1	1	10	5	...
19	...	1	1	9	5	...
20	...	...	1	4	5	...
21	...	...	5	5	3	1
22	...	...	4	4	2	...
23	...	...	4	6	1	...
24	...	1	4	4	4	...
25	...	...	3	4	6	...
26	1	1	3	5	3	...
27	1	1	3	3	1	...
28	...	1	3	3	1	...
29	...	1	3	4	...	...
30	...	1	6	4	...	...
31	...	...	5	2	...	...
Total	2	9	59	153	99	20

Source: S.N. Bhan, "Snowfall At Srinagar," *Indian Journal of Meteorology and Geophysics*, Vol. VII, 1956, pp. 295-300.

APPENDIX IV

Rainfall of selected stations by seasons and seasonal rainfall as percentage of the annual rainfalll
(1901-50)

Station	Winter	%	Spring	%	Summer	%	Autumn	%	Annual
Srinagar	191.00	29.0	240.25	36.0	160.25	24.0	71.50	11.0	663.00
Pulwama	138.50	32.0	197.75	33.0	153.00	26.0	52.25	9.0	591.95
Handwara	345.75	34.5	410.25	41.0	156.75	16.0	92.75	9.0	1005.50
Anantnag	209.50	33.0	188.50	30.0	150.30	24.0	74.50	13.0	622.80
Kulgam	308.35	34.3	286.50	32.0	206.00	23 0	97.25	11.0	898.10
Doru	471.50	39.0	379.50	32.0	232.50	20.0	111.50	9.0	1195.20
Ganderbal	154.00	24.7	223.75	36.0	184.25	29.5	61.00	9.8	623.00
Baramulla	319.60	34.7	373.00	40.0	149.00	16.0	80.25	9.2	921.85
Langet	272.50	31.2	388.75	44.5	136.00	15.6	76.00	8.7	873.25
Sopore	276.17	36.5	298.00	39.4	116.72	15.4	65.50	8.7	756 39
Gulmarg	N.A.	...	N.A.	...	289.75	...	67.00	...	N A.
Badgam	171.00	29.5	214.50	37.0	124.00	21.5	69.75	12.0	579.25

Based on actual monthly data of rainfall in cents (hundredth part of an inch) published in *Monthly and Annual Rainfall and Number of Rainy Days, 1901-50*, pt II, India Meteorological Department, New Delhi, 1965.

APPENDIX V

Srinagar—hours of bright sunshine
(1965)

Month	No. of days with duration				Total hours of sunshine	Percentage of possible hours of sunshine
	0.1 to 3 hours	3.1 to 6 hours	6.1 to 9 hours	above 9 hours		
January	7	5	...	...	31.8	10
February	7	4	6	...	75.4	33
March	9	5	5	9	156.7	42
April	7	5	6	6	146 8	38
May	1	5	4	17	240.9	56
June	2	3	4	21	283.0	66
July	3	4	7	16	253.3	58
August	3	7	7	14	236.6	57
September	0	3	7	20	273.6	74
October	1	3	8	17	238.7	72
November	5	8	11	3	159 2	51
December	5	0	20	0	158.3	51
Total	50	52	85	123	2254.3	50

Based on India Meteorological Department, *Monthly Weather Reports*, 1965.

APPENDIX VI

Srinagar—average monthly humidity (1932-51)

Month	1932	1933	1934	1935	1936	1937	1938	1939	1940	1941	1942	1943	1944	1945	1946	1947	1948	1949	1950	1951	Average (1932-51)
January	95	94	93	92	94	91	94	89	90	91	92	88	87	88	86	88	88	89	87	89	90
February	90	92	95	91	90	92	93	88	90	90	92	86	88	89	86	86	88	89	87	88	89
March	89	90	88	85	87	83	87	83	83	88	81	84	85	87	87	87	86	89	83	83	85
April	75	83	84	83	80	76	78	76	77	78	78	82	83	84	79	74	84	73	78	80	79
May	77	68	77	73	69	69	63	65	72	72	74	83	72	79	76	75	71	73	77	77	73
June	70	70	62	68	69	63	67	61	70	51	67	73	71	72	76	74	78	72	69	76	68
July	79	78	71	76	76	72	74	71	66	73	77	80	75	78	77	79	81	75	77	74	75
August	85	89	77	82	76	71	74	73	81	72	85	83	84	81	78	83	85	77	83	83	80
September	76	89	71	79	75	72	66	63	74	76	80	82	87	83	76	82	84	73	84	76	77
October	79	91	67	84	72	77	72	78	77	80	82	85	86	88	85	85	87	80	87	84	81
November	80	95	74	91	90	89	74	80	83	81	85	85	86	87	82	82	86	85	88	87	85
December	94	94	87	93	91	91	82	87	85	89	87	85	87	86	86	86	89	84	88	83	87
Annual Average	82	86	78	83	80	78	77	76	79	78	81	83	82	83	81	81	83	79	82	81	...

Source: India Meteorological Department, *Climatological Tables for Observatories in India*, 1931-60.

APPENDIX VII

The departmental files of the Central Water and Power Commission contain river discharge data for the following basins of the Kashmir Valley

River	Gauges	Period of data
JHELUM	Vetawathani (Nowpora)	1930-57
	Khanabal	1930-57
	Sangam	1930-57
	Awantipur	1930-57
	Padshahibagh	1930-57
	Chattabal	1952-57
	Gagarzoo	1931-57
	Munigund	1930-57
	Asham	1948-57
	Bunyari	1931-57
	Seer	1930-57
	Baramulla	1930-57
VISHAV	Arwani	1954-56
	Now	1954-55
REMBIARA	Hirpora	1955-62
	Nayiyna	1952-54
	Shopiyan	1952-55
	Nooh	1953-53
	Songul	1953-53
BRING	Wayil	1955-55
	Danter	1952-55
	Panchat than	1955-55
ARAPAT	Mir Danter	1952-55
	Thajwara	1952-55
LIDDAR	Kirkadal	1952-57
	Naniyal	1952-55
	Anjawal	1952-55
	Odur	1957-57
	Gur	1956-57
	Doru	1955-56
ARAPAL	Kadal Bal	1950-56
ROMUSHI	Bhu (Inder)	1952-55
	Pohu (Tail)	1952-56
SIND	Prang	1952-55
DUDHGANGA	Brenwar	1955-56
	Bandipur	1955-55
	Tsodar	1956-56
	Rupara (Tail)	1955-55
SHALIGANGA	Barzulla	1952-55
	Gopalpora	1954-54
SUKHNAG	Sukhnag Tail	1955-56
	Gudhkut	1955-56
POHRU (Lolab)	Kupwara (Tail)	1955-56
(Talar)	Siul	1956-56
(Mawar)	Nowgam	1954-56
	Dukalbal	1955-56
VIJI	Achhabal	1953-53
	Bijbura	1952-54
	Chukur	1952-54

Source: Central Water and Power Commission, New Delhi.

APPENDIX VIII

Intensity of rainfall
(millimetres per rainy day, based on averages for 1901-50)

Station	January	February	March	April	May	June	July	August	September	October	November	December
Srinagar	11.00	11.71	12.47	10.76	17.08	5.08	9.53	13.81	11.48	13.44	10.71	10.80
Pulwama	12.81	18.85	17.27	13.12	12.27	15.70	14 95	14.80	14.71	14.42	14.15	14.23
Handwara	16.11	18.93	18.86	17.71	14 83	10.58	12.13	13.55	13.35	15.87	13.16	12.09
Anantnag	13.67	14.64	12.54	7.86	12.00	11.69	13.23	13.23	19.56	15.29	10.08	12.65
Kulgam	18.55	17.49	15.50	17.17	13.78	12.79	15.50	15.18	19.29	15.11	14.92	17.12
Doru	20.49	26.27	24.71	16.68	15.42	16.25	18.31	17 51	21.91	17.37	19.09	23.64
Ganderbal	12.34	14.00	12.57	15.14	14.07	10.69	18.83	20.54	17.61	12.36	11.18	13.64
Baramulla	14.70	16.54	17.03	15.58	13.63	11.44	12.12	12.38	12.50	13.38	12.37	13.43
Langet	13.13	10.90	18.98	17.10	13.22	11.25	10.89	11.91	11.53	14.61	11.87	11.83
Sopore	13.32	13.66	14.97	12.69	11.90	10.25	9.37	4.66	11.76	10.58	11.13	12.95
Gulmarg	...	...	...	...	...	10.40	10.83	11.56	13.40	...	...	...
Badgam	10.96	15.21	12.86	12.63	11.37	9.52	12.18	11.41	17.21	14.53	11.54	10.39

Source: Based on actual monthly data of rainfall in cents published in *Monthly and Annual Rainfall and Number of Rainy Days*, 1901-50, pt. 2, India Meteorological Department, New Delhi, 1965.

APPENDIX IX

Distribution of occasions of rain according to amounts in 24 hours (1901-50)
(Srinagar)

Month	Number of occasions with rainfall (mm) per day									Total
	0.00	0.25-2.4	2.5-12.5	12.50-25	25-50	50-75	75-100	100-125	Greater than 125.0	
January	970	266 (46)	248 (42)	42 (7)	20 (3)	2	1	...	1	580
February	872	209 (43)	235 (44)	43 (8)	28 (5)	5	...	...	...	540
March	940	238 (39)	257 (42)	78 (13)	33 (5)	4	...	...	...	610
April	899	203 (34)	229 (48)	76 (13)	28 (5)	3	...	...	...	601
May	1001	266 (48)	223 (41)	39 (7)	19 (4)	2	...	...	...	549
June	1101	225 (60)	138 (35)	28 (7)	7 (2)	1	...	...	...	399
July	1063	242 (50)	188 (38)	39 (8)	16 (4)	2	...	...	...	487
August	1017	259 (49)	193 (36)	65 (12)	13 (2)	3	...	...	...	533
September	1212	162 (48)	129 (40)	31 (10)	12 (5)	3	...	1	...	338
October	1327	102 (45)	93 (42)	21 (?)	5 (2)	2	...	...	...	223
November	1379	65 (54)	39 (32)	15 (12)	2 (2)	...	...	...	...	121
December	1213	68 (20)	129 (36)	128 (35)	10 (3)	2	...	...	...	337

Source: S.N. Bhan, *Indian Journal of Meteorology and Geophysics*, VII, 1956.

APPENDIX X

Incidence of drought
(cases when drought extended over three or more consecutive months)

Over 3 consecutive months	Over 4 consecutive months	Over 5 consecutive months	Over 6 consecutive months
MAY-JULY (1913, 1919, 1928, 1953) JUNE-AUGUST (1905, 1954) JULY-SEPTEMBER (1895, 1949, 1961) AUGUST-OCTOBER (1902, 1959) SEPTEMBER-NOVEMBER (1892, 1912, 1919, 1925, 1927, 1943, 1946, 1948, 1951, 1952, 1958, 1960) OCTOBER-DECEMBER (1901, 1906, 1910, 1950)	MAY-AUGUST (1922) JUNE-SEPTEMBER (1896, 1914) JULY-OCTOBER (1899) AUGUST-NOVEMBER (1894, 1932) SEPTEMBER-DECEMBER (1897, 1907, 1916)	JUNE-OCTOBER (1963) JULY-NOVEMBER (1910) AUGUST-DECEMBER (1913, 1931)	MAY-OCTOBER (1918, 1936, 1946) JUNE-NOVEMBER (1920, 1934, 1945)

Courtesy: Meher-Homji, *Geographical Review of India*, Vol. XXXIII, 1, 1971.

APPENDIX XI

Flood control measures recommended
by various bodies[1]

LALA TULSI DASS PROPOSALS (1928)

The recommendations of Lala Tulsi Dass along with approximate cost of each scheme are briefly given below:

1) Providing openings in and remodelling formation of river bunds from Khannabal to Padshahibagh (head of floodspill channel).

2) Increasing the discharging capacity of the existing floodspill channel.

3) City bunds, their extensive raising, improving the city channels, improving and renewing their locks.

4) Periodic dredging of the Pohru river and other bars below Sopore, for preventing deterioration in the efficiency of the outfall channel.

5) Diverting the Pohru river (if investigations approved) from Doabagh to opposite Khojabagh into the Jhelum river, for stopping the recurring expenditure on dredging and also for reducing the silt transporting power of the Pohru river by increasing its length.

6) A cu from Gagarzoo to Anchar lake for relieving congestion of flood caused by outfall of the floodspill channel and also reclamation of Anchar lake and Shalabug swamps (9,000 acres).

7) Subsidiary floodspill channel for ensuring the security of the city of Srinagar by reducing the flood height and discharge to be passed by the city river channel.

8) River diversion from Asham to Ningal.

HARRIS PROPOSALS (1930)[2]

New Channels. 1) A cut capable of carrying a discharge of 16,500 cusecs to be made through the Dudhganga ridge to connect the Valley above Srinagar with Batmulla Nambal.

2) A new outfall channel capable of carrying 12,000 cusecs to be made from the Batmulla Nambal to the Jhelum river.

3) A channel with a capacity of 20,000 cusecs to be made from Jhelum river at Gagarzoo to Anchar lake. The bunds round the lake to be raised if necessary.

4) *Bunds.* The bunds on the bank of the Jhelum from Srinagar to Khannabal to be taken over by the government and raised above the maximum flood level by three to four feet and provided with escapes at different places for discharging 44,000 cusecs into the Valley.

5) Two new embankments to be constructed on the southwest of the Batmulla Nambal respectively and an escape made in the latter embankments to discharge 8,000 cusecs into the Hokarsar lake.

6) Sopore Bar not to be removed. The Pohru river not to

be diverted and dredging in the outfall channel to be suspended.

7) The five old bridges in the city of Srinagar to be replaced by new ones of the Safa Kadal type.

8) The old channels from Shadipur and Asham to Ningal and Mujgund to Wular to be reopened and their discharging capacity to be improved by widening and deepening.

UPPAL PROPOSALS (1956)[3]

1) Construction of a supplementary channel from Dogripura to Rambag and enlargement of old floodspill channel from Rambag to Wular lake.

2) Complete diversion of Pohru Nallah or sediment diversion only into Wular lake (Suil to Watlab).

3) A number of other small works, namely, diversion of Ningal Nallah into Hygam Jheel; stabilization of hill torrents between Baramulla and Khadanyar; cut-off of river Jhelum at Pampore, Munshibagh and Seer; inlet into Dal lake, removal of

footbridge at Baramulla; removal of the obstruction caused Ningal plantation; selective dredging of the outfall channel.

G.H. KHAN'S PROPOSALS (1961)[4]

1) Provision of two large flood-absorption basins above Srinagar with regulators at inlets and outlets.

2) Division of Dudhganga Nallah into Narakur Nambal, and diversion of Ningal Nallah into Hygham Jheel.

3) Enlargement and widening of the outfall channel from Sopore to Khadanyar.

4) Afforestation and soil conservation measures in the Pohru nallah catchment.

5) Opening of Shadipur and Vasikhan Nallah.

6) Regulators at the head of floodspill channel at Shadipur and at Vasikhan.

7) Strengthening the river and tributary embankments for predetermined discharges.

[1]H.L. Uppal, *Flood Control Drainage and Reclamation in Kashmir Valley*, Central Water and Power Commission, New Delhi, 1956, pp. 108-111.

[2]*Ibid.*

[3]G.H. Khan, *Irrigation, Flood and Food Problems of the Jammu and Kashmir State*, Srinagar, 1961, pp. 155, 159.

[4]*Ibid.*

APPENDIX XII

Area under commercial and non-commercial forests

Forest division	Commercial					Non-commercial	
	Deodar	Kail	Fir	Chir	Mixed broad leaved	Wooded	Unwooded
Kamraj	181.64	177.36	173.22	—	10.64	134.42	233.10
Langet	134.50	100.34	198.11	—	1.10	96.84	120.12
Sind	10.10	207.20	330.75	—	54.65	—	1441.85
Jhelum valley	94.53	59.57	113.18	—	—	937.42	47.55
Pir Panjal	9.40	131.29	330.17	65.18	10.47	41.72	749.46
Kashmir	27.45	314.94	225.07	—	55.17	1155.92	51.80
Plantation	20.02	26.94	—	—	73.85	—	83.84
Total	457.62	1050.62	1497.44	65.18	205.87	2365.32	2738.74

Source: Digest, Forest Statistics, Jammu and Kashmir, 1969.

APPENDIX XIII

No. 1. Soil profiles for Agriudolls*

(Locality—about six kilometres from Nawagam, on Nawagam Radhe Chowk road, in the northeast steep slopes of coniferous forest.)

Depth	Description
0-3 cm	Undecomposed and partly decomposed leaf litter of Blue Pine, Deodar
3-16 cm	Very dark brown (10 YR 2/2 M) moist; silt loam, weak fine crumb, friable, few gravels of 1 to 2 cm., high inorganic matter, many fine and medium roots, strongly acidic; gradual and smooth boundary
16-29 cm	Very dark greyish brown (10 YR3/2) moist, silt loam, weak fine sub-angular blocky; friable, many fine and coarse roots; about 5% coarse fragments; strongly acidic, clear smooth boundary
29-47 cm	Yellowish brown (10 YR 5/4) moist, silty clay loam; weak fine to moderate sub-angular block; sticky, firm, very few fine and coarse roots; about 5% coarse fragments; strongly acidic, clear and smooth boundary
47-129 cm	Dark yellowish brown (10 YR 4/4) moist, silty clay loam, moderate fine to medium sub-angular blocky; firm and sticky, very few fine and coarse roots; about 10% coarse fragments, clear and smooth boundary
129-154 cm	Olive grey (5 YR 5/2) moist, silt loam, massive; slightly hard, firm and slightly sticky, very few fine and coarse roots; about 10% coarse fragments; clear and smooth boundary
154-180 cm	Olive (5 Y 5/3) moist, silt loam, massive hard and slightly sticky, very few fine and coarse roots; about 20% coarse fragments

No. 2 Soil Profile for Hapludalfs

(Locality—near village Magam, in the nearly level Karewa top)

Depth	Description
0-13 cm	Dark brown (10 YR 4/3) moist and pale brown (10 YR6/3) dry, silt, loam; moderate medium and fine sub-angular blocky; slightly friable moist; slightly sticky; slightly hard dry, many fine and very fine interstitial pores; abundant medium roots; clear and smooth boundary
13-22 cm	Dark brown (7.5 YR 4/2) moist, silt loam, weak fine sub-angular blocky; slightly sticky; friable moist; many five and medium roots; clear and smooth boundary
22-43 cm	Dark brown (7.5 YR 4/2) moist silty clay loam; weak fine sub-angular blocky; sticky; friable moist; patchy thin cutans in roots channels and pores and in some bed faces; gradual and smooth boundary
43-63 cm	Dark greyish brown (7.5 YR 3.5/2) moist; silty clay loam, massive, sticky, firm moist, many fine and very fine roots

*Consultancy Report on Soil Conservation Planning for Pohru catchment (mimeographed) Soil Survey Division, Indian Photo Interpretation Institute, Dehra Dun, 1974.

APPENDIX XIV

Profiles of Highland Soils*

SOIL PROFILE No. 1

Locality	Khilanmarg, about 5.5 km from Gulmarg
Collected on	20.6.1955
Altitude	11,000 ft (3,353 metres) above sea level
Depth	0-22.5 cm
Colour	10 YR 6/3 (pale brown)
pH	5 to 6
Description	The area is a small flat plateau. The foot of the mountains covered with luxuriant growth of pine forests and "Doop" trees. The plateau itself has a sparse vegetation with small shrubs of wild flowers growing here and there and remains under snow for about six months. In this area hardly any day goes without a shower. The soil is moist and pale brown colour faded with depth

SOIL PROFILE No. 2

Locality	Chandanwari, about 17 km from Pahalgam
Collected on	23.6.1955
Altitude	10,000 ft (3,048 metres) above sea level
Depth	0-22 cm
Colour	2.5 Y 7/2 (Light grey)
pH	6 to 7
Description	The area is a mountainous slope with projecting cliffs and crags and constantly exposed to erosion. A good number of stones and boulders are found in the vicinity. Very little soil formation seems to have taken place and thus the soil shows prominent skeletal features. These soils are also not very deep

SOIL PROFILE No. 3

Locality	Anderwan, about 32 km away from Srinagar

Collected on   15.6.1955
Altitude   7,500 ft (2,286 metres), above sea level
Depth   0-30 cm
pH   6 to 7
Colour   10 YR 4/2 (dark grey brown) when dry, and 10 YR 3/2 (very dark grey brown) when moist
Description   This sample was collected from a ridge of the mountain which has very steep slope and a bushy growth throughout the area, vegetation of different grasses of small size covers the whole area. The area is uncultivated, though paddy and maize are grown on terraced fields

SOIL PROFILE No. 4
Locality   Chishmashahi (sheep breeding farm), about 7 km from Srinagar
Collected on   14.6.1955
Altitude   6000 ft (1,829 metres), above sea level
Depth   22.5 cm
Colour   10 YR 6/3 (pale brown) when dry and 10 YR 4/3 (dark brown) when moist
pH   7 to 8
Description   The area has a gentle topography with bushy growth but lentil is abundant. The texture of the soil appears to be clayey loam

*M.L. Kaul, Unpublished thesis of Indian Agricultural Research Institute, New Delhi, 1956.

APPENDIX XV

Mechanical analysis of the highland soils of Kashmir

Soil no.	Sample and locality	Height ft	Coarse sand 2.0-0.2 mm. %	Fine sand 0.2-0.02 mm. %	Silt 0.02-0.002 mm. %	Clay below 0.002 mm. %	Total
1.	Khilanmarg	11,000	1.0	15.3	48.0	23.0	100.6
2.	Chandanwari	10,000	36.0	11.2	30.2	18.2	101.4
3.	Dunad	8,200	3.4	16.6	12.5	50.0	102.7
4.	Dunad	8,000	3.0	22.0	21.8	38.5	102.6
5.	Tethar	7,800	1.3	20.7	30.8	31.7	100.1
6.	Anderwan	7,500	2.6	18.4	37.0	29.5	101.2
7.	Anderwan	7,200	4.3	22.7	29.5	32.3	102.9
8.	Anderwan	7,000	3.3	22.0	37.0	27.4	99.5
9.	Changilu	6,900	3.6	23.6	34.0	24.7	101.7
10.	Zaban	6,800	1.0	20.2	36.8	28.7	100.5
11.	Zaban	6,500	2.4	18.2	38.0	29.2	101.3
12.	Changilu	6,300	4.0	30.9	35.5	23.5	101.7
13.	Chishmashahi	6,000	6.7	30.0	35.3	20.0	98.6
14.	Chishmashahi	5,900	3.5	29.0	35.3	26.2	101.9
15.	H.Q. Banihal	5,300	4.0	30.3	34.0	24.0	101.5

Source   M.L. Kaul, Study of Soil at Different Altitudes in Kashmir State, unpublished assoc. thesis, SSAC, IARI, New Delhi, 1956, p. 37.

APPENDIX XVI

Chemical analysis of the highland soils of Kashmir

Soil sample no. and locality	Height ft	Organic carbon %	Organic nitrogen %	Organic matter %	C/N ratio %	Soil reaction (pH)	Total soluble salts %	C_aCo_3 %	Available nitrogen lbs/acre
1. Khilanmarg	11,000	3.35	0.358	5.77	9.3	5.2	0.023	0.5	580.0
2. Chandanwari	10,000	2.54	0.140	4.37	18.1	6.1	0.012	0.4	258.0
3. Dunad	8,200	8.49	0.540	14.50	15.6	6.1	0.021	0.7	704.8
4. Dunad	8,000	7.63	0.508	13.10	15.0	6.6	0.023	0.8	669.0
5. Tethar	7,800	6.96	0.442	12.00	15.0	6.7	0.021	0.8	655.6
6. Anderwan	7,500	5.22	0.342	8.90	15.0	6.3	0.021	0.9	596.8
7. Anderwan	7,200	5.49	0.372	9.40	15.0	6.5	0.012	0.9	605.0
8. Anderwan	7,000	4.28	0.292	7.30	14.6	6.8	0.021	0.9	508.8
9. Changilu	6,900	3.75	0.250	6.40	15.0	7.0	0.021	0.8	402.4
10. Zaban	6,800	4.28	0.330	7.30	13.0	6.4	0.021	0.8	543.2
11. Zaban	6,500	4.55	0.338	7.80	13.0	6.4	0.012	0.8	570.4
12. Changilu	6,300	2.05	0.144	3.50	14.0	6.7	0.012	0.8	322.0
13. Chishmashahi	6,000	1.34	0.994	2.30	13.0	7.0	0.012	0.8	203.6
14. Chishmashahi	5,900	2.27	0.220	3.90	10.3	6.7	0.012	0.8	336.0
15. H.Q. Banihal	5,300	3.46	0.298	5.90	11.0	6.7	0.021	0.8	448.0

Source: M.L. Kaul, Study of Soil at Different Altitudes in Kashmir State, unpublished assoc. thesis, SSAC, IARI, New Delhi, 1956, p. 51.

APPENDIX XVII

Highland soils

Place	Degree of weathering		
	Height	Clay %	Degree of weathering
Khilanmarg	11,000	23.0	43.2
Dunad	8,000	38.5	52.9
Anderwan	7,500	29.5	37.1
Changilu	6,300	23·5	33.0
Chishmashahi	5,900	26.2	41.0
H.Q. Banihal	5,300	24.0	37.0

Source: M.L. Kaul, Study of Soil at Different Altitudes in Kashmir State, unpublished assoc. thesis, SSAC, IARI, New Delhi, 1956.

Soil profiles from Pampore Karewas

Description	Depth (inches)	Morphological features	Mechanical composition (%)								Organic carbon	pH	Chemical constituent (%)			
			Gravel	Mois-ture	Loss on ignition	CaCO$_3$	Sand	Silt	Clay	N			Cation exch. cap.	CaO	MgO	P$_2$O$_5$
Soil growing saffron	0-9	Moist, loose structure, dark brown soil, plenty of roots of grasses and some corn or saffron flower	0.8	2.42	0.89	0.70	33.94	43.12	20.28	0.086	0.34	7.55	9.92	0.395	0.125	0.106
	9-15	-do- more compact	1.4	2.86	0.54	0.61	32.00	40.36	23.40	0.071	0.31	7.7	16.76	0.295	0.128	0.101
	15-36	Compact, concretionary, layer showing iron, manganese concretions, shining mica type material in the concretions against the seam	...	3.73	2.14	1.83	24.72	33.45	32.40	0.054	0.25	7.55	17.68	0.448	0.135	0.132
	36-42	More clayey, light dark brown soil, less compact than the third layer	...	2.82	0.68	14.05	21.33	34.68	25.40	00.50	0.31	8.21	13.20	7.567	0.221	0.156
Soil in which saffron does not grow	0-9	Light brown loam, structureless, plenty of plant roots	...	2.22	1.43	14.07	24.44	34.20	22.55	0.089	0.33	8.15	7.12	6.557	0.221	0.155
	9-20	-do- more compact, some seeming calcareous nodules	...	2.24	2.74	13.87	20.25	35.55	25.10	0.050	0.22	8.25	7.12	7.749	0.229	0.136
	20-36	-do- more compact than second layer and more calcareous than above	...	2.15	1.21	16.96	19.82	33.90	23.60	0.031	...	8.22	7.34	8.237	0.226	0.145
	36-48	Hard compact calcareous zone mixed with light brown soil	2.5	1.84	2.20	21.76	19.05	31.10	22.25	0.038	...	8.30	07.16	9.90	0.341	...

Source: S.P. Raychaudhuri, *et al*, *Soils of India*, Indian Council of Agricultural Research, New Delhi, 1963, pp. 105-110.

Index